CARPENTRY
AND
JOINERY
WORK

Second edition

By NELSON L. BURBANK

Formerly INSTRUCTOR
Building Vocational High School, Cincinnati, Ohio

SIMMONS-BOARDMAN PUBLISHING CORPORATION
30 CHURCH STREET, NEW YORK

INTRODUCTION

BUILDINGS, besides serving as one of the three basic essentials; food, clothing and shelter; needed to maintain life, are also classifed among the most permanent things we contact during our term upon this planet.

Archeologists study the remains of ancient buildings with avidity because structures erected by man, many centuries ago, are almost the only good clues to that nebulous--the history of civilization back through the ages.

In all recorded history the architect and the builder, as well as the fine craftsman, have been honored. The knowledge those men possessed was considered so valuable for centuries that it was imparted only to those sworn to preserve the secrets of the guilds. How successful this practice became can be judged by the fact that many great structures of antiquity--such as the Mayan buildings and the Pyramids--baffle analysis today, it being impossible to arrive at better than an indifferent conclusion regarding the methods of building them.

As civilization progressed, however, with the development of the printing press and other duplicating devices, more and more of the secrets of good craftsmanship have come to be recorded. As yet the knowledge so inscribed is all too meager, with much of the technical discussion in terms difficult for the modest craftsman to comprehend. Development of practical treatises on craftsmanship in the building industry is therefore, something to be greeted with acclaim. The dissemination of this useful knowledge is needed, yet the courage to blaze this educational trail has come to but a few.

In this book CARPENTRY AND JOINERY WORK the cardinal principles of residence construction are set forth simply and sincerely for the young man who would become a good journeyman carpenter. Mastery of the knowledge contained herein will serve as an important step toward a life of accomplishment and satisfaction.

The treatment of the many and complicated subjects is stimulating. The view-point is not a narrow one, but sends the mind off into delightful channels of exploration which, much to our surprise, ultimately come to be identified as both pertinent and logical. The earnest student will find his travels through this book most interesting. With a mounting curiosity as the whole field of knowledge is unfolded before him, the student will, I believe, regret that there is not more when the last page is reached.

Of course, no trade, business or profession should be embraced unless it offers abundant opportunity for the initiate. In residential building the outlook at this time is particularly encouraging. There is a great need for additional homes and improvements to existing structures. There is every reason to believe the next decade will see residential work more abundant than during any ten-year period of the past. In addition, the Bureau of the Census gave 73,897 as the number of apprentices to the building and hand trades in 1920, compared with only 40,133 in 1930. This obviously indicates that competition will be less during the next decade for the carpenter who is a master of his craft.

Nelson L. Burbank deserves great credit for producing a textbook of so comprehensive a nature, so interesting treatment and such apparent practical value. I am sure you will go through this text with as great pleasure as I have experienced in examining it. My personal wish would be that you reap to the fullest the many benefits I know you can obtain from its pages.

E. L. Gilbert,

New York, N. Y.
June, 1936.

Former Eastern Editor,
THE AMERICAN BUILDER.

————————

ACKNOWLEDGEMENTS

The author acknowledges the generosity of the following concerns and organizations for the use of illustrative material and certain copy which has been used verbatim.

These groups are the Stran-Steel Co., Detroit, Mich.; Architectural Forum, New York; United Brotherhood of Carpenters and Joiners of America, Indianapolis, Ind.; National Lumber Manufacturers Association, Washington, D. C.; American Forest Products Industries, Inc., Washington, D. C.; The Porter-Cable Machine Co., Syracuse, N. Y.; Truscon Steel Co., Youngstown, Ohio; Stanley Rule & Level Plant, New Britain, Conn.; American Rolling Mill Co., Middletown, Ohio; Metropolitan Life Insurance Company, New York; Weyerhauser Sales Company, Saint Paul, Minn.; General Timber Service, Inc., Saint Paul, Minn.; De Walt Products Corporation, Lancaster, Pa.; Skilsaw, Incorporated, Chicago; American Institute of Architects, Washington, D. C.; Insulated Steel Construction Co., Cleveland, Ohio; General Electric Co., Bridgport, Conn.; Forest Products Laboratory, Madison, Wis.; The J. R. Wood Supply Co., Cincinnati, Ohio; The Simmons Boardman Publishing Corporation, New York; Sears-Roebuck Co., Chicago; The C. F. Pease Co., Chicago; Eberhard Faber, New York; Masonite Corporation, Chicago; Concrete Engineering Corporation, Omaha, Neb.; Pencil Points, New York; The William B. Barr Co., Cincinnati, Ohio; Federal Board for Vocational Education, Washington, D. C.; Ohio Industrial Commission, Columbus, Ohio; Macober Steel Co., Canton, Ohio; Jones & Laughlin Steel Co., Pittsburgh, Pa.; Crex Patent Column Co., Chicago; Queen City Lumber Company, Cincinnati, Ohio; Samuel Cabot, Boston, Mass.; Wood-Fiber Board Co., New York; Keufel & Esser Co., New York; Hawthorne Roofing Tile Co., Cicero, Ill.; E. M. Long Co., Cadiz, Ohio; A. M. Lewin Lumber Co., Cincinnati, Ohio; Charles Parker Co., Meriden, Conn.; W. M. Ritter Co., Columbus, Ohio; Storm Lumber Co., New York; Hardwood Products Co., Neenah, Wis.; and the F. W. Dodge Corporation, New York.

CONTENTS

Chapter	Title	Page
I	Tools and Equipment	7
II	Tool Boxes	15
III	House Plans	19
IV	Excavations	33
V	Foundation Forms	39
VI	Foundations	47
VII	Sills	55
VIII	Girders	63
IX	Floor Joists	71
X	Sub Flooring	81
XI	Outside Framed Walls	89
XII	Inside Framed Walls	109
XIII	Plumbing Framed Work	119
XIV	Sheathing Walls	127
XV	Ceiling Joists	137
XVI	Roof Framing	153
XVII	Roof Sheathing	171
XVIII	Cornices	183
XIX	Roofing	191
XX	Porch and Bay Framing	197
XXI	Exterior Wall Covering	203
XXII	Interior Wall Covering	215
XXIII	Stairs	225
XXIV	Interior Trim	233
XXV	Windows	239
XXVI	Doors	251
XXVII	Hardware	259
XXVIII	Closets and Shelving	263
XXIX	Finish Flooring	267
XXX	Finishing	273

Tools and Equipment

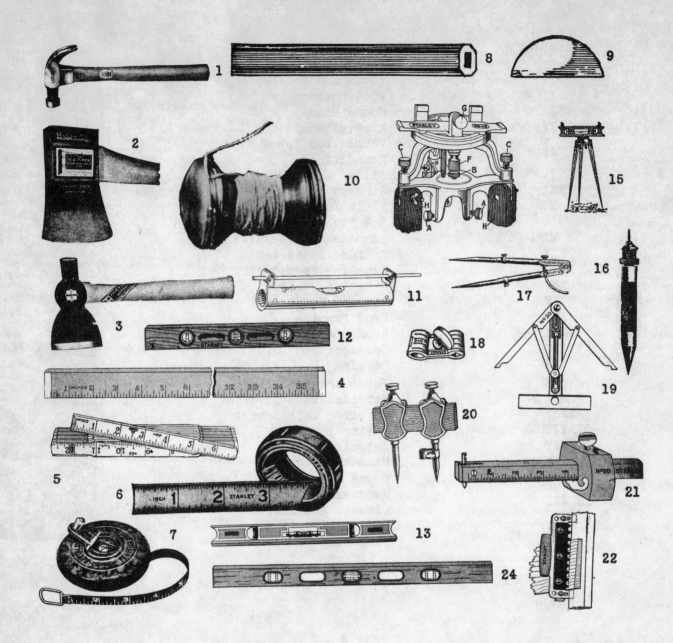

1 Claw Hammer	8 Carpenter's Pencil	15 Leveling Stand
2 Axe	9 Carpenter's Chalk	16 Plumb Bob
3 Shingling Hatchet	10 Chalk Line on Spool	17 Dividers
4 Yard Stick	11 Line Level	18 Pencil Clasp
5 Extension Rule	12 Carpenter's Level	19 Angle Dividers
6 Steel Rule	13 Plumb Level	20 Trammel Points
7 Steel Tape	14 Mason's Level	21 Marking Gauge
		22 Sliding Gauge

Chapter I

Tools and Equipment

Carpentry and Joinery Work is offered to the trade school student or apprenticed youth as a guide in his efforts to become a skilled journeyman carpenter. It has been organized around thirty phases of dwelling construction. Each phase is placed in construction sequence, which lends itself, with but few exceptions, to a psychological learning basis.

In each phase of activity typical building operations in wood and construction metal are dealt with. An exhaustive delineation of all building operations would be too voluminous and probably impractical to organize. The operations used in the erection of the newer types of metal houses have been given in so far as such information is available.

In this work the use of the steel framing square is dealt with in graphic detail. This is the only tool so described, as adequate reference material is available for all hand and powered tools. The following works are suggested as references: 'Hand Work in Wood' by W. S. Noyes; 'Principles of Woodworking' by Herman Hjorth; 'Light Frame House Construction' published by the Government Printing Office.

A two-fold program must be carried on by the learner. A program of study and a program of practical activities. The program of study involves:

A. Discussion   C. Related studies -   3. English
                     1. Drawing   4. Science
B. Practical job   2. Mathematics   5. Civics

Each subject involves studying, writing, drawing or performance.

The program of practical activities involves:

A. Discussion   4. Approval of instructor
                                 5. Stock selection
B. Practical job -   6. Laying out of work
   1. Sketch or drawing   7. Practicing
   2. Steps of procedure   8. Finishing
   3. Stock bill   9. Approval and rating

Each item above involves studying, writing, drawing, performance or practical construction or erection.

The words JOINERY WORK, do not refer in this text, to the joining of wood as practiced by the cabinet maker. The implication is the joining of metal or wooden prefabricated materials necessitated in dwelling construction, by the rough or finish carpenter. Certain organizations clearly define this as falling within the scope of carpentry operations.

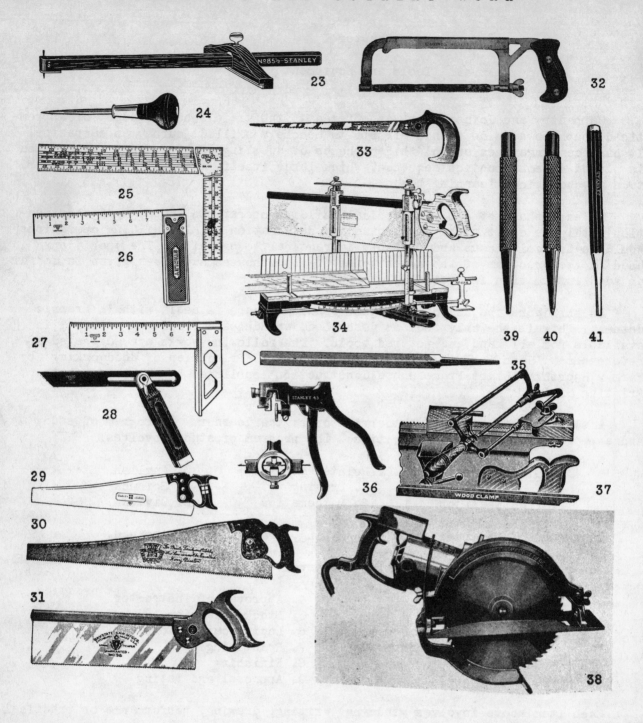

23	Panel Gauge	29	Cross Cut Saw	35	File
24	Scratch Awl	30	Rip Saw	36	Saw Set
25	Steel Square	31	Back Saw	37	Saw Filer
26	Try Square	32	Hack Saw	38	Portable Bench Saw
27	Try Square and Miter	33	Key Hole Saw	39	Nail Set
28	Sliding Bevel	34	Miter Box	40	Center Punch
				41	Drift Punch

Each of the foregoing involves much study, some writing and sketching, the making of a stock bill and the exacting performance of laying out, cutting and erecting of the parts involved in the job.

A suggested form for the recording of progress made by the student is shown below.

Name_____

Job_____

Job begun_____ Job finished_____

Rating on job_____Rating on related studies:_____

Drawing_____Mathematics_____English_____Science_____

Civics_____Other studies_____

Remarks_____

_____

Entire job and related studies_____

Approved_____

Instructor._____

The topics and lessons in this text can be pursued in sequence either horizontally or vertically. By horizontally is meant the use of each practical lesson, or each related drawing lesson, or each related mathematics lesson, etc., in order, wholly disregarding other lessons. By vertically is meant the use of each chapter in the full development of the topic, weaving in all available information, performances, studies or activities as a particular situation demands.

The first phase of activity involved in the construction of a dwelling is the study of tools and equipment. Since, as stated on pg. 7, adequate reference material is available for the study of fundamental tool processes, hand or powered, there is little need to add this to the study of carpentry. The beginner should make, at this point, adequate reference to texts or works on tool processes. After a 'brushing-up' on certain processes and the attaining of a desired level of skill in the use of the more fundamental tools, a study of the following practical jobs and related subjects will serve as an introduction to typical trade operations of house carpentry and joinery work. These include problems involved in the erection of framed dwellings of wood, pre-fabricated metal or pre-fabricated wood.

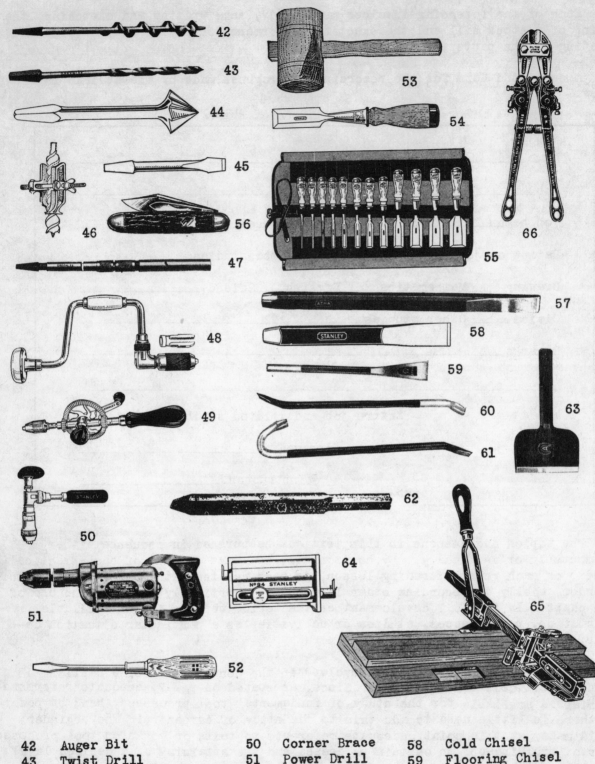

42	Auger Bit	50	Corner Brace	58	Cold Chisel
43	Twist Drill	51	Power Drill	59	Flooring Chisel
44	Countersink	52	Screw Driver	60	Ripping Bar
45	Screw Driver Bit	53	Mallet	61	Wrecking Bar
46	Bit Gauge	54	Butt Chisel	62	Crow Bar
47	Extension Bit Holder	55	Socket Chisels	63	Brick Chisel
48	Auger Bit Brace	56	Pocket Knife	64	Butt Gauge
49	Hand Drill	57	Rivet Chisel	65	Butt Mortiser
				66	Bolt Clipper

Practical Jobs

Study the illustrations of the foregoing tools and become familiar with the names. Secure trade catalogs and become acquainted with the tools. Make a list of references, as far as possible, of the foregoing illustrations.

Related Studies

Drawing

The drawing equipment used by a tradesman should be selected with as much care as the tools. The most important tool in drawing is the lead pencil. The chart below shows the several grades in which drawing pencils are made. A description of each grade, beginning with 6B is as follows: softest and blackest; very, very soft and very black; very soft and very black; very soft and black; soft and black; soft; medium soft; firm; medium; hard; very hard; extra hard; very, very hard; very, very hard and firm; extra hard and firm; extra hard and extra firm, and hardest and firmest.

Purchase three of four of these drawing pencils, say one each of 2B, 6H, 2H and HB grade. The harder grades are for line work and lettering and should be sharpened with a cone point. The softer grades are for shading and should be sharpened with a chisel point.
See illustrations below.

6B 5B 4B 3B 2B B HB F H 2H 3H 4H 5H 6H 7H 8H 9H

A cone point

A chisel point

Mathematics.

The value of tools will be better appreciated if something is known of their cash value. This information can be obtained from hardware catalogs or taking a list of tools to a hardware store supply house asking the several prices. As far as possible obtain the prices of the tools shown at the beginning of this chapter. Prices are often given in dozen lots and care must be taken to figure the cost of equipment. The various prices of pencils of different grades is also valuable information.

Science

The raw materials used in the construction of tools are selected with much care. These raw materials may be divided into two general classes, the metals and the woods. In the wood class the following kinds are generally used: wal-

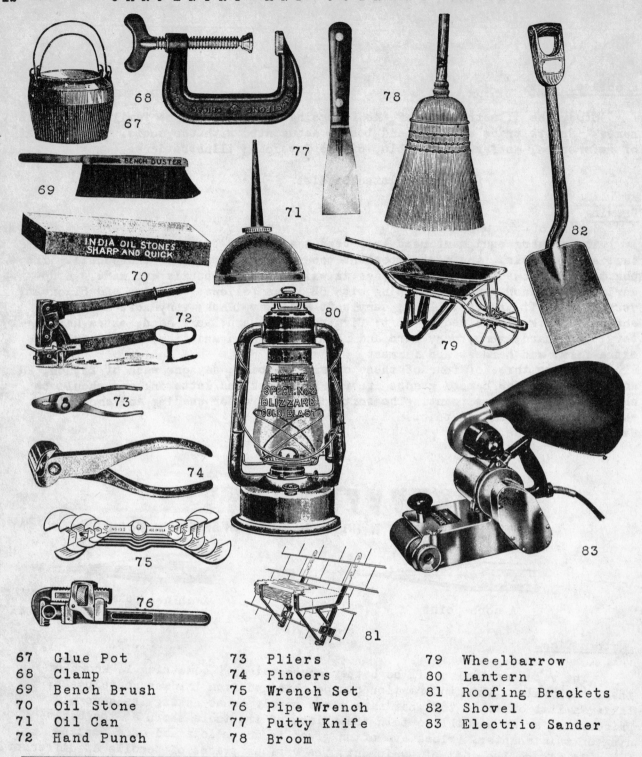

67 Glue Pot	73 Pliers	79 Wheelbarrow
68 Clamp	74 Pincers	80 Lantern
69 Bench Brush	75 Wrench Set	81 Roofing Brackets
70 Oil Stone	76 Pipe Wrench	82 Shovel
71 Oil Can	77 Putty Knife	83 Electric Sander
72 Hand Punch	78 Broom	

Note--The tools and items of equipment displayed on this and preceding pages have been carefully checked and recommended by Mr. Fred Gross of the Educational Department of the Stanley Rule and Level Co., New Britain, Conn.

The illustrations are by courtesy The Stanley Rule & Level Co., New Britain, Conn.; The J. R. Wood Supply Co., Cincinnati, Ohio,; DeWalt Products Corporation, Lancaster, Pa.; Skilsaw, Inc., Chicago, Ill.; The Porter-Cable Machine Co., Syracuse, N. Y.

nut, hickory, cherry, maple, mahogany, beech, rosewood, white pine, apple and oak. In the metal class the following kinds are generally used: steel, iron, brass, copper, aluminum, nickle, lead, bronze-chromium and bronze. Classify according to the foregoing classes, the tools shown at the beginning of this chapter. If parts of same tool are in both classes, list the parts accordingly. If possible, ascertain the weight of each tool.

English

One is often required to make a list of tools or write out an order for them. It is quite necessary to know the correct spelling of the names of the tools. Study the illustrations of the tools shown at the beginning of this chapter, paying attention to the spelling of the names and associate the name with each illustration.

Civics

Tools can be marked so that the owner can identify his tools when they become mixed with others. Great care must be taken to keep tools from being stolen. Why? Stolen tools can often be recovered at second hand stores. Tools should always be kept in shape and good working order. Why?

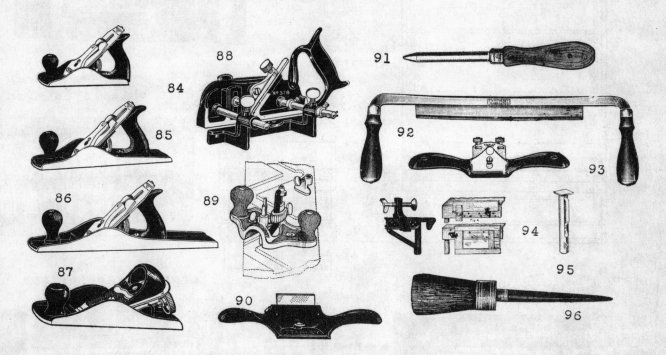

84	Smooth Plane	88	Rabbet Plane	92	Draw Knife	96	Glue Brush
85	Jack Plane	89	Router Plane	93	Spoke Shave		
86	Joiner Plane	90	Scraper	94	Bench Bracket		
87	Block Plane	91	Scraper Burnisher	95	Bench Stop		

A Tool Box

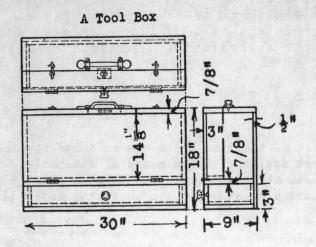

Showing tools in a chest

A Tool Chest

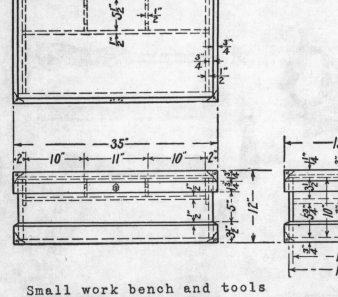

Showing tools in a box

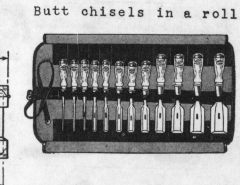

Butt chisels in a roll

Small work bench and tools

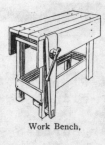

Work Bench,

Large work bench and tools

Chapter 11

Tool Boxes

Hand tools and equipment must be kept in an orderly way in boxes made for them. Tool boxes or containers may be divided into two classes, namely, carrying cases or large chests. Carrying cases are made for many of the smaller hand tools used by a journeyman. Each tool has a special place made for it. Place the spirit level so that it will not be broken. The pencil, pocket knife, chalk and chalk line may be wrapped in an apron. The saws must have slots and turn buttons made in order to hold them in rigid position. Place the hammer and half hatchet in such a position so that the cutting edge will not mar other tools. The steel square is usually placed on the side of the tool box with one portion of it extending out through a slot in the top of the box.

Large tool chests are used for storing tools so that they can be transported from job to job. These chests have, in addition to a place for tools, a place for nails, sandpaper and other smaller supplies. If tools cannot be kept in a secure place on the building premises be certain to find a place nearby where they can be kept. If need be take the tools to and from work each day. When tools are kept in a workshop each tool must have a place and be kept there when not in use. A definite procedure for storing and checking tools in a tool room should be followed.

Practical Jobs

The illustrations show two types of tool containers, the tool box and the tool chest. Study the drawings, giving attention to the method used in joining the pieces. What other types of joints could be used? The kind of hardware used varies a great deal. Before actual construction a stock bill is generally made. In the stock bill the number of pieces of material, their thicknesses, widths and lengths, quality and finish of each are listed. The hardware, also is listed and the costs of each separate item extended and totaled. A suggested form of a stock bill is shown below. This may be worked up on the drawing or obtained in printed form.

Quantity	T	W	L	Kind	Bd. Ft.	Cost

Related Studies

Drawing

In addition to careful selection of drawing pencils great care must be used in selecting paper on which to draw. There are many different kinds of drawing or drafting paper made to meet the exacting demands of the draftsman and the tradesman. The following points should be considered when selecting paper:
1. It should have body; 2. It should have erasing quality; 3. It should have a working surface; 4. It should have permanency. The first point involves such qualities as thickness, grade and color. The second point involves such qualities as the ability to withstand repeated erasing of either pencil or ink lines. The third point involves such qualities as smooth, toothed or pebbled face on which drawings

Common Joints

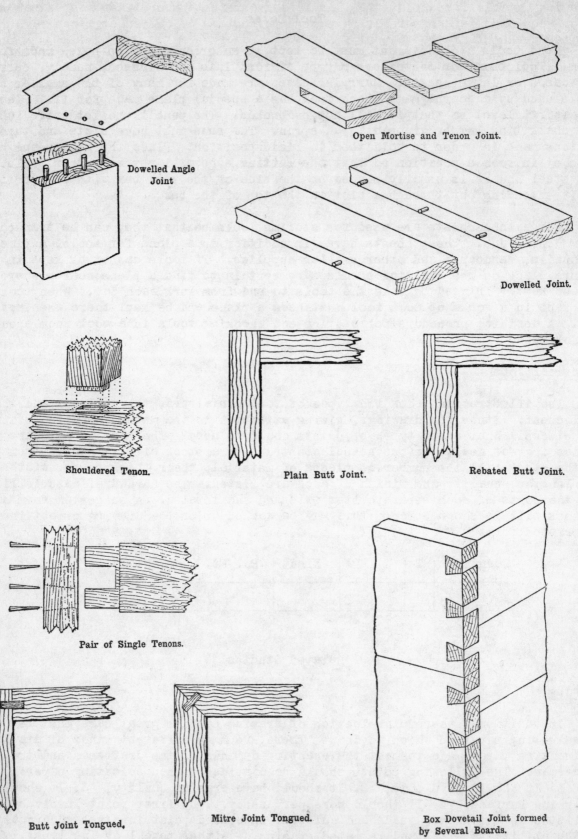

Open Mortise and Tenon Joint.

Dowelled Angle Joint

Dowelled Joint.

Shouldered Tenon.

Plain Butt Joint.

Rebated Butt Joint.

Pair of Single Tenons.

Butt Joint Tongued.

Mitre Joint Tongued.

Box Dovetail Joint formed by Several Boards.

are made. The fourth point involves such qualities as grade and kind of stock used.
The raw materials used in paper manufacture are cotton or linen rag, straw or bam-
boo, wood or jute. Paper having a high percentage of cotton or linen rags is the
better grade of drawing paper.

Secure samples of as many kinds of drawing paper as possible. Criticise them
in the light of the above points. Make a copy, using a good pencil and good paper,
of the tool box. Make this an exact copy, using only the pencil, eraser and paper.

Mathematics

The area of a surface is found by multiplying the width by the length. The
area is produced by multiplying two dimensions and the volume is produced by multiplying three dimensions. Thus if a piece of lumber is 1" t. and 24" w. and 24" l.,
the area of one large flat surface is found by multiplying the w. x l. or 12 x 24
which gives 288 square inches. In order to understand the method used in finding
board feet (which will be dealt with later) it would be well to find the area of the
back piece in the tool box. Also find the area of the bottom of the tray of the tool
box. Find the area of the top of the tool chest. Present the answers in terms of
square inches, just now, not square feet.

Science

A tool box should be large enough to carry the several tools intended and no
larger. Boxes or chests must be of sturdy construction in order to withstand much
rough usage. The following features must be embodied in a good tool box:
1. Good lumber (oak, birch, gum, pine or poplar); 2. Good hardware (lock, hinges,
corners, handles and straps); 3. Good construction (sturdy joints, workmanship,
finish); 4. Devices for holding tools in place.
Refer to Chapter 1 and select a group of tools you would like to have for a home
workshop. List the tools and if possible find the total weight. Will your group be
too heavy to carry in a box? Will you need to make a tool chest? Consider the size,
hardware and other features as given above for this box. Try to make a drawing of
the chest.

English

If one began the study of another language he would have to learn many new words.
The study of dwellings involves many new words and phrases. The correct spelling
must be known together with the correct meaning or definition.
A definition for a wheel barrow would be: Wheel barrow, n. A light piece of
carrying equipment with two handles and one wheel used to carry small loads. Note
in this definition that the word is given first, then the part of speech and lastly
a description.
Refer to the tool illustrations. List the names of the tools and then give
your own definitions. Refer to a dictionary after writing your own definitions.

Civics

Mankind has always used hand tools of some type. It is reasonable to assume
that the earliest hand tools were made of stones and branches, although little definite information of a historical nature is available. We do have, however, some facts
regarding the origin of the present day metal tools.
Refer to a book written by Frederick A. Collins, entitled, 'A Bird's Eye View
of Inventions', published by T. Y. Crowell Co., of New York. Gather facts on as many
tools as you can. Refer to any other history of tools or to an encyclopedia.

Common Joints

Plain Mitre Joint.

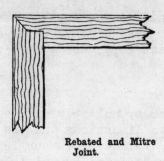

Rebated and Mitre Joint.

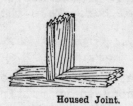

Housed Joint.

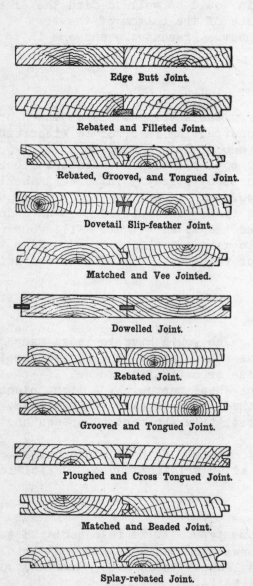

Edge Butt Joint.

Rebated and Filleted Joint.

Rebated, Grooved, and Tongued Joint.

Dovetail Slip-feather Joint.

Matched and Vee Jointed.

Dowelled Joint.

Rebated Joint.

Grooved and Tongued Joint.

Ploughed and Cross Tongued Joint.

Matched and Beaded Joint.

Splay-rebated Joint.

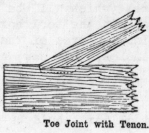

Toe Joint with Tenon.

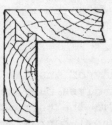

Mitred, Grooved, and Tongued Joint.

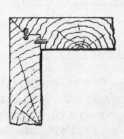

Rebated, Mitred, and Double-tongued Joint.

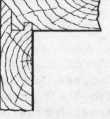

Glued Blockings.

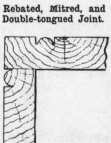

Butt Joint with Flush Beads.

Chapter 111

House Plans

With the selection of the tools and equipment for construction work, one must turn his attention to a very important phase of building, that of house plans and specifications. These, house plans and specifications, can be obtained in one of three ways. One way is to purchase a set of stock plans and specifications from organizations selling them. Another is the drawing and writing of these two units by a contractor. Still another is the hiring of the services of an architect. This way, of course, is the best, by far, since the architect takes charge of the entire job from the designing to complete supervision of construction. Many architects are not concerned with residence work but this field offers may rewards and is in need of aesthetic influence.

Practical Jobs

Visit the building lot on which the house is to be built. Note the slope of the land, the presence of trees or underbrush and the general appearance of the property. Refer to the set of plans and find the sheet marked PLOT PLAN. From the plot plan obtain the distance the house is to be placed from each property line. This will be the location of the excavation for the foundation. Refer to the sheet, in the set of plans, marked FOUNDATION or BASEMENT PLAN and note the points in common with the plot plan. Obtain a set of house plans and glance through the entire set. Obtain from the PLOT PLAN the distance the house is from the side line and from the front line of the lot. List this information. Read specifications pgs. 24-32

Related Studies

Drawing

An eraser is a device used to remove written or line marks from the drawing or writing paper. Erasers, for drafting purposes, are made in several types. They are, the ink line eraser, pliable pencil line eraser, soft pencil line eraser, soft ink eraser, ink and pencil eraser, art gum eraser and steel point eraser. The ink erasers contain more abrasive materials and are firmer in body than the pencil eraser. The art gum and pliable pencil eraser are used to clean a soiled drawing as well as to remove pencil markings. Steel erasers are made of tool steel sharpened to a point and mounted in a handle. Experience growing out of the use of erasers will give the best knowledge of the use of each particular kind.

Obtain a good eraser for pencil lines, also a good one for ink lines and a good art gum. Keep these erasers for use at all times.

Mathematics

One may classify the work on drawing as line work, lettering and figures. Line work and lettering may be slightly inaccurate but the figures must never be so on a worth while drawing. Dimensions must be checked for accuracy. The smaller dimensions must be checked to harmonize with the over all totals. One must learn to check over all dimensions against fractional or smaller ones. Refer to a floor plan drawing of a set of house plans. Locate the over-all length and width of the house. Mark it down. Locate the room dimensions and the wall thicknesses. Add the room

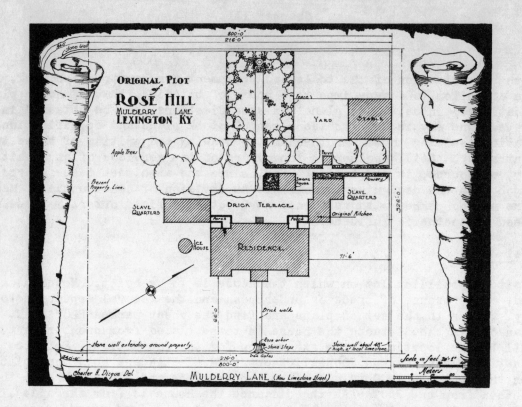

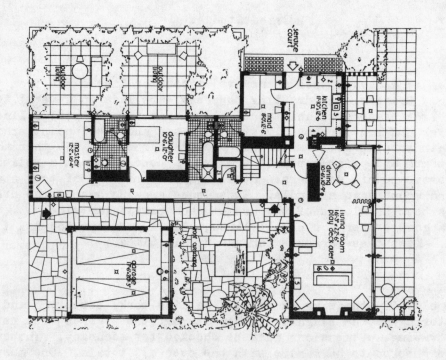

Plot Plans

dimensions and the wall thicknesses along the length of the house. Does it equal the total length given? What is the area of each room?

Science

The plans or directions for the actual construction work on a house consists of a set of house plans and specifications. The specifications are written instructions and regulations about the many detailed phases of the work. The set of house plans are a series of drawings. House plans are difficult to interpret completely but much information can be obtained from the several drawings by one of average experience. Careful observation will reveal much about a set of plans. Obtain a set of house plans. Find the FIRST FLOOR PLAN drawing. Study it carefully. From this study obtain the name and size of each room. Study the FRONT ELEVATION, SIDE ELEVATION and REAR ELEVATION drawings. Is the house to be built of brick or of wood? Study the PLOT PLAN. Where is the house to be located on the building lot? Study the specifications. What are they?

English

It is often necessary to ask for and tell about certain tools and pieces of stock. One should be able to use simple sentences in a correct manner. This sentence, for example, expresses a complete thought. THE CARPENTER TRIED TO LIFT FOUR LONG RAFTERS. Learn to express your thoughts in complete sentences. A fragment which has no meaning when read alone, or a sentence from which is omitted a necessary word, phrase or idea violates an elementary principle of writing. Use the following words as nouns in a complete and simple sentence. Each sentence should not be over ten or twelve words in length. The words to use in simple sentences are as follows: trade, building, property, level, saw, rule, house, land, foundation, pencil, hammer and square.

Civics

An architect is one who consults any party contemplating the erection of a building, draws the necessary set of plans and supervises the construction unto completion. An architect must have professional as well as practical training and usually specializes in some phases of construction, such as small houses, public buildings, office buildings, churches, bridges, roads, etc.

The architect acts as the representative of the owner in dealing with the building contractors and building materials supply houses. Construction contracts are made with the architect. The architect is versed in the requirements of the city building code and complies with the building ordinances set by the city authorities in the building code.

The architect consults the prospective owner, renders several free hand sketches, obtains the desires and requirements of the prospective owner, draws a set of plans which are approved by the owner, signs a contract to build the house, lets the construction work out on contracts, obtains the building permits (there are several), and carries the work to completion.

What is the function of an architect? What is the relation of the architect to the builder?, to the city authorities?, to the owner?. What steps of procedure does the architect take in building a house? Find the names of several architects from a telephone directory. Write to the AMERICAN INSTITUTE OF ARCHITECTS, OCTAGON HOUSE, Washington, D.C. for information explaining the functions and purposes of this organization.

Floor Plans

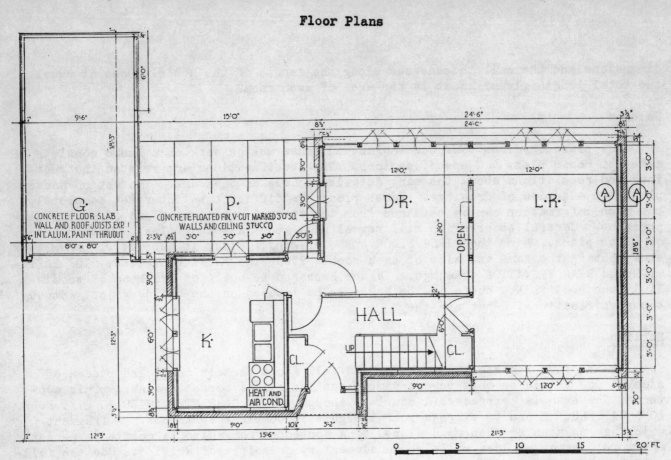

FIRST FLOOR PLAN

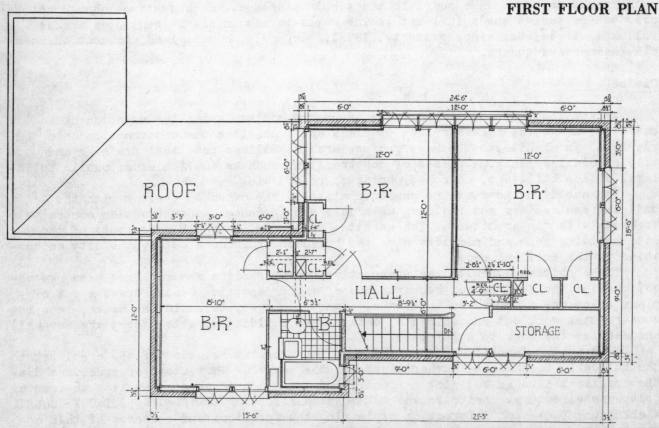

SECOND FLOOR PLAN

Floor Plans

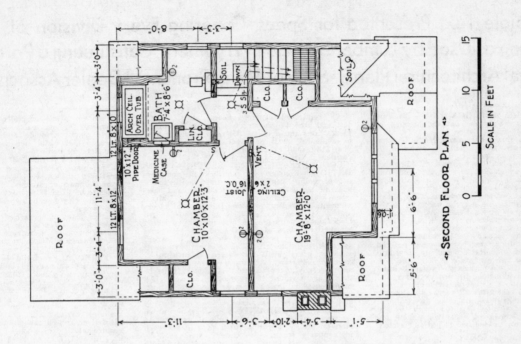

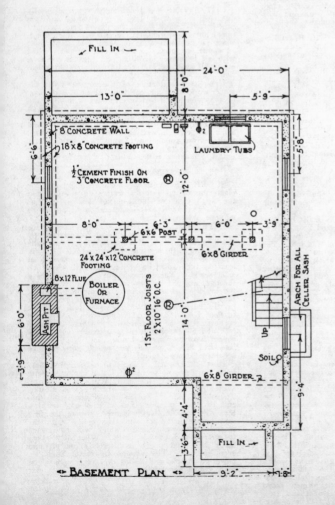

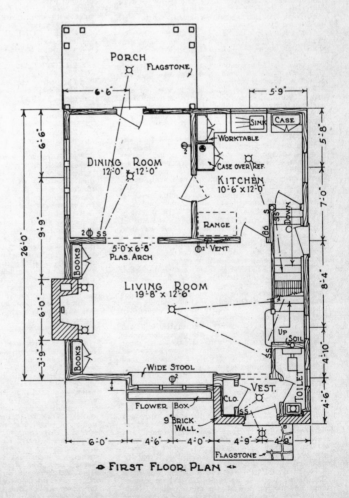

Model Set of Open Specifications

Complete Text Presented for Specs. Covering Every Division of Home Building as Used by Lumber Dealers Everywhere, Constituting a Part of the Official Architectural Plan Service of Many Prominent Dealer Associations

EXCAVATING

EXCAVATING AND GRADING:—The contractor shall accurately lay out the building as directed by the owner.

All trees and shrubs that are liable to be damaged during construction shall be protected by temporary casings or boxes.

Remove all top soil to a depth of 12 inches from that area which is to be excavated and from an additional area of six feet beyond all sides and place in a pile where directed.

Excavate for basement, foundation walls, areas, piers and all footings as may be necessary to the proper depth as shown on plans. All bottoms of walls and piers must be level, solid, undisturbed and kept free from surface drainings.

Fill in around masonry walls where directed by owner. All filling must be thoroughly puddled and tamped and must be brought up to within 8 inches of the finished grade.

Earth removed from excavations should be used for grading and filling as directed by owner and then covered with 8 inches entirely of top soil. Contractor shall cart away all earth not used for filling and grading unless otherwise directed. All grading shall be covered 8 inches with the top soil which has been piled separately. This top soil shall be evenly graded and sloped as directed.

MASONRY

CEMENT:—All cement shall be portland cement of approved brand and shall conform to the specifications of the American Society for Testing Materials.

SAND:—All sand shall be clean, sharp, well graded and free from loam or foreign matter.

GRAVEL OR CRUSHED STONE:—Shall be clean, sound and free from sand and loam and shall range from ½ inch to 1¼ inch in size.

CONCRETE:—All concrete (except when reinforced) shall be composed of one part of portland cement, three parts sand and five parts of gravel or crushed stone.

Reinforced concrete shall be composed of one part of portland cement, two parts sand and four parts of gravel or crushed stone.

WATER PROOFING:—Integral water proofing shall be mixed with concrete walls below grade and the basement floor.

FORMS:—All forms shall be erected to resist bending and buckling under load. They shall be straight, plumb, true and water tight. Forms shall not be removed until all concrete has set thoroughly. All concrete shall be poured into forms immediately after mixing and shall immediately be thoroughly tamped after pouring. All exposed concrete shall have a smooth, uniform, finish in which no surface stones must appear.

CONCRETE FOUNDATIONS FOR WALLS, PIERS, AREAS AND FOOTINGS:—Build of solid concrete according to plans. Concrete shall be spaded next to forms on the surface walls so that mortar will flush to the outside and prevent irregular surfaces. Any rough or hollow space shall be filled or pointed with cement.

CEMENT FLOORS:—This contractor shall make sure that all furring, pipes, floor drains, outlets, and all other work which shall go in or under the floors is in proper condition. Floor drains shall be furnished by the plumbing contractor but the mason contractor will cement in the floor drains and also give the plumber the correct elevations to which the drains will sit. All earth shall be leveled off and thoroughly tamped into a hard surface. If the earth floor of basement is sand the concrete can be applied directly to same; if of clay, then a leveling bed of cinders approximately 4 inches shall be used. Same to be carefully tamped in place. Over the entire basement floor this contractor shall lay concrete to a thickness including the top finish as shown on plans. Thoroughly tamp the concrete into place and carefully pitch to floor drains. Top surface shall be ½ inch thick and composed of one part of portland cement to one part of clean, coarse, sharp sand thoroughly mixed and troweled to a smooth even surface. This finished surface must be laid before the under concrete has been allowed to set so that it will harden well and act as one solid stone.

Porch floors, terraces, slabs when shown in plans shall have ¾ inch finish. Where cement steps and coping are shown on the plans, build of concrete with troweled facings making solid stone.

All reinforced concrete floors, slabs, lintels, footings, etc., as shown on plans shall conform to drawings and details. All reinforcements shall be expanded metal of exact size as shown on plans and shall be carefully placed in the exact position as indicated on plans.

CONCRETE BUILDING BLOCKS—FOUNDATION:—Construct all exterior walls and piers out of hollow concrete blocks as shown to be such on the drawings. All foundation and basement walls to rest on a concrete footing. Measurements are given on plans for sizes of blocks and a ¼ inch mortar joint is infended. All blocks must be made of one part of portland cement, two parts of coarse sand and two parts of mixed gravel or crushed stone not to exceed ⅝ inch in diameter. The greater portion of stone or gravel shall not exceed ¼ inch to ½ inch in diameter. All to be thoroughly mixed and carefully manufactured. All blocks must be thoroughly seasoned before placing in wall. All mortar used in laying must be one part of portland cement to three parts of coarse, sharp sand and used as soon as mixed.

STONE FOUNDATIONS:—All stone walls, footings and piers shall be built to conform to sizes on plans. The stone used shall be approved local quarry stone. The lower course shall be extra large flat stones equal in length to width of footing or wall. All shall be carefully bedded on their widest face and laid in mortar composed of one part cement to two parts coarse sand. Each layer to have well flushed joints on both sides with mortar and firmly bonded. Walls to be neatly pointed on both sides.

CINDER CONCRETE BUILDING BLOCKS:—Blocks shall be.. laid according to manufacturers specifications. All shall conform to plans and drawings.

STRUCTURAL CLAY TILE WALLS, PIERS, ETC.:—Tile shall be.. laid according to manufacturers specifications. All shall conform to plans and drawings.

STRUCTURAL CLAY TILE—GLAZED:—Tile shall be.. laid according to manufacturers specifications. All shall conform to plans and drawings.

STONE WORK ABOVE GRADE:—All exterior facing above grade except cut stone trim shall be local quarry stone. Same to be furnished in random irregular sizes, but shall be 4 inches thick except bond stones which shall be 8 inches thick. Joints shall not be more than ½ inch wide and shall be racked back ¼ inch at the time stone is set. All stone shall be set in non-staining cement mortar and shall be laid up to conform to drawings.

BRICK WORK:—Face brick shall be furnished by the contractor but selected by the owner. The contractor shall allow $30.00 per thousand for the brick delivered on the job. The difference between $30.00 and the cost per thousand to the contractor for the brick selected by the owner shall be the unit price for computing the amount to be added to or subtracted from the contract price. All face brick shall be protected from damage. Face brick shall be laid in lime mortar mixed in proportions of one part of lime, one part of cement to four parts of sand. All shall be laid strictly in accordance with designs as shown on drawings and shall be well bonded to backing. All joints shall be neatly struck.

Common brick used for backing and about the building, unless otherwise specified shall be hard burned common brick laid wet in cold dry weather and dry in warm damp weather. All common brick shall be laid in fresh lime and sharp sand mortar. All exposed joints in the brick work shall be neatly struck. All shall be well bedded, tied in every 7th course and laid in regular bond, leaving no empty spaces in walls. Work in seasoned lath every 12th course inside of enclosing walls and walls shown as furred. All common brick for facing exterior walls shall be extra hard burned brick with joints and exposures as per plan or as directed by owner. Fill in and back close all facing work. Set all door and window sills. Cover the walls from weather and brace them thoroughly. If bricks are laid below grade use only cement mortar composed of one part pure cement and two parts coarse sharp sand. When brick sills are shown on plans, carefully lay same in mortar composed of one part portland cement to two parts sand. Provide and install metal joints, anchors and metal ties as may be required to complete all work.

CHIMNEY:—Build all chimneys of.................. as per plans, neatly topped. Flues to be smoothly plastered inside. Finish and put in all thimbles where shown or directed. Brick chimney smoke flues to be lined from basement to above roof with best fire clay flue lining (see sizes on drawings) neatly cut out for stove thimbles. The flue for heating plant to be carried up individually of all other flues. Ventilating flues to be built where shown on plans. Construct chimney cap as shown on drawings. Mortar to be one part cement to three parts sand.

FIREPLACE:—Build hearth supports at the same time chimney is built and build fireplace according to plans. Mantel face brick to be ....laid with.. mortar. Joints to be of color to suit owner. Provide and lay fire clay brick lining with fire clay mortar as shown on plan. Hearth floor to be built of.. Install doors and ash dumps provided by another contractor.

CLEANING:—All brick shall be left clean and free from mortar stains or other defacements. Any division of joint shall be carefully pointed up.

CUT STONE:—All cut stone shall be locally quarried stone when possible. Must be uniform in color and quality and free from imperfections impairing its durability. Shall be cut in neat, sharp angles according to sizes and dimensions as shown on plans, and delivered properly fitted with all necessary drillings and lugs or anchors, etc. All shall be laid according to its stratification.

Upon the completion of the mason work the stone work shall be carefully cleaned with soap or soap powder, boiled in clean water applied and brushed with a stiff fiber brush. No acid shall be used in cleaning stone work. Joints shall be raked out and brushed clean ¾ inch deep and after a thorough wetting shall be pointed flush with mortar consisting of one part stainless cement, two parts clean white sand and cold lime putty to make a stiff mixture as can be worked.

PLASTERING AND STUCCO

SCOPE OF WORK:—This shall include the plastering of all interior walls and ceilings and the application of lath, corner beads, etc., as necessary and all exterior stucco and lathing as may be shown on plans.

INTERIOR LATHING:—Plaster base to be ....applied as directed by the manufacturer; if of wood lath, cover all walls and ceilings throughout with dry No. 1 lath. Joints broken every 12 or 14 inches and lath at least ⅜ inch apart on ceiling but little closer on side walls. There must not be any lathing through angles from one room to another. Should the lathers find any corners not properly secured they must not lath until it is made permanent by the carpenter and in all cases lath shall go to floor behind base and wainscoting. All inside corners shall be reinforced by strips of metal lath and all exposed corners protected with metal corner beads. Expanded metal lath weighing not less than 2 5/10 pounds per square yard shall be securely fastened to all arch soffits.

PLASTER:—All surfaces to be plastered shall have two coats of prepared plaster applied strictly in accordance with the manufacturer's directions. Water only to be added to the prepared plaster. Thoroughly mix before using. Finish with thin coat of finish plaster. Put on each coat of plaster with considerable pressure. Broom the first coat before it is set and then follow with the second or browning coat, which will be rodded to a true and even surface. When dry apply finish coat and bring to perfectly smooth and even surface. The plaster contractor shall remove all debris and leave the job broom clean upon completion of his work.

Keene's cement shall be used for all wainscoting 4 feet 6 inches high in kitchen, bath and toilets. Mark off in tile patterns, as may be directed by the owner.

EXTERIOR LATHING:—All exterior metal lath when shown on plans shall be expanded, painted or galvanized and shall weigh not less than 3 4/10 pound per square yard.

STUCCO:—All stucco shall be mixed and applied according to the specifications of the Portland Cement Association. Color and texture of finish coat shall be selected by owner....................

CARPENTRY

FRAMING AND DIMENSION LUMBER:— All shall be sound, well seasoned, free from large, loose or dead knots, or other imperfections liable to impair the strength or durability of the timber. All shall be No. 1.

For sizes of framing timber see plans and sections. All floor joist must be sized to widths and set crowning-edge upward. All joist, studding, rafters and other framing timbers shall be set 16 inches on centers, unless where otherwise mentioned on drawings. Frame double-headers and trimmer joist, well spiked together, around all stairways, chimney breasts, etc. All joist under partitions shall be set double and triple. Bearing partitions shall be cross-bridged. All door and window studs shall be set double; truss over all openings in bearing partitions in a substantial manner. Angles of rooms must be made solid. All joist shall be well cross-bridged with good sound stuff, well fitted at the angles and put in as soon as joists are leveled. Frame horizontal collar beams to rafters above the upper ceiling joist, well spiked to long rafters. Nail 1x1 grounds around all door openings, around all rooms for base, also where chair rail and hook strips are to be placed. Outside wood steps shall have substantial carriages set not over 3 feet apart unless otherwise shown on plans. All furring, blocks, etc., shall be worked according to plans.

SHEATHING FOR OUTSIDE WALLS:— All box sheathing shall be 1x8 shiplap No. 2 .... All shall be well nailed at each bearing with three 8d nails. All joints shall be broken. Sheathing to extend from foundation walls to rafters. Care should be taken to avoid unnecessary waste at door and window openings. All loose knots shall be cut out.

SUB-FLOORING:—Cover the floor joists with 1x6 No. 2 All shall be laid close and nailed to every joist. All joints shall be broken on bearings only. All flooring damaged by plumbers, gasfitters, furnace men or other mechanics must be replaced by the carpenter in first-class condition before it is covered with the building paper and finished floor. When shown on plan strip with 1x2 pieces before laying finish floor

BUILDING PAPER:—Cover the entire exterior sheathed surface with.................... Building Paper, all joints well lapped at least 6 inches and run in under all casings, around windows and doors and shall lap around all angles and corners. Also cover all rough floor surface with one thickness of.................... Building Paper after all plastering is completed and dry.

ROOF SHEATHING:—Roof boards shall be .... laid as per plans, and shall be nailed with 8d nails on every rafter with joints broken on bearings only. Strip roof boards with.................... when shown on plans.

SIDING:—All siding as shown on plans shall be....................and laid with....................lap. Cut close joints against all casings, corner boards, etc., and properly nailed with six or eight penny nails every 16 inches. The carpenter is to notify the painter to prime all siding as soon as it is placed in position.

SHINGLES FOR WALLS—STAINED:— Shall be.................... laid....................inches to weather and nailed with....................d.................... nails....................to each shingle.

SHINGLES FOR ROOF:—The entire roof shall be covered with.................... laid....................inches to the weather. Make perfectly watertight around all chimneys, etc. All shingles shall be nailed with at least two galvanized or cut shingle nails to each shingle. The carpenter must see that all sheet metal flashing is properly set in place while shingling, as he will be held responsible for all leaks in the roof after all shingling is completed. All shingles over 8 inches in width shall be split before using.

EXTERIOR FINISH AND TRIM:—All exterior finishing lumber, such as facias, verge boards, planciers, friezes, watertables, belts, corner boards, treads, risers, etc., shall be.................... All finished lumber shall be well fitted in place and primed by painter as soon as work is completed. All shall conform to the plans, elevations and detailed sections.

All exterior mouldings such as crown mould, bed mouldings, etc., must be put in position and well fitted at corners so as to leave the whole in a perfect condition when completed. All shall be worked to conform with detail drawings as shown on general plans. Casing nails are to be used for this work. Cornice soffits shall be built up as shown on plans. If one-piece stock, or ⅝ inch ceiling is to be used, the same shall be well driven up and laid with close joints and blind nailed with 6d casing nails. Where half timbers are used with stucco walls, the inside corners shall be grooved to create a solid bond and joint. All half timbers shall be securely nailed to backing in a substantial manner.

• Place all columns, newel rails, balusters, etc., as indicated on drawings, all shall be well nailed and put up in a proper mechanical manner, and all nails shall be properly set. All lattice work where shown on plans shall be worked out as indicated on drawings. All shall be done in first-class, workmanlike manner and left ready for the painters. Porch ceiling, unless otherwise shown, shall be ⅝ inch narrow beaded and shall be driven up close and blind nailed with 6d casing nails.

PORCH FLOORING:—Shall be.................... and shall have at least ¼ inch drop to every foot in depth and shall be laid in one-piece lengths to cover entire porch and allow for.................... nosing. Shall be driven up close and blind nailed with 8d casing nails.

ATTIC FLOORING:—Attic flooring shall be ....and shall be laid close and nailed with 8d nails. Blind nail and face nail.

FINISH FLOOR:—After all plastering and cement work is completed and dry and all plumbing, tubing and pipes have been installed, cover the entire rough floor surface with.................... as before specified, and then lay the finish floor as follows:

Oak Flooring....................for....................
Maple Flooring....................for....................
Yellow Pine Flooring....................for....................
Fir Flooring....................for....................

All shall be smoothed, scraped, sand-papered and thoroughly protected. Smooth all uneven places and clear off all stains, finger marks, etc., from floors before turning over to painter.

DOOR AND WINDOW FRAMES, LOUVRES, ETS.:—Shall be clear Cypress or White Pine stock. Outside door frames shall be of sizes as marked on plan, shall be rabbeted ½ inch by thickness of doors. All inside door jambs shall be ⅞ inch thick by thickness of partitions, of same wood as trim of wood in which it faces and fitted with ⅜x1¾ inch stops. All single sash frames shall be regular plank frames, rabbeted ½ inch by thickness of sash. All frames for check rail windows shall be of the form, styles and dimensions as marked on plans; all pulley stiles shall be ⅞ inch thick and fitted with pulleys.

DOORS:—All doors shall be of the size and style as indicated in the drawings. Front doors shall be....................
Balance of outside doors shall be....................
Inside doors shall be....................
Provide and install door or panel at base of bathroom partition as shown on plans, which shall be fitted with suitable casing, jambs and trim.

WINDOWS, SASH, TRANSOMS AND SHUTTERS:—If of wood, shall be clear Cypress or White Pine stock. Windows shall be of the size and style shown on plans. All check rail or double hung windows shall be plowed and bored for weights and shall be properly fitted and evenly balanced. If windows are put into frames before the house is plastered, they should be refitted and balanced on weights after the plaster is dry. Care must be taken that all are well and evenly balanced and work freely in the pulley stiles. All casement sash and transoms shall be hung to swing as desired by owner, where not otherwise mentioned. Provide and hang all shutters as indicated on plans.

INSIDE FINISH:—All finish shall be clear, sand-papered clean and smooth. Install and place picture moulding where directed. All windows to have proper stools and aprons. Outside doors shall be fitted with thresholds. Provide and put in place beam ceilings, wainscot, columns, seats, book cases, mantel shelf and all cabinets, etc., where same are shown on plans. Provide and place angle beads where required. Construct and set in place all shelving as shown on plans and as directed by the owner, all shall be complete in every respect and ready for use. Closets shall be trimmed with plain casings and base, and to have hook strip fastened to walls and to extend around entire closets with hooks fastened to same about 8 inches apart. All inside finish shall be ....unless otherwise mentioned below, in which case the room mentioned after the kind of wood shall have trim of that wood.

Oak ....
Birch ....
Gum ....
Yellow Pine ....

Fir ....
Cypress ....
White Pine ....
The style of casings, base, picture mould, etc., shall be selected by owner.

CABINETS:—Provide and install all cabinets and mantels as per plan. All shall be of same finish as room in which they are located. All cabinets shall be placed and set in a proper and workmanlike manner.

STAIRWAYS:—Build all stairs as per drawings, in the most substantial manner, or as hereinafter specified; all made from thoroughly seasoned materials; treads and risers tenoned and grooved together, both front and back; balusters dovetailed and wall-strings glued to treads and landings. All treads and risers housed into wall-strings, wedged and glued thoroughly. Stair builder to box, cover and protect stairs from injury, and fur off all soffits ready for plastering.

Rear and attic stairs, if such are shown on drawings, shall have 2x10 carriages, 1⅛x10-inch treads, ⅞ inch risers and ⅞ inch wall string. Shall be fitted with cove mould under nosings. Provide suitable hand rail for attic stairs. Cellar stair shall have 2x10 carriages, 1⅛x10 treads and 1x8 risers. Shall be provided with 2x4 rails, 4x4 posts and completed in a first-class manner.

CLOTHES CHUTE:—If shown in plan shall be lined with.................... Provide and install doors as per plan. Doors shall be fitted with suitable hardware. Doors and trim shall match room or closets into which they open. Provide suitable receptacle in basement.

SCUTTLE:—Construct a scuttle door in ceiling, where shown on plans and case in neat manner.

HARDWARE:—All finishing hardware will be furnished by owner. Same shall be received, sorted, cared for and installed by this contractor. He shall sort and store finishing hardware immediately upon delivery and shall notify the owner of any hardware not delivered or incorrectly delivered. This contractor shall be solely responsible for all hardware after delivery and shall make good at his own expense any hardware which may be injured or lost following delivery.

All rough hardware of every kind required for the finishing of the building shall be furnished and installed by this contractor, including all spikes, nails, screws, sash weights, window pulls, cord, joist anchors and wall plate anchors and any and all other like items of rough hardware.

PROTECTION:—This contractor shall provide protection for all carpentry work installed by him during the execution of this contract, same to be saved from all injury until completion of the building and he shall replace any work injured due to his failure to properly protect it.

IRON AND STEEL

SCOPE OF WORK:—This contractor shall deliver to the building site all miscellaneous steel and iron necessary for the completion of the building. This includes wrought iron gates, grills, hinges, hinge plates, steel windows and steel sash, fireplace equipment and all steel columns, beams and lintels. Steel windows and iron grates, grills and railings shall be installed by this contractor. The remainder of steel and iron to be placed by other craftsmen as needed. All work specified herein must be installed by experienced craftsmen, only the highest type of workmanship being acceptable.

This contractor shall take all measurements at the building and may be required to make all work set exactly and he shall be responsible for the accuracy of such measurements. All materials shall be of standard quality as required by the standard specifications covering the material in question. Unless otherwise definitely mentioned this contractor shall set in place all of the work covered in this contract, same to be in strict accordance with the detailed drawings. He shall do all drilling which may be required and shall furnish all necessary bolts, rivets, screws, etc. Provide and install coal chute when shown on plan.

This contractor shall give all items included in this contract a shop coat of paint. Paint except for damper shall consist of a lead and oil paint. Before applying the paint this contractor shall make certain that all rust, dirt and grease spots are removed.

ROOFING AND SHEET METAL

ASPHALT, ASBESTOS OR PREPARED SHINGLES:—Provide and cover..roofs with.. shingles, and lay according to the specifications issued by the manufacturer. Care should be taken to see that all joints are well lapped and solidly nailed with large head nails as furnished. The contractor for this work shall see that the roof sheathing is properly laid and well nailed before beginning.

CANVAS ROOFING:—Over.. lay 12-ounce duck. Thoroughly soak in water before laying. First paint the D. & M. sheathing with thick coat of white lead and oil paint, then stretch the canvas and nail it in position with large headed roofing brads. The canvas shall receive first coat of paint before it begins to dry.

SLATE ROOFING:—The entire roof surface shall be covered with extra heavy slating felt and over this surface slate the roof with roofing slate. Slate shall be.. Each slate must have at least two copper slating nails and must be so laid so that the third course will lap the first at least three inches. All hip and valley slate shall be cut to the proper bevel and must be well bedded with slaters' cement. All slating must be done in a thoroughly mechanical manner and be water tight at completion and to the satisfaction of the owner. Slater shall see that the roof is properly stripped before proceeding with this work. The contractor shall furnish a written guarantee for a period of five years.

TILE ROOFING:—Cover roof as shown on plans with.............................. roofing tile according to the manufacturers' specifications. Provide ridges, finials, copings, etc., in a complete workmanlike manner. None but skilled mechanics shall do this work. Roofer shall see that roof is properly laid and wood strips in proper position before proceeding with this work. The contractor shall furnish a written guarantee for a period of ten years.

COMPOSITION ROOFING:—This contractor must see that the entire roof sheathing surface and all wall strips for gutter flashing have been properly and securely set in place. He must make certain that all brick and stone masons have completed the top of all walls so that the roof will not be used as a work platform after the felt has been laid. Cover the entire roof surface with a four-ply tar and gravel roof composed of best tar roofing felt well cemented together and to sheathing board with hot tar so laid that there will be a thickness of four layers in all places well flashed along walls and when nailing is required, nail with 4d nails and tin washers. Cover the entire felt surface with a thick layer of hot tar even flowed on and coarse clean gravel which must be thoroughly dry and spread on the tar before it gets cool. All this work must be done by expert roofers and must when completed be perfectly water tight and to the satisfaction of the owner and the contractor must furnish a written satisfactory guarantee to the owner to keep the roof in a perfect water tight condition for a period of five years from the completion of the work.

SHEET METAL—Gutters and Down Spouts:—Gutters shall be detailed without pitch. Provide and place outlets and mitres as needed. Support outer side of gutter with metal straps on roof every three feet. Down spouts shall be corrugated and approximately three inches in diameter. Down spouts shall be approximately 10 foot lengths and joints shall be lapped turn inside and outside and well soldered. Slip joints shall be provided in gutter and conductor. Down spouts shall be fitted in drain tile and joints shall be neatly cemented up. Down spouts shall be held clear of wall by metal hooks; a wire strainer shall be provided where water enters down spout. All the above sheet metal shall be ....

Flashing:—Whenever vertical surfaces of any kind intersect the roof the joints shall be carefully flashed. Where vertical surfaces are stucco the flashing shall form a stopping bead for the stuccoing. Where flashing occurs against brick, the flashing shall be let into a brick joint and the joint pointed with elastic mortar. Ribb flashing shall be 8 inches wide lapped and soldered. Flashing shall be..

METAL ROOFS:—Metal roofs where shown on plans shall be.. laid over rosin sized paper. Seams shall be locked, standing seams soldered. Form drip at edge of eaves.

VENTS AND CHUTES:—Place No. 24 gauge galvanized iron vents in kitchen and for clothes chute lining as may show on plans.

GUARANTEE:—The contractor shall guarantee all of the above work for a term of five years from the date of completion and acceptance of the work. Such guarantee to protect the owner against all defects in material or workmanship. If any such defects develop this contractor shall make all necessary repairs without cost to the owner.

TILE WORK—INTERIOR

SCOPE OF WORK:—This shall include tile floors for..
Tile base in..
and tile wainscot in..

MATERIALS:—Floor tile for.............................. shall be.............................. Tile base for .... shall be.............................. Tile wainscot for.............................. including Bull nosed jamb, shall be standard 4x4.............................. glazed. Shall be.............................. high except over the tub, which shall be.............................. high, with molded cap. All walls to receive tile shall first be covered with metal lath.

TILE FLOORS:—Over the entire surface to be covered this contractor shall first lay a thickness of heavy asphalt saturated building felt, same shall be lapped at least two inches and turned up at walls two inches.

CONCRETE SETTING BED:—This contractor shall install over the building paper as specified above a concrete setting bed consisting of one part portland cement to two parts sand and four parts gravel, into which there shall be imbedded a layer of 2"x2" mesh No. 12 gauge wire reinforcing. Concrete setting bed shall be brought up to a point sufficiently below the finished floor line to allow for the tile and a ½" thick mortar setting bed.

MORTAR SETTING BED:—The concrete setting bed shall be thoroughly saturated before applying the mortar setting bed. Mortar for setting bed shall consist of 1 part cement to 3 parts sand and shall be not less than ½" thick. Mortar setting bed shall be laid just before tile is laid.

SETTING TILE:—The setting bed shall be dusted with dry cement before setting the tile. The tiles shall be placed upon and firmly pressed and tamped into the mortar, until exactly true and even surfaces even with the finished floor line are obtained. All joints shall be grouted with portland cement grout. All surplus grout shall be removed and the faces of tile left clean.

PROTECTION:—After being cleaned, the floor shall be closed to traffic until the tiles are firmly set. All completed tile work shall be turned over in a clean condition.

PREPARATION OF SURFACE:—This contractor shall apply to the surfaces to be tiled a scratch coat of mortar mixed in the proportions of one part portland cement to three parts sand with hydrated lime added at the contractor's option not to exceed 10% of the volume of the cement mortar. The scratch coat shall be at least ½" thick and shall be brought to true and even surfaces. While still plastic the scratch coat shall be deeply scored horizontally.

SETTING:—Wainscot must be set in neat manner to make a finished job with true and even surfaces. Tile shall be set on a thoroughly dampened scratch coat. Use setting mortar composed of three parts sand to one part cement with 1/10 part hydrated lime.

CLEANING:—Upon completion of the various portions of his work, the tile contractor shall remove all unused materials, rubbish, etc., in connection with this contract and shall give the tile work a thorough cleaning at completion.

PAINTING AND GLAZING

SCOPE OF WORK:—This branch of work shall include the finishing of all wood trim both interior and exterior and the finishing of all wood floors, the enameling of plaster surfaces in the kitchen, bath and lavatory and the painting of all iron work and all of the glazing.

MATERIALS:—
Exterior paint shall be..
Exterior stain shall be..
Interior stain shall be..
Interior varnish shall be..
Floor varnish shall be..
Spar varnish shall be..
Enamel shall be..
Metal preservation paint shall be..
Paste wood filler shall be..
Shellac shall be..

Putty as used herein under painting shall consist of whiting with basic carbonate white lead mixed with pure, raw linseed oil.

OUTSIDE WOOD WORK:—All outside wood work such as .... shall be painted. All shall be given a priming coat of paint directly after erection. Nail holes and imperfections shall be neatly puttied before finish coats are applied. Two finish coats in color as selected shall be applied after all other work is completed. Particular care being taken not to apply any coat until the remaining coat is dry. No painting of any exterior work in wet or freezing weather will be permitted. All outside wood work such as.. shall be stained three coats of creosote stain. Front door shall be..

INTERIOR WORK:—The painter must see that all work is in proper condition to receive the first coats before proceeding with the work. The following rooms and work shall be painted, varnished, stained or enameled as specified below:
Living Room and..
Dining Room and..
Chambers and..
Bath and Toilets and..
Kitchens and..
Entries and..
Main Stairway..
Other Stairways..
Plaster Walls in..
Closets..
Floors..

INTERIOR PAINT WORK:—All interior work which is to be painted unless otherwise specified shall receive a priming coat composed of white lead, pure linseed oil, turpentine or flatting oil and drier as well as two additional coats of the same white lead paint.

INTERIOR ENAMEL WORK:—Apply three coats of paint as specified for interior paint work, then apply two coats of enamel.

INTERIOR VARNISH WORK:—All inside wood work which is to be varnished shall be stained and filled as soon as delivered to building and all oak floors shall be filled as soon as laid and properly smoothed by carpenter. All oak and porous wood shall be filled with paste filler in colors as selected. All other wood work shall be filled with.. Over all filled wood work and trim apply two coats of varnish. Over floors and main stair treads apply two coats of floor varnish. Allow 48 hours between coats. All shellac and varnish to be well rubbed between coats. Over all other wood work not specified apply..............................

MISCELLANEOUS WORK:—The interior of cabinets and drawers, trays, closet shelves and pulley stiles of windows and all other like items shall be filled with two coats of linseed oil, brushed on.

METAL WORK:—All miscellaneous steel and iron work such as cast iron doors, fireplace equipment, wrought iron ornaments, steel sash and all similar items shall be given two coats additional to the priming coat of metal protective paint same to be in colors as selected.

At the completion of the work contractor shall remove all varnish or paint spots and blemishes that may have accumulated on the work of other contractors and leave such work in the same condition as he found it. Any paint work which becomes marred or which develops imperfections shall be refinished by this contractor.

GLAZING:—Measurements shall be taken at the building and this contractor shall be responsible for accuracy of such measurements and for the fit of the glass. Approximate sizes for glass are shown on elevations. All glass except in doors shall be set in putty. Such glass shall be back puttied and set with glazier's points or hooks and then shall be face puttied brought out even to the width of the rabbet. Glazed doors shall be provided with glazing mould. Glass in these locations shall be bedded in putty and the mould securely set with screws.

Putty used for glazing shall be approved putty used for glazing steel sash.

Cellar Sash to be glazed with.............................. quality of.............................. glass.

Attic Sash to be glazed with.............................. quality of.............................. glass.

Sash over 24"x24" in size to be glazed with .... quality of.............................. glass.

Sash less than 24"x24" in size to be glazed with .... quality of.............................. glass.

Steel Sash to be glazed with D. S. A. glass. Glass of less thickness shall not be used. Glaze according to the manufacturer's specifications.

Front Door to be glazed with.............................. quality of.............................. glass.

Rear Door to be glazed with.............................. quality of.............................. glass.

Grade Door to be glazed with.............................. quality of.............................. glass.

Sash Doors to be glazed with.............................. quality of.............................. glass.

French Doors to be glazed with.............................. quality of.............................. glass.

Plate Glass..
for ....

Art Glass to be set in and cost..........................
per square foot.
Florentine Glass ....
for
Miscellaneous ....
This contractor shall protect all glass installed
by him. All glass broken as a result of this contractor's failure to properly protect it shall be
replaced by him at his own expense.

ELECTRICAL WIRING

SCOPE OF WORK:—This contractor shall
provide all labor and material necessary to install
the electric wiring complete as shown on plans
and as herein specified.

CODE RULES:—All work shall be done in
accordance with the rules of the National Electric
Code, and any local department having jurisdiction. All necessary certificates to be obtained by
contractor at his expense.

No materials shall be used in any part of the
work except those that have been approved by
the National Board of Fire Underwriters and
having their stamp shown plainly on them.

GUARANTEE:—The contractor shall guarantee to make good any defects in the wiring system that shall develop within one year from date
of acceptance, due to faulty materials or poor
workmanship.

WIRING SYSTEM:—This shall be as selected
by owner or as dictated by the construction and
the rules of local departments having jurisdiction.

FIXTURES, APPLIANCES, ETC.:—All shall
be as approved by owner and a list of same to
be furnished shall be attached to contract.

PLUMBING

SCOPE OF WORK:—This contractor shall
provide all labor and material and fixtures necessary to install the waste and sewage system,
water and supply system complete as shown on
plans and as herein specified.

CODE RULES:—All work shall be in strict
accordance with all city or state laws, ordinances,
etc., and in every case in accordance with the
standard of first-class construction.

MATERIALS:—All materials shall be the best
of their respective kinds.

FIXTURES, APPLIANCES, ETC.:—All fixtures and appliances shall be as approved by
owner and a list of same with a detailed description shall be made a part of contract.

GAS FITTING:—The owner will notify gas
company and provide for bringing the main into
building. He will also give location of gas outlets as desired. Contractor shall provide and run
pipes from the supply of gas to each outlet all
of a sufficient capacity to give ample supply and
all shall be put in in accordance to rules and
regulations of gas company. All pipes to be
properly fastened and secured. Locate meters
where directed or shown. Contractors shall furnish owner a certificate of inspection by gas company. Any and all gas fixtures shall be furnished by the owner and shall be installed by
the contractor.

GUARANTEE:—This contractor shall guarantee to make good any defects in the plumbing
system that shall develop within one year from
date of acceptance due to faulty materials or
workmanship.

HEATING

HEATING SYSTEM:—The heating system
shall be as selected by owner, and installed in
accordance with specifications and the highest
standard of good practice in heating design.

The contractor shall furnish the owner with
a copy of heating layout showing the complete
system, together with a description of all parts
and appliances. This layout and description shall
form a part of the contract after being approved
in writing by the owner.

GUARANTEE:—This contractor shall guarantee the system installed to heat all rooms in this
house to 70 degrees Fahrenheit when the outside
temperature is 10 degrees below zero.

This contractor shall also guarantee to replace
or make good any part of heating equipment
which shall become defective within one year
from date of acceptance, due to faulty material
or workmanship.

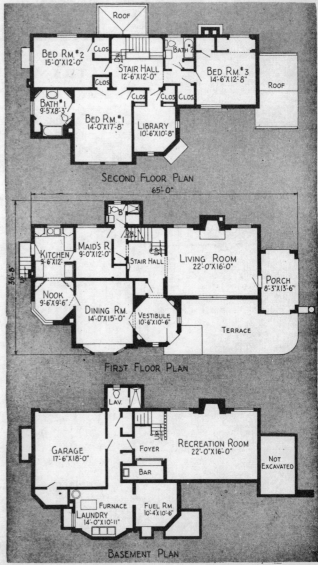

Second Floor Plan

First Floor Plan

Basement Plan

THIS HOUSE is notable in that, early in the 1935 season,
it aroused public interest in Cincinnati in home building
and in quality construction. Among the first of the truly
modern type homes to be opened to the public, this perfect example of design and construction was acclaimed
by the newspapers and by the home seeking public. Its
unusual talking point was the Stran-Steel frame, rigid, safe,
and practical

STRAN-STEEL HOUSE

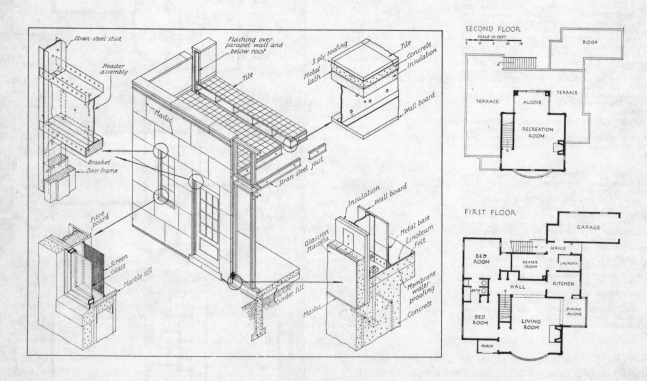

Framing details and floor plans

SPECIFICATIONS

of materials and labor required for the construction and completion of the Stran-Steel Exhibition House, Housing Group, A Century of Progress, Chicago, Illinois. 1933 and 1934. Built for Mr. Carl A. Strand, Detroit, Michigan, in conformity with the accompaning drawings prepared by

H. Augustus O'Dell--Wirt C. Rowland
Associate Architects
Detroit, Mich.

ARCHITECTURAL TRADE. Excavating. Properly excavate to depths shown for all foundation walls. A neat cut may be made the width of continuous footings, provided banks will hold themselves during the construction of the footings, otherwise provide trench 12" wider of footings and form for same.

Crock drains. Lay a 4" crock drain where shown on foundation drawings. Lay with good uniform grade and connect to 6" crock drawing at trap as shown, after which 6" crock drawing is connected to sewer.

Backfill. Backfill against walls with good earth tamped solidly.

Cement, gravel, sand, etc. All the cement used in the work to be an approved brand Portland cement of uniform quality. All cement must be delivered at premises in original packages and stored on wood platforms under suitable shelter. All sand to be good, clean, sharp building sand. Gravel must be thoroughly clean, free from loam, and to be suitable size for the work.

Footings. Pour, 1:2:4, concrete footings under walls where indicated, providing re-inforcement in same as indicated on drawings.

Foundation walls. Build foundation walls to underside of first floor slab, properly forming same. Provide re-inforcement as indicated.

First floor plan. Provide and install monolythic first floor slab on the ground as shown by plan. Provide 6 x 6 # 10 wire mesh through out. Provide integral waterproofing of an improved brand in slot. Along exterior walls and at interior bearing partitions install wood nailing blocks flush with top of concrete where indicated by carpenter. Trowel surface of slab perfectly smooth and level, removing all trowel marks and leaving same in first class order.

Steel frame. Install complete steel frame above first floor as provided by the Stran-Steel Corporation and in accordance with their structural drawings. At first floor level anchor sill plates to wood blocks embedded in face of concrete by means of 3/8" lag screws at approximately 6' centers. Erect the first floor studding at 2' centers as shown on drawings. Connect bottoms of steel studs to steel plates by means of 1/4" stove bolts, holes being provided in sill plates and in bottom of studs for this purpose. On top of first floor studs connect channel plates with flanges turned down and bolt to top of studs in similar manner as to sills. Erect second floor and roof joists at second floor level spaced at 2' centers or as indicated on second floor drawings. Connect ends of joists to channel plates by means of 1/4" stove bolts, two bolts being placed in the end of each joist. Properly frame for stairs as indicated.

STRAN-STEEL

PURPOSE. The house was built to demonstrate new steel materials, a substitute for lumber framing and siding. The cost was $7,500, with $2,500 additional for special equipment. It is intended for a family of four, with one guest room and a one-car garage.

CONSTRUCTION AND FINISH. Built on a reinforced concrete wall with a 6 in. reinforced concrete slab, the house has a patented type of steel framing, which is bolted together, with the collateral materials nailed to the nailing grooves of the frame. The exterior wall surface is of porcelain enameled steel panels 2′ x 8′, pointed with mastic. The walls are insulated with 2-ply, ½ in. insulation board overlapped. The second floor is of 1½ in. monolithic concrete construction, with the metal lath reinforcement nailed to the steel joists, which are 2 ft. on centers. The finish floors are linoleum except in bedrooms which have wood blocks laid in mastic. The windows are steel casement with ultra-violet ray glazing. Interior partitions are of insulating wallboard nailed to steel studs, and finished in washable wall covering. The kitchen wainscoting is formica and that in the bathroom is linoleum.

EQUIPMENT. The house is completely air conditioned, having a gas-fired boiler. The kitchen equipment is specially designed, and includes gas range with a ventilating hood, steel shelving, and electric washer.

UNIQUE FEATURES. The type of construction permits speedy erection, is fireproof, has high insulating value.

Close up photo of exterior wall construction showing the sheets of Celotex, 1 inch thick, nailed to the Stran-Steel studs; then the Macotta units are attached by means of right angle nailing clips of steel. Photo shows the Enduro stainless steel edge around each Macotta unit. The joint is filled with caulking mastic.

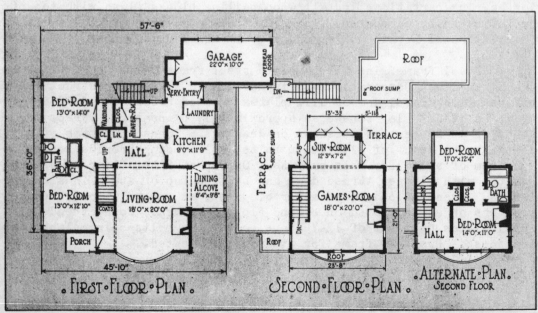

An alternate plan of the first floor would turn the heater room into a maid's room. The space below is then to be excavated for a heater room. The second floor may be made into a recreation room, or into two bedrooms with a convenient bathroom as shown.

Sub-floors. Over all joists at second floor level and over joists in roof of recreation room install layers of one-half inch cellotex. Stagger joints and nail solidly at 6" intervals by means of large headed, galvanized nails

Siding. Similarly to sub-floor install double layer of one-half inch cellotex over entire outside wall surfaces of house, staggering joints and using the same type of nail as for sub-floor.

Concrete slab for second floor and roof. Over the sub-bases for the second floor and roof pour concrete slab 1 1/2" thick of 1:2:4 concrete. Provide in this slab one layer of 6 x 6 #10 wire mesh. Trowel surface of concrete perfectly smooth and level, excepting for roof surfaces, which are to properly slope to drains. Remove all trowel marks and leave same in first class condition.

Concrete sub-stairs. Construct inside concrete stair slab spanning between first and second floor level. Slab to be 7" thick and to be provided with re-inforcement consisting of 5/8" rounds at 6" on center lengthwise of slab, and 3/8" rounds at 18" on center crosswise.

Brick flue. Build brick flue and around the flue lining as indicated on drawings. Flue to have 8" square fire clay flue lining 4" of common brick. Brick to be laid in mortar composed of one part Portland cement, two parts of lime and nine parts of sand. Flue to extend above roof as indicated on plan.

Glass iron macotta. The entire exterior wall surfaces are to be covered by sheets of glass iron macotta according to detail drawings furnished manufacturer. Generally this glass iron macotta is furnished in sheets 2' x 6' and being approximately 1 1/2" thick. Sheets of macotta are to be fastened to studs by means of angle clips, also provided by manufacturer and spaced according to his directions.

Steel sash. Steel sash to be provided through out and to be Fencraft special casement type with frames complete. Sash to swing out and to be provided with glazing beads. Hardware to be of bronze and of type to operate through stationary screens. Provide and install steel frame screens. Wire mesh to be # 18, bronze wire. Screens to be of removable type.

Ornamental iron work. Provide and install wrought iron trellises around front porch, outside steel stairs at rear of house, and inside stair railing, all as shown on drawings.

Roofing. Cover all roofs, except roof over garage and over recreation room with three ply-ten year guaranteed Barret roofing. Over garage and recreation room apply Barrett's tar and gravel roof. Roofs to be laid in accordance with the manufacturer's specifications for these types of roofs over concrete slab.

Sumps. At outlets to conductors from roof provide an approved type of sump with flat grating. Gratings to be set in elastic cement.

Metal flash. Properly flash all copings under French leading from solarium to terrace roof and elsewhere required to make all water tight. Provide metal roofs for bay window and front porch. Provide all conductors leading from roofs to drains under first floor.

Tile. On terrace roof and in front porch slab apply 6" x 6" red tile furnished by Ludiwici Caledon Co. Tile to be laid in Portland cement mortar composed of one part Portland cement to three parts of sand. Joints of tile to be one-half inch apart in both directions and to be grouted solid with Portland cement grout. Provide proper expansion joints through out roof and fill same with an approved type mastic.

Elevations and floor plans.

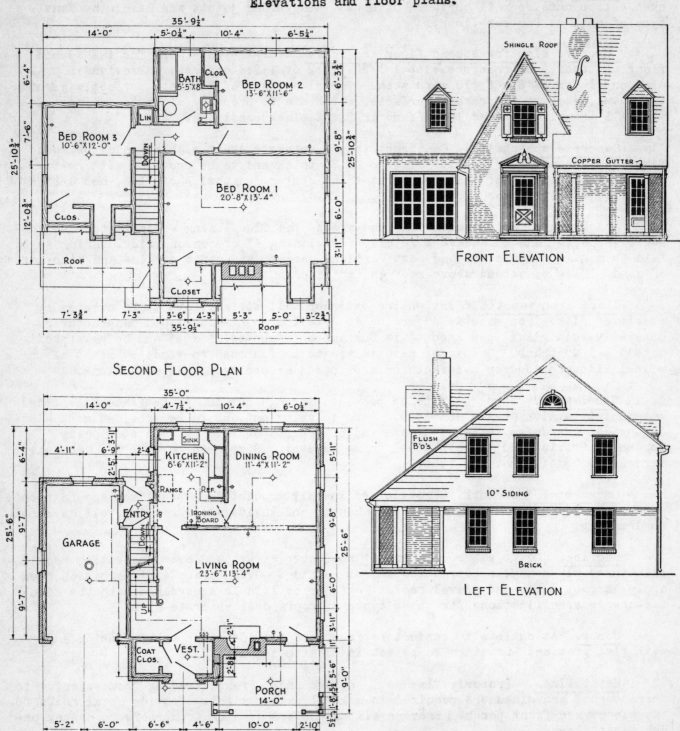

Chapter lV

Excavations

Actual work in the erection of a house begins with the digging of the earth for the foundation. No work, of course, could be done without the ideas, plans, specifications, contracts and building permits. But with the starting of the foundation excavation the work of the journeymen craftsmen begins. It is necessary that the CARPENTER AND JOINER understand all these steps.

Newer types of houses often have no basement or cellars, as space is provided for the heating plant, laundry or automobile in rooms on the same level as the kitchen, dining room, etc.

Locating Site for Excavations

In locating the place, on the building lot, for the foundation find the property line stakes on the lot or other surveyor's marks. If these stakes have not been placed the local community will authorize a surveyor to locate the property lines, the street line and the sidewalk line. Obtain the distance the foundation is to set over from one of the side property lines from the plan on the sheet marked PLOT PLAN. Measure in with the steel line and locate the outside lines of the foundation wall. Nail together the batter boards as shown and place in position. Stretch chalk line, measure and drive stakes as shown. Attach chalk line to stakes. Obtain the width and length of the foundation of the house from the PLOT PLAN or from the BASEMENT PLAN and lay off these lines.

Check each corner for squareness by using the six-eight-ten method. Mark off with a spade the line of excavation so that the excavating contractor will have a mark on the ground to use as a guide. Remove the chalk line but not the stakes to allow the workmen to remove the earth.

Observe the grading and hauling contractor as he removes the earth from the marked off area where the house is to be built. See that enough earth is removed to allow the worker to build up forms for the foundations if forms are to be used. See that the floor of the excavation is fairly level and that proper excavation is made for wall and post footings. See that the side walls of the excavation are trimmed and that proper ditches are made for drainage. Study very carefully the illustrations on the next page.

Practical Jobs

The making of a tool box may prove too difficult at this time. If so, the following jobs offer very elementary procedures. It is to be understood that the use of, and acquaintance with many hand woodworking tools has been made. If one has not become acquainted with many hand tools and their uses a study should be made using the list of references furnished in the introduction.

Foundations forms and
runs ready for pouring.

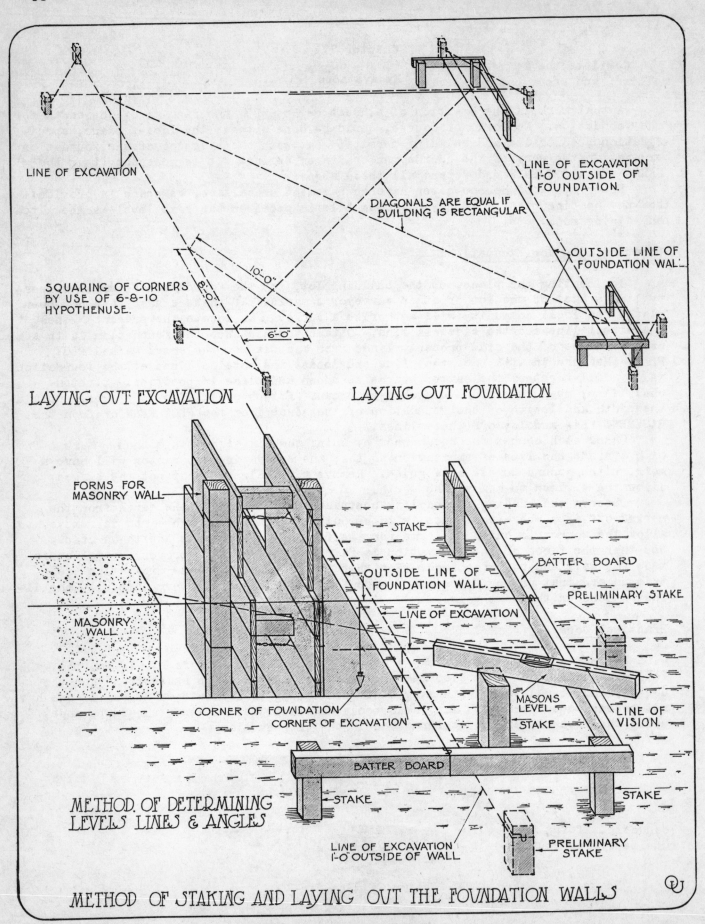

LINE OF EXCAVATION

LINE OF EXCAVATION
1'-0" OUTSIDE OF
FOUNDATION.

DIAGONALS ARE EQUAL IF
BUILDING IS RECTANGULAR

OUTSIDE LINE OF
FOUNDATION WALL

SQUARING OF CORNERS
BY USE OF 6-8-10
HYPOTHENUSE.

10'-0"

8'-0"

6'-0"

LAYING OUT EXCAVATION

LAYING OUT FOUNDATION

FORMS FOR
MASONRY WALL

STAKE

BATTER BOARD

OUTSIDE LINE OF
FOUNDATION WALL.

PRELIMINARY STAKE

MASONRY
WALL

LINE OF EXCAVATION

MASONS
LEVEL

LINE OF
VISION.

STAKE

CORNER OF FOUNDATION

CORNER OF EXCAVATION

BATTER BOARD

METHOD OF DETERMINING
LEVELS LINES & ANGLES

STAKE

STAKE

LINE OF EXCAVATION
1'-0" OUTSIDE OF WALL

PRELIMINARY
STAKE

METHOD OF STAKING AND LAYING OUT THE FOUNDATION WALLS

Complete the following jobs: Chop a stake, A: square a board, B; join boards by nailing, and erect batter boards, D. Refer to illustration on page 34.

Typical door and window details. See pgs. 239-251.

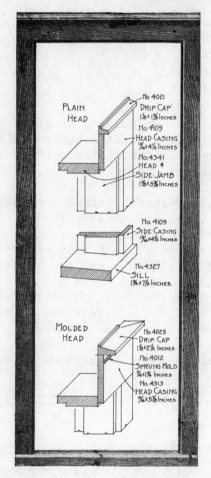

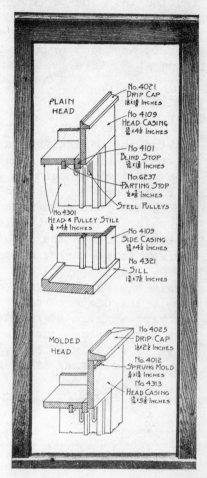

Related Studies

Drawing

Refer to the tool illustrations. These are what is known as photographic reproductions, that is, the things seen by the eyes or the eye of the photographer's camera. If these photographs were reproduced in pencil or pen lines they would appear about the same and would be known as perspective sketches. These drawings, as you see, have no dimensions and are used merely to give an idea of the appearance of the object or objects. It is very important to acquire the ability of distinguishing perspective drawings or sketches or reproductions from other types of drawings. What does a picture show? What does a pencil or pen line sketch show? Draw the perspective views of several of the hand tools.

Mathematics

The volume of any solid is found by multiplying the thickness by the width by the length. The amount of earth removed in excavating is obtained by multiplying these three dimensions in order to estimate the cost. What is the depth, width and length of the excavation? What is the content in cubical feet? In cubical yards? What is the cost of removing the earth for the foundation of the accompanying set of plans at $1.25 a cubic yard?

Science

It is a common practice to place distance of 24 inches or less on drawings by stating the dimensions in terms of inches only. The distance of six inches would be stated 6", of twelve inches 12", of twenty-four inches 24". The distance of two feet-ten inches would be stated 2'-10", of two feet-ten and one-half inches, 2'10$\frac{1}{2}$", of three feet-no inches 3'-0".

A two-foot rule is generally used in the measuring of short distances on stock. The rule is held in the left hand, edge down while markings are made by the pencil or knife held in the right hand. This is done to get the divisions as near to the surface to be marked as possible. The inch distance is related to a standard measure called the METER. The meter, a unit of length, was and is approximately the ten-millionth part of a fourth of the earth's meridian. The standard meter is the distance between two defining lines on the International Prototype Meter bar kept at zero degree temperature at Sevres, Paris, France. Accurate copies of this distance are supplied to various countries to serve as national standards. The meter is exactly .39.37 U.S. standard inches long.

The following table gives the relation of the inch to other measures

U. S. WEIGHTS AND MEASURES

LONG MEASURE (Measures of Length)

Ins.	Feet	Yards	Fath.	Rods	Furl.	Mile
12 =	1					
36 =	3	= 1				
72 =	6	= 2	= 1			
198 =	16½	= 5½	= 2¾	= 1		
7920 =	660	= 220	= 110	= 40	= 1	
63360 =	5280	= 1760	= 880	= 320	= 8	= 1

6080.26 Feet = 1.15 Statute Miles = 1 Nautical Mile or Knot.

What is measuring? Why measure objects? What are the divisions of the inch? How is a rule placed? What are the divisions of the foot and their relation to other distances?

English

It is necessary to ask for one thing or one item. At times it is necessary to ask for more than one thing or item. In making a list of tools or parts we must list the word that means just one tool or part and against we must list the word that means two or more parts or tools. The word HAMMER calls to mind just one tool while the word HAMMERS calls to mind more than one tool.

The following words call to mind just one tool or part: apron, pencil, building, saw, shop, plane.

List the above words in a column, numbering each word and after each word write the word that means more than one. An example is: 1. tool, tools. These words add s for plural.

List the following words and write the plural: box, pitch, cross, inch, brush, truss. These words add es for plural.

List the following words and write the plural: Study, sky, property, lady. These words add ies for plural.

List the following words and write the plural: workman, footman. These words change a to e for the plural.

It will often be found necessary to write a list of tools to use. Study the following way of listing, then, using this form, make a list of tools, adding the names of about 24 others in addition.

A List of Tools

No.	Kind	
1	Block plane	watch the spelling
3	Nail sets	
1	Pencil clasp	Plural or singular endings?
1	Saw set	
1	Miter box	

Civics

Visit or call to mind, a building lot on which will be found grass, brush, trees, water, etc. Building lots are not always level. Some slope from front to rear, others rear to front and may have exposed rock formation. A house must be placed to advantage on a building lot and it must harmonize with the houses in its immediate surroundings. One should study the houses in a particular place trying to learn just why such conditions are as they are. Study the virtues and vices of buildings in certain localities. Pick out a section of buildings, two or three city squares in area and describe the buildings. Are any too good, any too poor? What is the nature of the lots on which the buildings are built? Are there any vacant lots? Is there any reason for it remaining vacant?

Many cities have a plan for the future. A plan of civic betterment. The city of Cincinnati has a plan called THE OFFICIAL PLAN OF CINCINNATI, OHIO published in 1925 by the City Planning Commission. This is a plan for a bigger and better city. It should be read with interest.

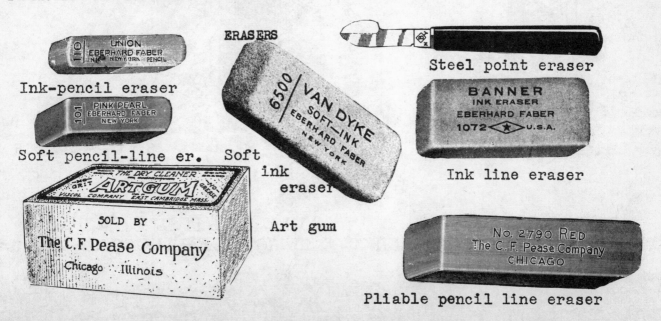

ERASERS

Ink-pencil eraser

Soft pencil-line er.

Steel point eraser

Ink line eraser

Soft ink eraser

Art gum

Pliable pencil line eraser

Forms for poured foundation walls

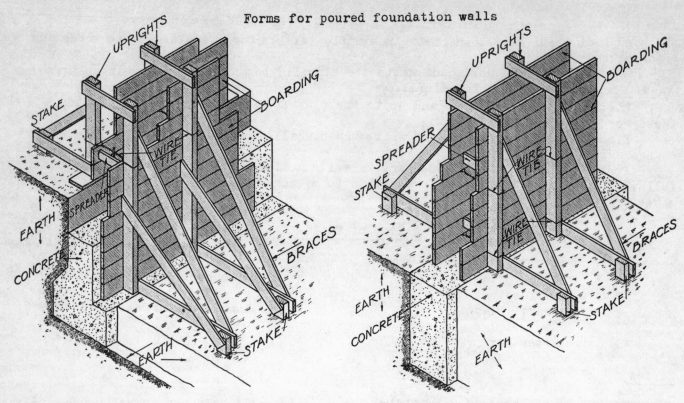

FORMS FOR WALL IN SOLID EARTH

FORMS FOR WALL ABOVE GRADE

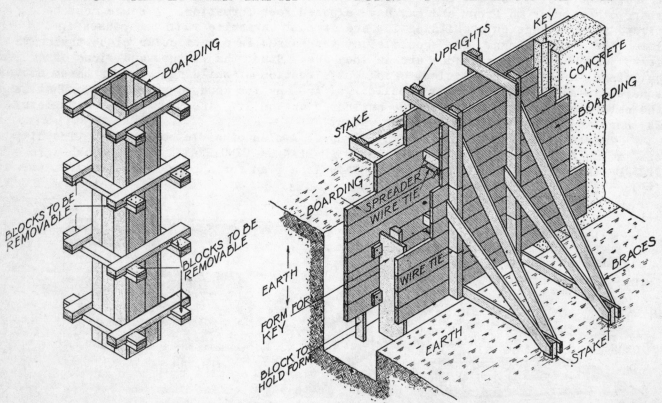

FORMS FOR PIERS

FORMS FOR WALL IN SOFT EARTH AND
METHOD OF KEYING WALL FOR A HALT IN CONCRETE

NATIONAL LUMBER MANUFACTURERS ASSOCIATION

Chapter V

Foundation Forms

In most sections of the country a large room or space is provided under a house for the purpose of housing certain conveniences, for insulation, storage, laundry and work space.   This space or room is commonly known as the basement. Some present day dwellings, making use of the more recent developments in household conveniences, do not require a large space and hence no large room is made available.

It is necessary, however, under any circumstances to provide a substantial foundation for a dwelling. If a basement is not needed, then proper walls and footings to hold the upper structure will be required. THE LOCAL BUILDING CODE WILL NEED TO BE CONSIDERED IN ALL CASES PECULIAR TO EACH LOCALITY.

Obtain the sizes and locations of all footings, both for the foundation wall and girder posts, from the details in the set of house plans. If the footings are to be formed by the shapes of the trenches in the earth, no wood or other types of forms will be necessary. The side walls of the earth should be carefully measured and trimmed. The concrete is then poured into these trenches and allowed to set for at least three days in dry weather and six days in damp weather. Concrete is most generally purchased by the cubic yard and sent to the job from a common mixing point by certain companies which specialize in supplying ready made concrete.

If footings have forms, erect these according to the details in the plans or study the following illustrations. Obtain the height of the foundation walls from the details. Mark off the height on a pole and erect it in one of the corners of the excavation near the batter boards. If this height does not exceed the height of the batter boards that have been placed in the ground for the excavation layout, then a chalk line can be restrung on the batter boards and the height of the outside wall line of the forms can be lined up by use of the original chalk line layout.

If the height of the foundation cannot be measured on the batter boards, then longer stakes must be erected at the batter boards and the chalk line strung on the stakes to the proper height.

The type of forms to use will, of course, be specified in the specifications and on the drawings. The following illustrations show forms of wood sheathing, metal and manufactured wood. See pg. 42 for practical jobs.

Related Studies

Drawing

The use of the rule is explained in Chapter IV, in the SCIENCE study. This study will deal with the relation of the rule to a certain tool used in the drawing work. It is called a scale. This tool is really a series of scales, there being as many as eleven different scales on some types of tools.

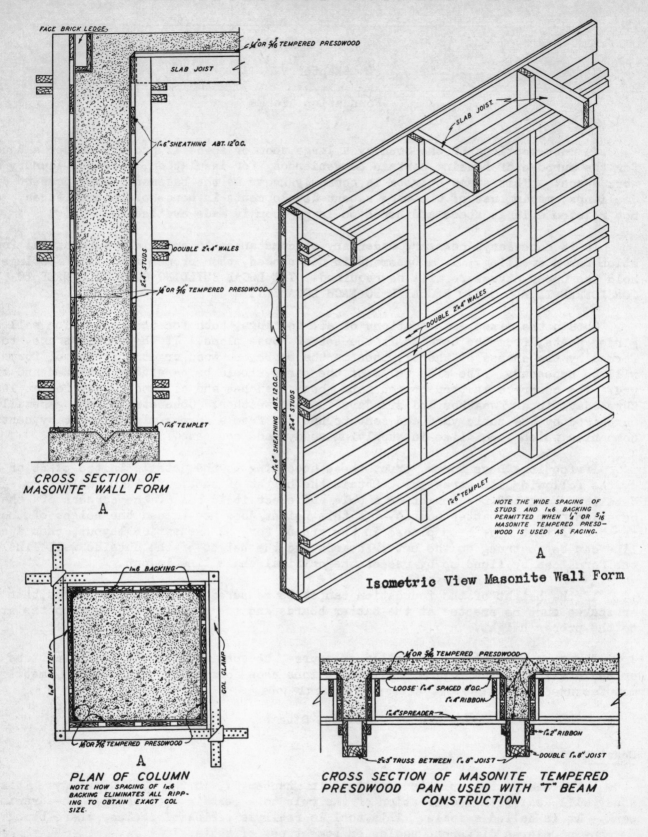

FACE BRICK LEDGE

¼" OR ⁵⁄₁₆" TEMPERED PRESDWOOD

SLAB JOIST

1" x 6" SHEATHING ABT. 12" O.C.

DOUBLE 2" x 4" WALES

2" x 4" STUDS

¼" OR ⁵⁄₁₆" TEMPERED PRESDWOOD

1" x 6" TEMPLET

CROSS SECTION OF MASONITE WALL FORM

A

SLAB JOIST.

DOUBLE 2" x 4" WALES

1" x 6" SHEATHING ABT. 12" O.C.

2" x 4" STUDS

1" x 6" TEMPLET

NOTE THE WIDE SPACING OF STUDS AND 1 x 6 BACKING PERMITTED WHEN ¼" OR ⁵⁄₁₆" MASONITE TEMPERED PRESD-WOOD IS USED AS FACING.

A

Isometric View Masonite Wall Form

1 x 6 BACKING

1 x 4 BATTEN

COL CLAMP

¼" OR ⁵⁄₁₆" TEMPERED PRESDWOOD

PLAN OF COLUMN
NOTE HOW SPACING OF 1 x 6 BACKING ELIMINATES ALL RIPPING TO OBTAIN EXACT COL SIZE.

A

¼" OR ⁵⁄₁₆" TEMPERED PRESDWOOD

LOOSE 1" x 4" SPACED 8" O.C.

1" x 4" RIBBON

1" x 4" SPREADER

1" x 2" RIBBON

2" x 3" TRUSS BETWEEN 1" x 8" JOIST

DOUBLE 1" x 8" JOIST

CROSS SECTION OF MASONITE TEMPERED PRESDWOOD PAN USED WITH "T" BEAM CONSTRUCTION

A. Showing use of manufactured wood PRESDWOOD for concrete forms.
Courtesy Masonite Corporation, Chicago, Ill.

The drawing of an object or objects often must be made larger or smaller, than actual size. This process is called drawing to scale or making the drawing in a relative proportion. The most commonly used standard proportions or scales are:

Full size. 12" on drawing is equal to 12" on the object.
Half size. 6" on drawing is equal to 12" on the object.
Quarter size. 3" on drawing is equal to 12" on the object.
Eighth size. 1½" on drawing is equal to 12" on the object.

Obtain a scale and a rule. Place the rule in the left hand and the scale on the right hand. Turn the scale to any one of the different faces or scales and see that the zero on the scale is at the first mark on the rule. If the quarter scale is used, see how the quarter scale divisions match up with every quarter inch on the rule.

All drawings must have on them the scale used and they are designated as follows: $\frac{1}{4}$" = 1'-0" or $\frac{1}{4}$" = 1'-3" or 1" = 3" or $\frac{1}{2}$" = 1' and so on.

The following shows the relation of the rule to the scale, the scale being turned to the $\frac{1}{4}$" scale:

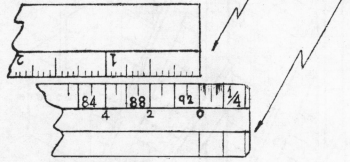

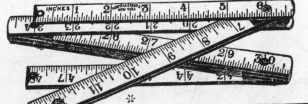

The ordinary folding rule used by the carpenter

A flat scale having four scales. Used by the architectural draftsman

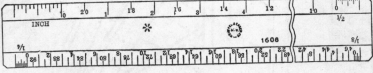

Study the flat scale, the triangular scale and the rule. Obtain the catalogs of several drafting room supply dealers and inspect the illustrations of the scales. Price the scales and read the important descriptive matter as given in the catalogs.

Practical Jobs

The following jobs, as shown in a unit of form work below, are the ones which follow those of making batter boards:

    a. Construct a form for a section of a footing.
    b. Construct a form for a section of a side wall.
    c. Construct a form for a key.
    d. If available use manufactured wood for the above
       wherever there are large flat areas.

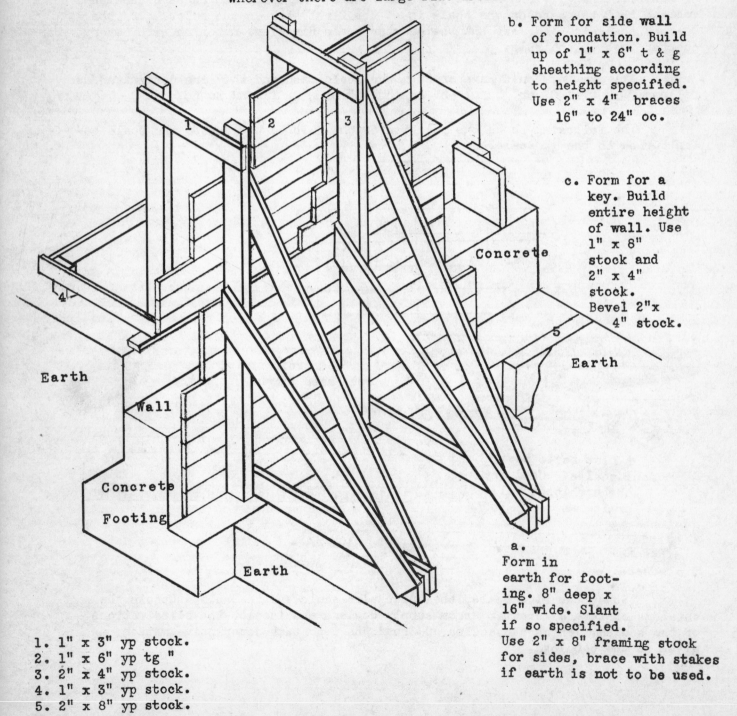

b. Form for side wall of foundation. Build up of 1" x 6" t & g sheathing according to height specified. Use 2" x 4" braces 16" to 24" oc.

c. Form for a key. Build entire height of wall. Use 1" x 8" stock and 2" x 4" stock. Bevel 2"x 4" stock.

a. Form in earth for footing. 8" deep x 16" wide. Slant if so specified. Use 2" x 8" framing stock for sides, brace with stakes if earth is not to be used.

1. 1" x 3" yp stock.
2. 1" x 6" yp tg "
3. 2" x 4" yp stock.
4. 1" x 3" yp stock.
5. 2" x 8" yp stock.

Mathematics.

The methods used to find the area of a surface is explained in Chapter II, in the Mathematics study. This method has a very close relation to the method of finding the number of board feet in an object or objects. By board feet is meant the relation of the area of one square foot to the thickness, usually one inch or multiples. That is, if a piece of lumber twelve inches wide and twelve inches long has one hundred and forty-four square inches in its surface, it will have one board foot of lumber for a board foot is 1" x 12" x 12". Each additional inch thickness of lumber adds another board foot. One way to calculate the board feet (b. f.)in lumber is to use this formula

$$\frac{\text{Thickness" x width"}}{12} \times \text{Length'}$$

The way to read this formula is to state; multiply the thickness in inches by the width in inches, divide the total by twelve and multiply the quotient by the length in feet. Lumber of less than one inches thickness is counted as one inch in thickness. $1\frac{1}{2}$" thickness as 1"; 1-3/4" thickness as 2"; $2\frac{1}{4}$" thickness as 2", etc. That is, calculate thicknesses in multiples of the inch; if a thickness is over the inch and not over the next half-inch, do not work with the half-inch, but if the thickness is over the half-inch and not quite to the next whole inch, calculate it as the next whole inch.

Note that board measure involves cubic measurement, one board foot being 1/12th of a cubic foot, or the lumber contained in a piece 1" thick by 12" wide by 12" long. In other words, twelve board feet equals one cubic foot.

Find the amount of tongue and groove material to be used in making forms for the foundation of the house in the accompanying set of house plans. This is done by finding the area of all forms. As the tongue and groove stock is not quite one inch thick, the board feet will be the square feet. Find the amount of braces by calculating the studding or 2" x 4" stock, as spaced every two feet. These pieces extend the entire height of the form wall in most cases and pieces are used for braces. List this material and work up a stock bill as shown in Chapter II. Add twenty pounds of 8 penny common nails every 1000 board feet. Add 3" of wire (annealed # 20) per every three board feet. Keep these estimates in a separate record, as this is the first division of the very important task of estimating the amount of material required to construct a house. The amount of labor needed to construct forms will be dealt with in Chapter VI.

Science

The inventor or inventors of the steel square are not known. Many prehistoric people understood how to square building materials, as evidenced in the findings in old ruins. The Egyptians and Greeks had a tool called the square and understood its use. The predecessor of the modern square was a clumsy and often inaccurate tool made in England during the Seventeenth century. It is believed the immediate predecessor of the modern tool was made in New Haven, Conn. during the Nineteenth Century. There are many steel squares on the market today. A few by name are: Topp's Framing Square; Combination Square and Level; Van Namee Framing Square; Nicholl's Square; Bridge Builder's Square; Machinist's Square; Combination Square and others.

A Construction Crew at Work

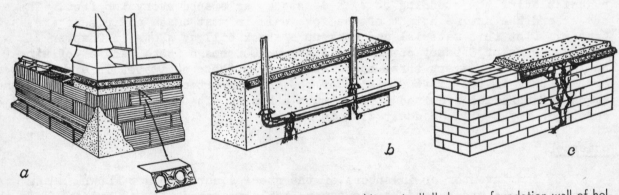

Methods of preventing damage by termites or white ants; "a" shows a foundation wall of hollow tile surfaced with stucco; note the metal termite shield; the top of the wall is capped with slate and concrete; "b" shows a concrete wall with termite shields on the wall and around the pipes; "c" shows brick wall with termite shield capped with concrete. (Courtesy of the Bureau of Entomology.)

The Nicholls Square, a popular favorite, has on it the various inch graduations, the rafter or framing table, the Essex Board Measure table, the brace table, the octagon scale and the hundredths scale.

Find out about some of the facts regarding the steel square. Refer to Stanley Rule & Level Plant's steel square booklet. Refer to a book by T. F. Hodgson, "Practical Uses of the Steel Square". Describe the tables found on the steel square. What is the cost of a good steel square?

English

In the English study in Chapter IV the use of singular and plural words was studied. One can continue to the next step, which is the forming of these words into complete sentences. A sentence expresses thought.   The thought must consist of a complete flow of reasonableness or logical expression. An example of incomplete thought will be found in these words -- The man -- Here we find nothing complete in expression or logic. We must build on to these words adding something about -- The man -- so we can say -- The man used the saw -- and we have a complete expression. This complete expression is called a sentence. For convenience we can divide a sentence in to parts which are; The object or thing talked about or the <u>subject</u>, the word of action or the <u>verb</u> and the thing said about the object or the thing on which action was taken or the <u>predicate</u>.

Use the words given in the English study in Chapter IV for elements of thought in complete simple sentences.

Civics

Write a letter or postal card to the AMERICAN INSTITUTE OF ARCHITECTS, Octagon House, Washington, D. C., asking for a folder describing the AIA system of filing or cataloging advertising material and technical data. The carpenter or apprentice will be interested in keeping some advertising material and technical data at hand. It is well to learn of a system of keeping this information in a logical and usable form.

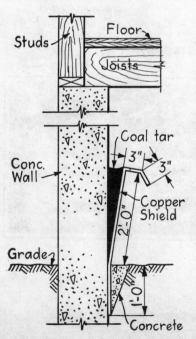

TERMITE shield for unprotected existing building. To install, rest shield against wall with bottom edge in shallow trench. Fill trench with concrete. When concrete hardens, pull top of shield away from wall and fill space with coal-tar pitch.

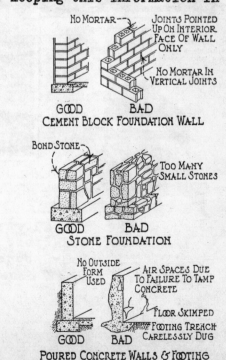

Showing concrete being poured into forms.

Illustrations showing the use
of metal forms.   This method is
very successful in large structures.

Placing Meyer Steelforms
Note the simple open wood centering
required—a feature that saves time,
labor and materials

Meyer Steelforms in Place
Ready for placing of concrete. Results like
this, delivered on time, save money all along
the line

Meyer Steelforms
Extremely rigid, thus maximum
re-use is·secured

Right: **View of Open Ceiling**
Illustrating the clean-cut attractive results
of concrete joist floor construction

Chapter VI

Foundations

The job of erecting a foundation is not done by the carpenter but it is
very necessary that he understand something about the construction of foundation walls and footings. The job of erecting foundation forms for concrete
construction is of course one for the carpenter and this type of foundation
is very popular. There are other types of foundation walls which are often
specified in dwelling construction, some of which are: brick, stone or concrete block.

Brick is suitable in very dry soils and then only for interior basement
partition walls. Stone walls are much stronger than brick walls, especially
if the stones are uniformly flat and hard. Concrete block walls made of good
Portland cement concrete is quite suitable to small dwelling work. These
blocks are well seasoned before being used, have the advantage of hollow construction which can be re-enforced with poured concrete at points and do not
necessitate form work.

One great objection to any built up wall is in the use of concrete or
mortar between the voids. This space at the meeting of these bricks, stones
or blocks forms an ideal opening for moisture and water to enter into the
basement. Hollow tile walls are often specified for walls in some localities.

Check over each detail of the concrete form construction. See that each
wall of the form is in place and PLUMB. Be sure that proper runways and platforms have been built for the men to work. When concrete is mixed in a concrete mixer on the job it must be wheeled in wheelbarrows from the mixer, up
a runway to the top of the forms and over platforms to the several places where
it is poured into the forms. Each batch of green concrete must be worked in
with a tamp so that no air pockets are formed. All of the forms must be filled
at one time while the concrete is still green, so that the entire job will form
one solid mass and dry uniformly. Anchor bolts must be placed in the walls as
designated in the plans.

If the whole job cannot be done at one time, a key must be used as shown
in Chapter V.

A concrete block foundation is generally built on a poured concrete footing. The blocks do not require a form, but each one must be erected with care
for plumb and spacing.

Stone or tile walls require great care in bonding.

After green concrete has been poured and allowed to set until it has become hardened, the several forms and runways are to be removed. A good way to
test concrete for firmness and quality is to attempt to scrape away a grain of
sand or piece of gravel with the thumb nail or a sharp tool. If sand and gravel can be removed by this process, the concrete is either green or of poor qual-

The following is a reproduction of a pencil and pen sketch of a dwelling. All the items true about the above illustration are true and in addition one can see the short strokes of the pen as they are made light and dark so that form is given to the sketch and one is given the idea of the picture of a dwelling even though it does not actually exist.

Vertical lines vanish at an infinite distance, hence are generally considered as parallel at all times.

The eye can 'vanish' horizontal lines but never can vanish vertical lines.

The following is a reproduction of a pencil and shading pencil sketch of a corner construction. The facts given about the first illustration on this page are true about this one and in addition much care has been given to the details of construction. All these illustrations are perspectives.

Vertical lines are parallel.

The use of two VP in order to give emphasis on just one side or phase of the sketch.

This illustrates a pencil and pen drawing of a dwelling not classified as a perspective one. Note its straight lines, both horizontal and vertical. Keep in mind that a camera could never take a picture like this of an actual dwelling.

Vertical lines are parallel.

Horiztonal lines are parallel.

An architectural drawing.

○ FRONT ○ ELEVATION ○

Horizontal line.

A mechanically made drawing.

Made for construction purposes. A WORKING DRAWING.

Vertical line.

ity. Remember, the foundation is to carry the full weight of the structure and
it must be of good quality.

      In taking away the forms, use a heavy claw hammer or wrecking bar. Carry
the boards or sections away from the concrete work. Save as much as possible
for future use. Do not allow pieces to drop down to the floor of the basement.
Do not needlessly rip or tear the lumber. If the forms are to be knocked down
entirely, remove the nails from the pieces and stack in an orderly pile on one
side of the building lot away from activities • In removing the forms from the
walls do not pry against the concrete wall to the point of injuring it.   Take
care not to chip pieces from the top edges of the wall. If a foundation wall
is very high or particularly hard to reach, a run-way must be built.   A ladder
is often used in these situations.

      A carpenter should be very careful to see that all points in good construct-
ion have been observed, as the foundation is the base of his own superstructure
and often good carpentry work is ruined by poor foundation work. A foundation
must be built so that it holds together and settles uniformly, otherwise uneven
settling causes bad breaks in upper construction work.

      The illustrations on page 50 show a few types of foundation materials.
Place sill anchor bolts as designated in plans. See pages 54 and 55 for illustrations of sill anchor bolts.

      Practical jobs. Observe and check over operations of cement contractor as
foundations are poured.

Related Studies

<u>Drawing.</u>

      In Chapter IV the study in drawing dealt with perspective sketches. This
study will continue the topic of pencil or ink perspectives and try to point out
certain important parts.

      A perspective sketch represents an object as it appears to the eye.   This
sketch is expressed through the medium of pencil or pen lines. Sketches are made
up of short, freehand (lines not drawn against a straight edge) lines so placed
as to give the appearance, as far as possible, of what a camera will show or what
the eye sees.

      Below is a reproduction of a camera photograph of a dwelling. Note that the

parts nearest you appear   largest and the parts in
the distance smallest.   Note how these lines tend
to grow smaller and seem   to come together on a line
which is commonly called   the horizon line.

Lines coming together   * Eye level
at vanishing point, VP.   or horizon
                                                               or center of
                                                               vision on
                                                               which all
                                          horizontal lines seem to
                                          vanish VP.

ROCK FACE BROKEN RANGE ASHLAR WALLS
USING ONE & TWO·MAN GRANITE RUBBLE

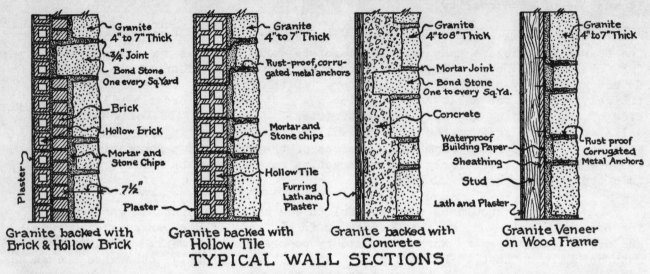

Granite backed with Brick & Hollow Brick
- Granite 4" to 7" Thick
- 3/4" Joint
- Bond Stone One every Sq. Yard
- Brick
- Hollow Brick
- Mortar and Stone Chips
- Plaster
- 7½"
- Plaster

Granite backed with Hollow Tile
- Granite 4" to 7" Thick
- Rust-proof, corrugated metal anchors
- Mortar and Stone chips
- Hollow Tile
- Furring Lath and Plaster
- Plaster

Granite backed with Concrete
- Granite 4" to 8" Thick
- Mortar Joint
- Bond Stone One to every Sq. Yd.
- Concrete
- Waterproof Building Paper
- Sheathing
- Stud
- Lath and Plaster

Granite Veneer on Wood Frame
- Granite 4" to 7" Thick
- Rust proof Corrugated Metal Anchors

TYPICAL WALL SECTIONS

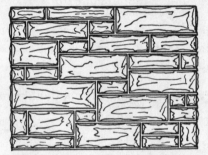

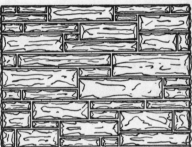

Typical Wall Pattern Rise 6" to 18" Length 1½ to 2 times rise

Moderate Elongated Pattern Rise 6" to 16" High pieces averaging 12". Length about three times rise

Extreme Elongated Pattern Rise 4" to 12". Length five to six times rise. Wall leveled every 22".

ELEVATIONS·SHOWING STYLES OF FACE JOINTING

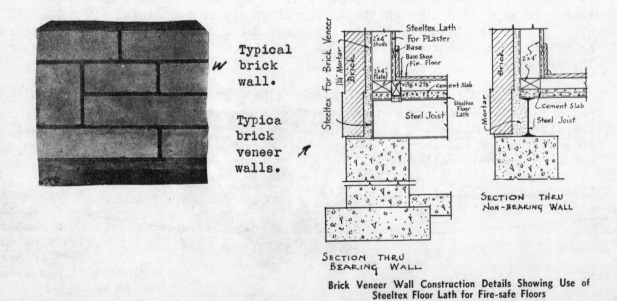

W   Typical brick wall.

Typical brick veneer walls.

Steeltex for Brick Veneer — Steeltex Lath for Plaster — 2"x4" Studs — Base — Base Shoe — Fin. Floor — ¼" Mortar — Brick — 2"x4" Plate — 1⅜" x 2⅝" — cement slab — Steel Joist — Steeltex Floor Lath

SECTION THRU BEARING WALL

Brick — Mortar — 2"x4" — Cement Slab — Steel Joist

SECTION THRU NON-BEARING WALL

Brick Veneer Wall Construction Details Showing Use of Steeltex Floor Lath for Fire-safe Floors

Study very carefully the foregoing explanations about perspective sketches. What is a horizontal line? What is a vertical line? What is the horizon, What is a vanishing point? What is the first tool (pencil or pen) used in making a pen sketch? At what point is the horizon placed in a perspective sketch? What do light lines and heavy lines tend to bring out in perspective sketching? Are long sweeping strokes used in sketching? For what purpose is a perspective drawing made? For what purpose is a photograph taken? What essential points of similarity exist between a photograph and a perspective drawing? What essential points of difference exist between a photograph and a perspective drawing. Copy the first, second and third illustrations as shown on page 48.

Mathematics.

A carpenter can usually frame up about one thousand board feet of form work in two eight hour days. This cost, based on an hourly rate, must be added to the cost of material of form construction as given in the preceding chapter. In foundation construction where no forms are used, this labor cost of course will not be considered, but the cost of masonry labor must be taken into consideration. Building code requirements must be considered in each locality, as some cities prohibit the use of hollow time for foundations, while others have certain restrictions. The cost of foundations walls of other than solid concrete is not considered in this text, as solid concrete walls are generally considered the best for dwellings.

Solid concrete construction is estimated, that is the cost, by the cubic yard. This simply means the finding of the number of cubic yards of mass in the walls, footings, bases, etc., and multiplying this by the cost per cubic yard for material and labor. The cost of concrete, including material and labor, is approximately $7.00 per cubic yard. This cost, of course, varies greatly with each changing locality and condition of construction. Find the cubical contents of concrete required in the footings and walls of the house, add to it the labor costs and keep in separate listing with the foundation form work estimates.

Science.

Concrete is composed of cement, sand, aggregate and water. These ingredients may be mixed on the job or purchased ready to pour. Artificial cement is composed of silica, alumina, iron oxide and lime in certain close ratios. These ingredients are mined from the earth. A good grade of Portland Cement is composed of the following parts. LIME 62 parts. SILICA 23 parts. ALUMINA 8 parts. IRON OXIDE, MAGNESIA, SULPHURIC ACID 7 parts. The last three parts are considered as impurities. Natural cements were used before artificial cements but their use has practically ceased with the innovation of artificial cements. Concrete is mixed by hand or in a mixing machine. If concrete is mixed by hand, the following steps are taken: a. prepare platform, b. spread on sand, c. spread on cement, d. mix with shovels and hoes, e. mix in water, f. mix in gravel, g. mix till slush mixture is obtained.

How is concrete mixed? What are the ingredients of concrete? Of cement? What is natural cement? What is artificial cement? How is concrete used in cold weather? Mix up a batch of concrete, using the foregoing ingredients as listed in the first sentence of this study. Refer to KIDDER'S ARCHITECTS AND BUILDERS HANDBOOK for additional information about concrete and cement.

English.

A series of complete sentences, closely related in meaning, are grouped into a unit of writing called a paragraph. Try to write a series of closely related sentences in which are described the characteristics of a pen or pencil sketch. Form sentences that convey but one meaning. The paragraph should contain about seventy-five words.

Civics.

Concrete is an artificial stone made by uniting cement, water and aggregate of sand and broken stone. Concrete for house foundations is mixed in the following proportions: 1 part cement, 2 parts sand and 4 parts coarse aggregate. It is dishonest and unfair for any builder to use a poor mixture of concrete. A poor mixture will result in accidents when the heavy structure is erected upon it.

In order to secure the utmost safety in concrete construction, cities have set up certain requirements embodied in laws known as a building code. The city of Cincinnati, in its building code, states as follows: 'Aggregate must be sound, clean and free from all foreign matter, such as clay, loam or combustible material. Proportions are to be $1-2\frac{1}{2}-5$.

Manufacturers recommendations are about the same as strict code laws.

Give several examples of poor concrete construction. What effect has poor concrete construction on a foundation? What are cement manufacturers recommendations for a good cement mixture? What are several code requirements for concrete mixtures?

Foundation and framing details.

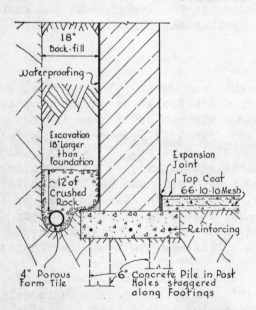

Note proper drainage, waterproofing, expansion joints, reinforcing and concrete pile supports to counteract earth shrinkage

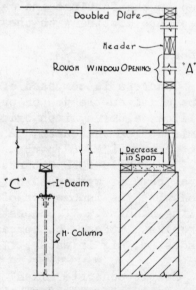

· FRAMING · DETAIL · ·

Two mud sills are used in joist framing at foundation line, one at inside and one at outside, thereby decreasing effective joist span about 12 inches. Plate on I-beam at C equalizes shrinkage.

A Pen and Ink Perspective Sketch

One's attention can be called to the following points as indicated.
A. Second tree is smaller than first. As distance becomes greater objects become smaller. B. Distinctive lines are indicated through the sketch. C. Heavy lines and light lines are used. This gives appearance of lights and shadows.

The following illustrations show typical construction details in light frame house construction. The several titles and accompanying notes offer adequate explanation.

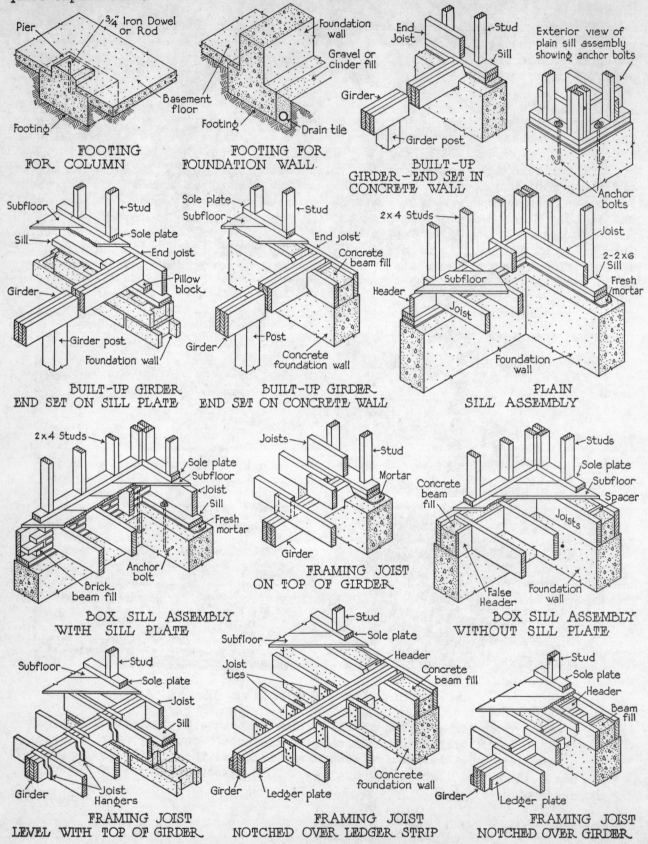

FOOTING
FOR COLUMN

FOOTING FOR
FOUNDATION WALL

BUILT-UP
GIRDER-END SET IN
CONCRETE WALL

BUILT-UP GIRDER
END SET ON SILL PLATE

BUILT-UP GIRDER
END SET ON CONCRETE WALL

PLAIN
SILL ASSEMBLY

BOX SILL ASSEMBLY
WITH SILL PLATE

FRAMING JOIST
ON TOP OF GIRDER

BOX SILL ASSEMBLY
WITHOUT SILL PLATE

FRAMING JOIST
LEVEL WITH TOP OF GIRDER

FRAMING JOIST
NOTCHED OVER LEDGER STRIP

FRAMING JOIST
NOTCHED OVER GIRDER

Chapter VII

Sills

The work involved in sill construction is a very important one for the carpenter. The concrete wall is the foundation on which all upper structures rest. The sill is the foundation on which all framing structures rest and it is the real point of departure for actual carpentry or joinery activities.

Sills are bases for wood or metal framing. Study the sills in the accompanying set of plans and refer to any other available plans. The illustrations show the typical methods of constructing sills for wood and metal framed houses.

After studying the house plans and learning the type of sill required, clean off the top of the foundation wall and see that each metal anchor bolt is ready for use. Secure good straight stock of the size required. Square off one end of the stock. Place bed plate on the foundation wall against the anchor bolts and mark off places where bolts are to enter the plate. Bore holes in this plate and then build up the sill as required. Use twenty penny common nails throughout. In making joints for the bed plate of header, use a lap joint as indicated below. Build the sill up, place over bolts, securely fasten down, level off, shim up where necessary and chop off any crown in the wood. Square all corners by use of the 6, 8, 10 method.

Lap joint of bed plate.

The following illustrations give a graphic idea of some of the necessary operations:

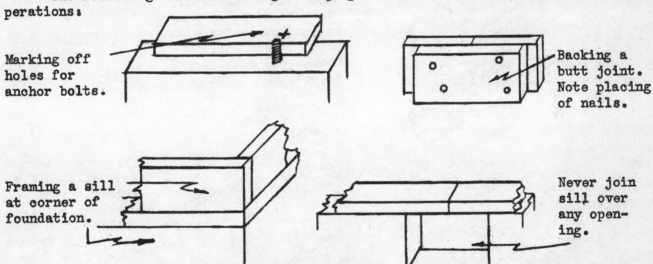

Marking off holes for anchor bolts.

Backing a butt joint. Note placing of nails.

Framing a sill at corner of foundation.

Never join sill over any opening.

If the plans and specifications call for a structural steel sill, build up according to plans.

Practical jobs: a. Build up a box sill as shown on page 54.
        b. Build up a structural steel sill as shown on page 56.
        c. Construct a corner of a 'T' sill.
        d. Level off and shim up sills.

Study the following illustrations of typical sill constructions.

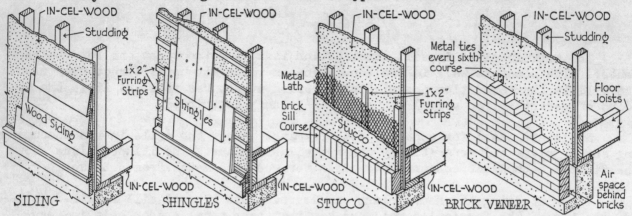

SIDING SHINGLES STUCCO BRICK VENEER

Details showing 'L' shaped box sills. In-cel-wood is a manufactured insulating material used in place of t&g sheathing. Beveled siding, Wood shingle, Stucco and Brick veneer walls are shown. Courtesy Cornell Wood Products Company, Chicago, Illinois.

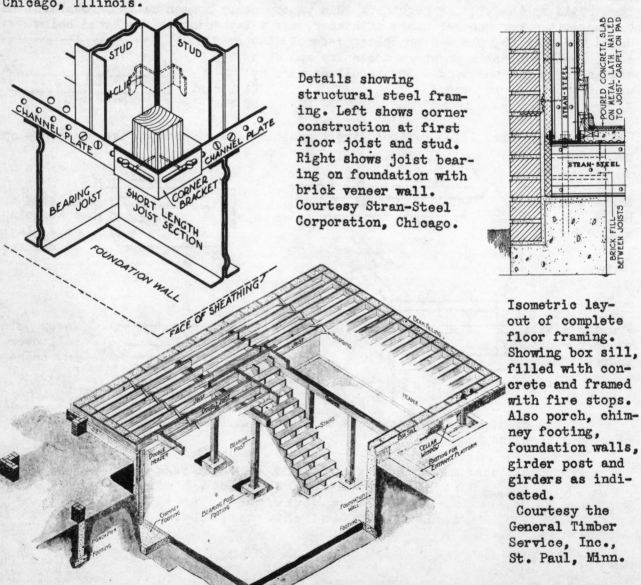

Details showing structural steel framing. Left shows corner construction at first floor joist and stud. Right shows joist bearing on foundation with brick veneer wall. Courtesy Stran-Steel Corporation, Chicago.

Isometric layout of complete floor framing. Showing box sill, filled with concrete and framed with fire stops. Also porch, chimney footing, foundation walls, girder post and girders as indicated.

Courtesy the General Timber Service, Inc., St. Paul, Minn.

Related Studies

Drawing

It has been shown that a freehand perspective sketch has many points in common with a photograph. In a highly developed technical work such as house construction one can understand readily that picture drawings are quite limited in their usefulness. Nature builds and expresses herself in curved and irregular lines, while man builds and expresses himself in straight lines, horizontals and verticals. Man has even devised a way of working out a perspective drawing by the use of straight lines. A pencil, scale and straight edge are used so that no line or point is suggested or faked according to methods of freehand perspective.

The following diagrams show the exact steps to take in the construction of what is known as two point and one point perspective drawing, not sketching. Follow these steps in their numbered order, so as to construct an angular perspective and a parallel perspective drawing. This is man's way expressed through geometrical or mechanical perspective to draw (not sketch) a picture.

The first layout shows a two point perspective drawing. It is also known as an angular perspective drawing.

The second layout shows a one point perspective drawing. It is also known as a parallel perspective drawing.

Each step in construction is numbered. Think through each layout, following the steps in numerical order.   See diagram on pg. 60.

Mathematics

Wooden or steel sills are built up on the job. Wooden sills usually consist of a bed member and an upright member called a header. Steel sills are of one piece, manufactured in certain widths ready for assembling on the job. Since these members are placed on top of the foundation wall and are the first members of the main frame, great care is taken in placing each part.

Wooden sills are estimated by taking the actual length needed to cover the top of the foundation wall. This length will equal the perimeter of the foundation wall wherever the sill member is required. Add one in number for every ten members used because of squaring of stock and lap for joints. If the bed plate and header are of the same size (2" x 8") or (2" x 10") standard lengths of the stock can be ordered. If the entire perimeter is 185', this length will be divided by 8 or 10, which will give the number of pieces required, plus the several added for squaring and joining.

Steel sills can be ordered by the length, size and stock number of style designated in the specifications. The labor costs can be figured as about twenty hours for every 1,000 board feet of lumber and about ten hours for every 1,000 linear feet of steel sill stock.

Estimate the number of pieces of stock (wood or steel) needed in the sills in the accompanying set of house plans. Estimate the entire cost, material, bolts, nails and labor. Keep these estimates in a separate record, along with similar estimates as described heretofore.

A Popular Cape Cod Colonial House with Garage

Another Popular Demonstration House

Science

There are several types of sills in use in modern house framing, the chief ones being: balloon frame sill, braced frame sill, box or western sill and 'T' sill.

Sills are constructed of pine or oak wood. The bed plate should be anchored every 10' or so by use of a 5/8" or 3/4" anchor bolt about 18" long, which is set in the concrete foundation wall as it is being poured.

Sills generally have bearing under their entire length. The chief factors of a sill should be its resistance to cross grain crushing and ability to withstand decay and insect attack. All wood has more resistance against crushing lengthwise or with the grain than it has in crushing across the grain. No. 1 common grade of Douglas fir can withstand a load of 1100# per square inch with the grain but only 325# per square inch across the grain.

This is an illustration of a mature termite or white ant. These ants live in the earth and carry on their activities from there. If they are shut off from the moist earth they will die. These ants can eat their way through poorly made masonry walls and get to wood members. Preventative means, such as using sills treated with creosote or zinc chloride, termite metal shields or slate pieces imbedded in good cement can be used.

Illustrate a method of framing a sill over a basement window. What points should be observed? What is the crushing strength of several commercial woods? Obtain several samples of wood about $\frac{1}{2}$" square and 3" long. Crush each piece in a vise of C clamp, first against the grain, then with the grain. Which offers the greatest resistance, crushing with the grain or against the grain?

English

One of the essential jobs in estimating material is that of order writing. Stock is estimated and orders written for it. The following is a typical order on a mill for stock for a sill Pg. 61.

HERE is the "danger zone" in any building, which should be of treated lumber to guard against termites and decay.

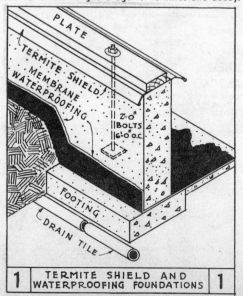

1 | TERMITE SHIELD AND WATERPROOFING FOUNDATIONS | 1

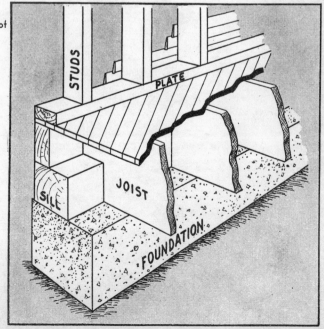

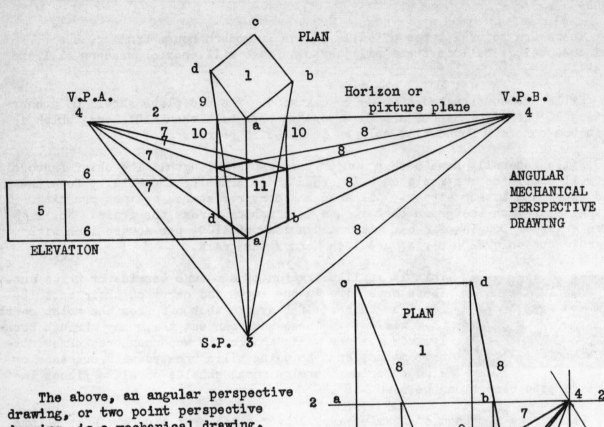

ANGULAR
MECHANICAL
PERSPECTIVE
DRAWING

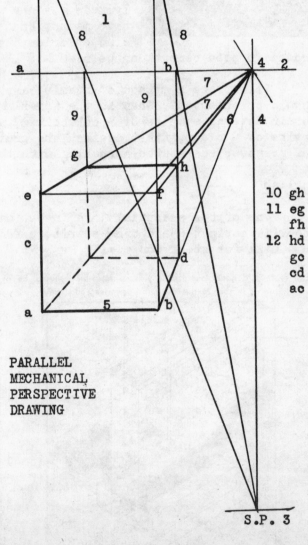

The above, an angular perspective
drawing, or two point perspective
drawing, is a mechanical drawing.
Each step is numbered. The plan
is placed in position, line ab not
horizontal, the line #2, or horizon,
drawn as shown and each point and
line placed in numerical order.

Draw the above and the drawing
to the right, place each number and
letter in position as shown.

See pg. 57.

PARALLEL
MECHANICAL
PERSPECTIVE
DRAWING

· AGREEMENTS ARE CONTINGENT UPON STRIKES, LOCKOUTS AND OTHER CAUSES BEYOND OUR CONTROL

WM. B. BARR, President   ELMER C. BARR, Vice-Pres.   S. S. NICHOLSON, Sec'y and Treas.

Remodeling and
Repairing Buildings   **The William B. Barr Co.**   Office Partitions
                                       BUILDERS   and Railings

Store Fronts and   Phone PArkway 0250   Special Attention
Show Windows   to
                                       545 and 547 East Thirteenth Street   All Kinds of Repairing
Counters and Shelving   Cincinnati, Ohio

                                                                        October 3, 1935.

Superior Lumber Company,
2630 Spring Grove Avenue,
Cincinnati, Ohio.

Gentlemen:

        Please deliver to job # 26, Baker Place, Avondale, City on
October 10th., the following items of stock:

        8 pcs., 2" x 8" yp. framing stock, 10' lengths, select S2S.
        8 pcs., 2" x 6" yp. framing stock, 10' lengths, select S2S.

        Deliver before 3 P. M. on day of delivery.

                                        Very truly,

                                        William B. Barr
                                        William B. Barr,
                                        President.

                            ——————————

        Note the special items in the order. The job is given a number.
The stock is ordered by the piece. The width, thickness and length is given.
Select stock calls for the best pieces obtainable. yp. means yellow pine.
Delivery is requested before the workmen quit work for the day. Write an order
for stock for the sill material required for the house in the accompanying set
of plans.

Civics

        A city building code is a set of laws pertaining to building construction.
If a city were without building laws there would be no uniformity in construction,
no safety features and every builder would build to suit his fancy.

        A building code may be obtained in printed form from the city authorities,
usually the building commissioner.

        A code contains all laws, ordinances, requirements and suggestions for the
safe and practical erection of residence structures, public buildings and monu-
mental buildings.

        Obtain a copy of a building code. Study it. What sections pertain to sill
construction? Write these down.

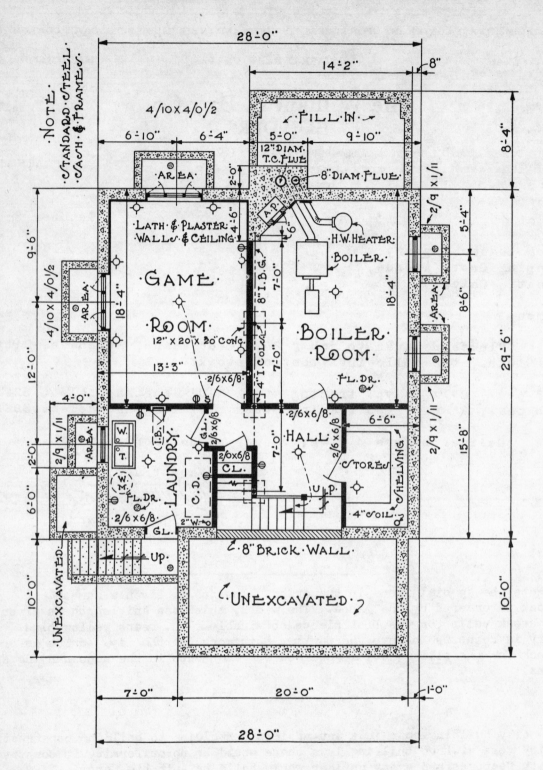

· BASEMENT · PLAN ·
· SCALE · ⅛" = 1′0" ·

Chapter VIII

Girders

Girders are foundations, as well as sills are foundations, upon which all upper structures rest. Girders are needed to support floor joists wherever the width or length of the house make it impossible to use joists over the full span. The full span is considered to be from foundation wall to foundation wall.

Building code requirements limit a 2" x 10" long leaf yellow pine joist, having a load limit of 66 pounds per square foot to a span of about 18'. Since but few dwellings are as narrow as this, an intermediate bearing member known as a girder is needed.

Girders for dwellings are most always specified as steel I beams. An I beam of 8" depth has a load strength of 8.08 tons if supported every 10'. It can readily be seen that a steel I beam makes the ideal type of girder.

Girders can be built up of wood, too, if select stock is used. Be sure it is straight and sound. Square off ends of stock. If the girder is to be built up of 2" x 8" or 2" x 10" stock, place pieces on the saw horses and nail together. Use the piece of stock that has the least amount of wind or warp for the center piece and nail other pieces on sides of center stock. Use a common nail that will go through the first piece and nearly through the center piece. Square off the ends of the girder after the pieces have been nailed together. If the stock is not long enough to build up the girder the entire length the pieces must be built up in the following manner.

If the girder supporting post is to be built up it is to be done in the same manner as described for the girder. Obtain the size of the metal dowel in the post footing and bore a hole in one end of the post to receive this dowel pin. Place the girder post in position and brace it until the girder is put in place.

Plan view of girder showing method of staggering joints.

If the girder is solid or built up safe sizes are as follows:

Span	Width	Depth	Load
10'	4"	8"	1988 lbs.
6'	4"	8"	2488 lbs.

If a Stran-steel joist is used a girder support is required over any span more than 18 feet. An I beam girder, as described elsewhere, can be used with Stran-steel joists as well as wood joists. If open truss steel joists are used a span of 32 feet can be made. If clearspan truss joists are used a span of 56 feet is permitted. If work other than wood girders or girder posts is done the structural steel worker does the work.

Practical Jobs

The very next job for the carpenter or joiner to perform after the sills have been built is the job of erecting the girder supporting posts and the girder or girders. Study the details in the set of plans and erect the type of girder required if a wood or Stran-steel girder is designated. Follow the details as shown on page 64 as regards the size and method of placing or building up girders.

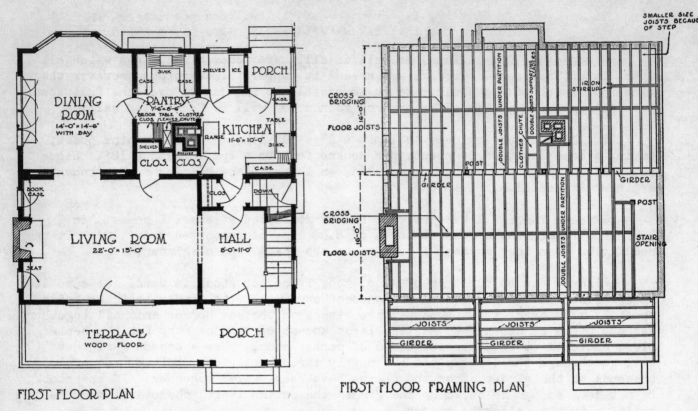

FIRST FLOOR PLAN

FIRST FLOOR FRAMING PLAN

A first floor plan showing location of posts, girders and joists.

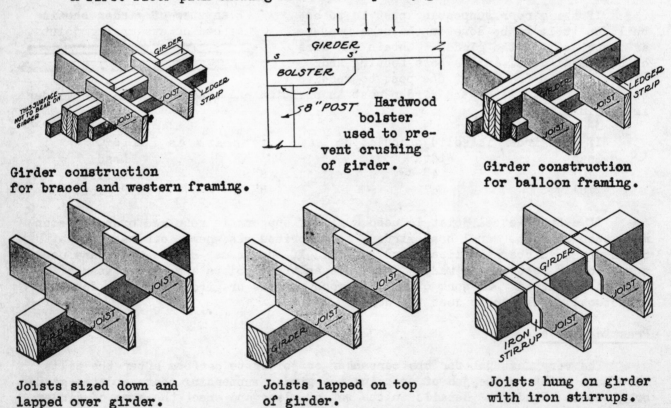

Girder construction
for braced and western framing.

Hardwood
bolster
used to pre-
vent crushing
of girder.

Girder construction
for balloon framing.

Joists sized down and
lapped over girder.

Joists lapped on top
of girder.

Joists hung on girder
with iron stirrups.

Courtesy FEDERAL BOARD for VOCATIONAL EDUCATION.

Drawing

Study very carefully the detailed steps taken on page 60 to illustrate the steps taken in the drawing of one and two point perspective drawings. Produce the following illustrations in two point then in one point perspective. Use just a pencil and rule or pencil, scale and straight edge. Use the thicknesses and widths given and make the length about 10 or 12 inches.

Inside door jamb with stop. 3/4" x 3½". Stop 3/8" x 1" placed 1-3/8" from edge.

Inside door jamb with double rabbet. 1-3/8" x 5½" with 3/8" x 1-3/8 rabbet on both sides.

Mathematics

Girders are built up or cut to size on the job. The cost of girders is based on the actual number of pieces needed, plus the labor, nails or other hardware. The cost of girder supporting posts will be the same as girders. The stock is listed piece by piece. The hardware is listed, item by item. It will take about 20 hours of labor to erect every 1000 board feet of girder or girder posts. Estimate the number of board feet of lumber and the hardware needed in the construction of the girders and girder posts for the house in the accompanying set of plans. The size is determined by the load to bear. Study the following discussion.

Science

The following diagram shows the live and dead loads in a frame house. There are various tables and data for use in determining the correct sizes of wood columns, girders, joists and rafters. Reference should be made to standard handbooks. The diagram is the courtesy of the General Timber Service, Inc., of St. Paul, Minn. Study the diagram and calculate the loads on the girders and girder posts of a typical frame house. See pg. 67.

English

The report on page 67 covers industrial occupational injuries in Ohio during the year 1933. This report has been taken from the MONITOR, a monthly publication of the Ohio Industrial Commission. Read the report carefully. Make a list of five good sentences found in the report. List five nouns, five verbs, three punctuation marks and one paragraph. List the main thoughts as expressed in each paragraph.

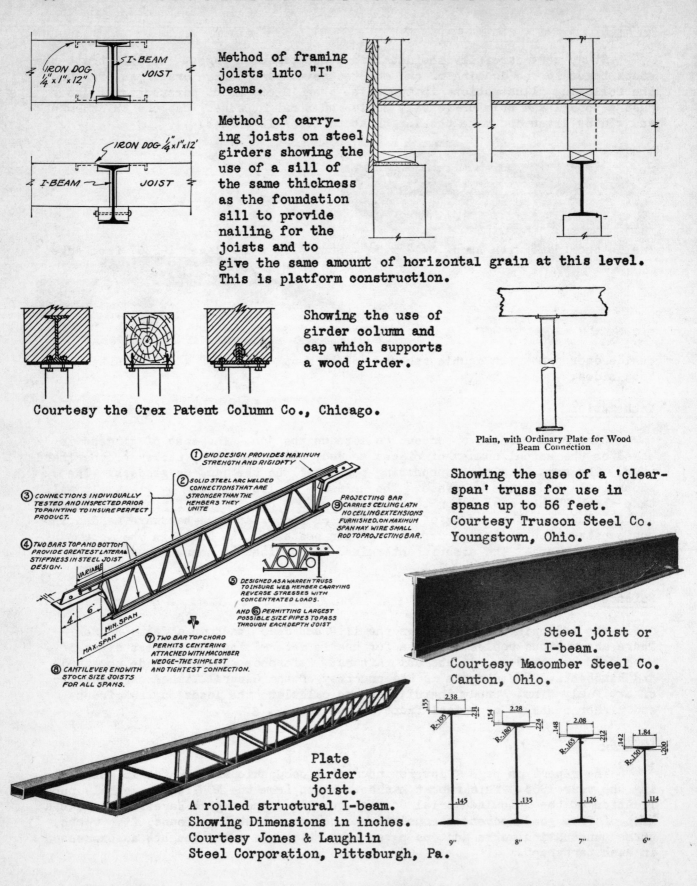

IRON DOG ¼"x1"x12"   I-BEAM JOIST

Method of framing joists into "I" beams.

IRON DOG ¼"x1"x12'

I-BEAM   JOIST

Method of carrying joists on steel girders showing the use of a sill of the same thickness as the foundation sill to provide nailing for the joists and to give the same amount of horizontal grain at this level. This is platform construction.

Showing the use of girder column and cap which supports a wood girder.

Courtesy the Crex Patent Column Co., Chicago.

Plain, with Ordinary Plate for Wood Beam Connection

① END DESIGN PROVIDES MAXIMUM STRENGTH AND RIGIDITY

② SOLID STEEL ARC WELDED CONNECTIONS THAT ARE STRONGER THAN THE MEMBERS THEY UNITE

③ CONNECTIONS INDIVIDUALLY TESTED AND INSPECTED PRIOR TO PAINTING TO INSURE PERFECT PRODUCT.

⑨ PROJECTING BAR CARRIES CEILING LATH NO CEILING EXTENSIONS FURNISHED. ON MAXIMUM SPAN MAY WIRE SMALL ROD TO PROJECTING BAR.

④ TWO BARS TOP AND BOTTOM PROVIDE GREATEST LATERAL STIFFNESS IN STEEL JOIST DESIGN.

VARIABLE

4'   6'

MIN. SPAN

MAX. SPAN

⑤ DESIGNED AS A WARREN TRUSS TO INSURE WEB MEMBER CARRYING REVERSE STRESSES WITH CONCENTRATED LOADS.

AND ⑥ PERMITTING LARGEST POSSIBLE SIZE PIPES TO PASS THROUGH EACH DEPTH JOIST

⑦ TWO BAR TOP CHORD PERMITS CENTERING ATTACHED WITH MACOMBER WEDGE-THE SIMPLEST AND TIGHTEST CONNECTION.

⑧ CANTILEVER END WITH STOCK SIZE JOISTS FOR ALL SPANS.

Showing the use of a 'clear-span' truss for use in spans up to 56 feet. Courtesy Truscon Steel Co. Youngstown, Ohio.

Steel joist or I-beam. Courtesy Macomber Steel Co. Canton, Ohio.

Plate girder joist. A rolled structural I-beam. Showing Dimensions in inches. Courtesy Jones & Laughlin Steel Corporation, Pittsburgh, Pa.

.155 2.38 .231 R-.195 .145 9"

.154 2.28 .224 R-.180 .135 8"

.148 2.08 .212 R-.162 .126 7"

.142 1.84 .200 R-.190 .114 6"

DIAGRAM SHOWING METHOD OF FIGURING LOADS FOR HOUSE FRAMING

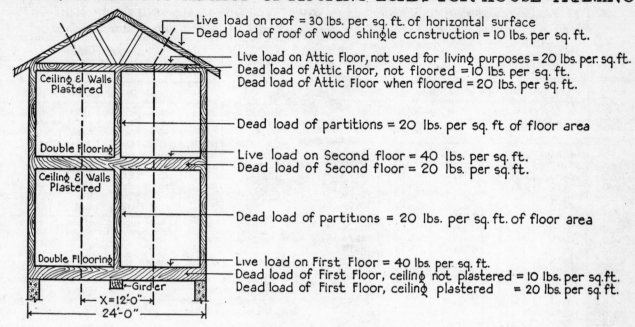

Live load on roof = 30 lbs. per sq. ft. of horizontal surface
Dead load of roof of wood shingle construction = 10 lbs. per sq. ft.

Live load on Attic Floor, not used for living purposes = 20 lbs. per. sq. ft.
Dead load of Attic Floor, not floored = 10 lbs. per sq. ft.
Dead load of Attic Floor when floored = 20 lbs. per sq. ft.

Dead load of partitions = 20 lbs. per sq. ft of floor area

Live load on Second floor = 40 lbs. per sq. ft.
Dead load of Second floor = 20 lbs. per sq. ft.

Dead load of partitions = 20 lbs. per sq. ft. of floor area

Live load on First Floor = 40 lbs. per. sq. ft.
Dead load of First Floor, ceiling not plastered = 10 lbs. per sq. ft.
Dead load of First Floor, ceiling plastered = 20 lbs. per sq. ft.

Ceiling & Walls Plastered

Double Flooring

Ceiling & Walls Plastered

Double Flooring

Girder

X = 12'-0"

24'-0"

English

Study the following taken from the 1934 report on industrial accidents in Ohio.

STUDY OF INJURIES TO WORKERS
DISCLOSES SOME AMAZING FACTS

In no study included in this report does the reader get a clearer conception of the havoc wrought by industrial mishaps than the one on the succeeding pages, showing the nature of injuries sustained by Ohio workers and the parts of the body affected.

Cuts and lacerations furnished the basis for more occupational injury claims last year than any other form of injury, as they have in preceding years. The claims due to this class of injury numbered 68,271, or 15,228 more than in 1933.

Crushes and bruises, with 29,810 cases, were second in frequency. Sprains and strains gave rise to 21,834 claims, puncture wounds 12,930, fractures 10,168, burns and scalds 10,987, dislocations 651, traumatic amputations 570, concussions 169, asphyxiations 175, drownings 3 and unclassified 3,680. These figures represent increases over 1933, with the exception of concussions, drownings and unclassified cases.

The amputations reported represent the loss of 2 arms, 4 hands, 548 fingers, 2 legs and 14 toes.

An analysis of the record shows that the fingers of workers in Ohio industries are more susceptible to injury than other parts of the body, 41,749 claims being based on injuries of this nature. Eye injuries were second with 27,195 cases, the trunk had 22,604, legs 15,565, arms 15,841, hands 12,898, head and face 10,192, feet 7,739 and toes 5,465.

A comparison of these figures with those for 1933 shows that the increase was general, and with few exceptions, in about the same ratio. The heaviest increase was in eye injuries and injuries to the fingers, with injuries to other parts of the body increasing in about the same percentage. No small part of this abnormal increase in eye and hand injuries is, we fear, due in great measure to failure to provide guards and goggles or laxity in their use when provided. Many specific instances of this failure have been noted in the reports on disposition of claims.

Included in the 10,168 fractures reported in claims for compensation were 1,945 of fingers, 1,883 of toes, 1,349 of arms, 1,354 of ribs, 1,063 of legs, 834 of feet, 390 of hands, 294 of the skull, 348 of teeth, 261 of vertebrae, 144 of the nose, 136 of the pelvis and 88 of the jaws. The extent of the incapacity due to this one type of accident alone, is shown in the fact that workers sustaining fractures suffered a time loss of 1,782,790 days, or more than 22 per cent of the total for all injuries.

Safeguarding and safety education on a much broader scale than has been practiced in the past is the crying need of the hour in Ohio industry. Recognized methods of inculcating safety consciousness whose value has been practically demonstrated, are available to every industry.

SIZES OF BUILT-UP WOOD GIRDERS FOR VARIOUS LOADS AND SPANS
Based on Douglas Fir 4-SQUARE Guide-Line FRAMING
Deflection not over 1/360 of Span—Allowable Fiber Stress 1600 lbs. per sq. in.

Load per Linear Foot of Girder	Length of Span				
	6'-0"	7'-0"	8'-0"	9'-0"	10'-0"
	Nominal Size of Girder Required				
750	6x8 in.	6x8 in.	6x8 in.	6x10 in.	6x10 in.
900	6x8	6x8	6x10	6x10	8x10
1050	6x8	6x10	8x10	8x10	8x12
1200	6x10	8x10	8x10	8x10	8x12
1350	6x10	8x10	8x10	8x12	10x12
1500	8x10	8x10	8x12	10x12	10x12
1650	8x10	8x12	10x12	10x12	10x14
1800	8x10	8x12	10x12	10x12	10x14
1950	8x12	10x12	10x12	10x14	12x14
2100	8x12	10x12	10x14	10x14	12x14
2250	10x12	10x12	10x14	12x14	12x14
2400	10x12	10x14	10x14	12x14	
2550	10x12	10x14	12x14	12x14	
2700	10x12	10x14	12x14		
2850	10x14	12x14	12x14		
3000	10x14	12x14			
3150	10x14	12x14			
3300	12x14	12x14			

The 6-in. girder is figured as being made with three pieces 2 in. dressed to 1⅝ in. thickness.

The 8-in. girder is figured as being made with four pieces 2 in. dressed to 1⅝ in. thickness.

The 10-in. girder is figured as being made with five pieces 2-in. dressed to 1⅝ in. thickness.

The 12-in. girder is figured as being made with six pieces 2-in. dressed to 1⅝ in. thickness.

Note—For solid girders multiply above loads by 1.130 when 6-in. girder is used; 1.150 when 8-in. girder is used; 1.170 when 10-in. girder is used; 1.180 when 12-in. girder is used.

Reference—Page 33, Bulletin No. 145, National Committee on Wood Utilization, U. S. Department of Commerce, "Light Frame House Construction."

Instructions for Determining Girder Sizes

First—Refer to diagram on page **67** and using it as a guide, determine for each floor the length of joist spans that are to be supported by the girder. For the first floor it is equal to one-half the total distance from center line of girder measured **both** ways to the next girder, basement bearing partition or foundation wall, **except** when joists are continuous over this girder and broken over nearest support on each side, in which case it is equal to ⅝ this total distance. Use the same method for second and third floors and roof when part of that weight is to be supported by the girder through the bearing partition, struts, etc. In the case illustrated in diagram on page 19, it is equal to 12 feet for all three floors and 18 feet for the roof.

Second—Multiply the load per square foot, as indicated on the chart, for each of these floors and roof by the various spans, including 20 lbs. per square foot of floor area for first and second story partitions. (In this case it is 2880 lbs.)

(First Floor plus partitions........70 lbs. × 12 ft.— 840 lbs.)
(Second Floor plus partitions......80 lbs. × 12 ft.— 960 lbs.)
(Attic Floor, not floored..........30 lbs. × 12 ft.— 360 lbs.)
(Roof ....40 lbs. × 18 ft.— 720 lbs.)
(Total ....2880 lbs.)

The total represents the load to be supported by the **girder** for each foot of its length.

Third—Determine length of girder span (distance between columns).

Fourth—Refer to table, read down in column at left to load already determined—then across to column corresponding to length of span to be provided for, the figure at this intersection represents the size of girder required.

SIZES OF WOOD COLUMNS FOR VARIOUS LOADS AND COLUMN HEIGHTS
Based on Use of No. 1 Common Douglas Fir

Load on Column (lbs.)	Length of Column					
	5'-0"	6'-0"	6'-6"	7'-0"	7'-6"	8'-0"
	Nominal Size of Column Required					
10,000	4x6 in.	4x6 in.	4x6 in.	4x6 in.	4x6 in.	4x6 in.
15,000	4x6	4x6	4x6	4x6	6x6	6x6
20,000	6x6	6x6	6x6	6x6	6x6	6x6
25,000	6x6	6x6	6x6	6x6	6x6	6x6
30,000	6x6	6x8	6x8	6x8	6x8	6x8
35,000	6x8	6x8	6x8	6x8	6x8	6x8
40,000	6x8	6x8	8x8	8x8	8x8	8x8
45,000	8x8	8x8	8x8	8x8	8x8	8x8
50,000	8x8	8x8	8x8	8x8	8x8	8x8
55,000	8x8	8x8	8x8	8x8	8x8	8x8

Reference—Page 50, Bulletin No. 145, National Committee on Wood Utilization, U. S. Department of Commerce, "Light Frame House Construction."

Instructions for Determining Column Sizes

First—Use the total load per linear foot of girder obtained when determining girder sizes.

Second—Determine length of girder span being supported by column (see diagram, page **67** (this is equal to one-half total distance from column measured both ways to next column or bearing wall, except when the girder is continuous over this column and broken over the column or bearing wall on each side in which case it is equal to ⅝ this total distance).

Third—Multiply the length of this span in feet by load per linear foot.

Fourth—Refer to table. Read down in column at left to load already determined—then across to column corresponding to length of column (distance from concrete footing to under side of girder). The figure at this intersection represents the size of column required.

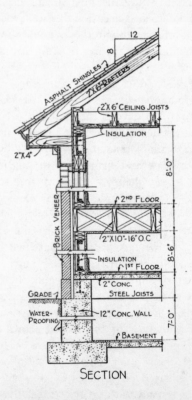

SECTION

Civics

Refer to a building code or a hand book and find the answers to the following questions:

What is the code requirement on girder widths and thicknesses?

" " " " " " " lengths or spans?

List this information, working it out in the light of some definite set of house plans.

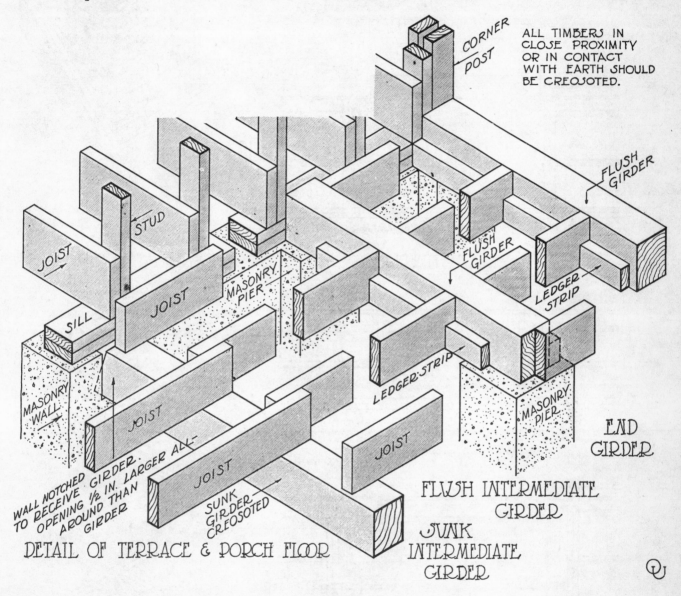

CORNER POST

ALL TIMBERS IN CLOSE PROXIMITY OR IN CONTACT WITH EARTH SHOULD BE CREOSOTED.

FLUSH GIRDER

STUD

JOIST

JOIST

MASONRY PIER

FLUSH GIRDER

SILL

LEDGER STRIP

MASONRY WALL

LEDGER STRIP

JOIST

MASONRY PIER

END GIRDER

JOIST

JOIST

WALL NOTCHED TO RECEIVE GIRDER. OPENING ½ IN. LARGER ALL AROUND THAN GIRDER

SUNK GIRDER CREOSOTED

FLUSH INTERMEDIATE GIRDER

SUNK INTERMEDIATE GIRDER

DETAIL OF TERRACE & PORCH FLOOR

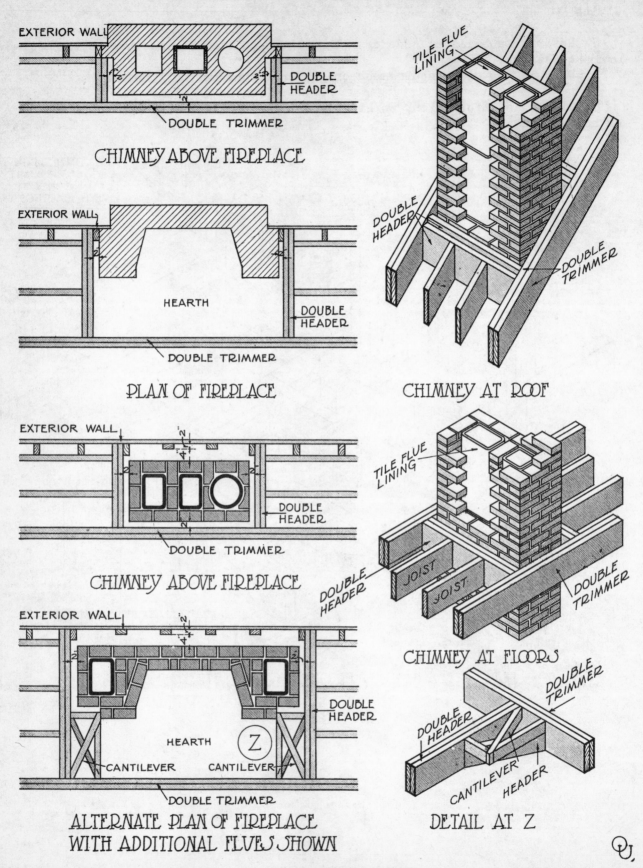

EXTERIOR WALL
DOUBLE HEADER
DOUBLE TRIMMER

CHIMNEY ABOVE FIREPLACE

EXTERIOR WALL
HEARTH
DOUBLE HEADER
DOUBLE TRIMMER

PLAN OF FIREPLACE

EXTERIOR WALL
DOUBLE HEADER
DOUBLE TRIMMER

CHIMNEY ABOVE FIREPLACE

EXTERIOR WALL
DOUBLE HEADER
HEARTH
Z
CANTILEVER   CANTILEVER
DOUBLE TRIMMER

ALTERNATE PLAN OF FIREPLACE
WITH ADDITIONAL FLUES SHOWN

TILE FLUE LINING
DOUBLE HEADER
DOUBLE TRIMMER

CHIMNEY AT ROOF

TILE FLUE LINING
DOUBLE HEADER
JOIST
JOIST
DOUBLE TRIMMER

CHIMNEY AT FLOORS

DOUBLE TRIMMER
DOUBLE HEADER
CANTILEVER   HEADER

DETAIL AT Z

Framing Details

Chapter IX

Floor Joists

Floor joists are the framed members on which the floor is placed. They
form the backbone of the platforms known as floors. Observe the framing details in the set of plans which pertain to the floor joists. Note the method
of framing at the sills, chimney, fire place and any other opening or well.
Select the floor joist stock with care being sure each piece is straght and
sound. Obtain from the set of house plans the length of the joists. Use the
first joist cut of each length for the pattern in marking off similar lengths.

Wood joists are generally spaced 16" apart, center to center measure.
The location of each joist should be marked on the sill and on the girder.
Place pieces of stock of equal length in place on the sill and girder. Do
not nail until all joists of equal length are in place. If there is a bow
or crown in any joist, place the crown to the top. If the widths of joists
vary trim off where needed. This trimming can be done by use of a hatchet.

If structural steel joists are used place each in position as shown in
the plan. Stran-steel joists can be spaced about 24" or 36" apart cc, according to the span.

After wood joists have been placed and properly sized they should be
nailed in position by 20 d. common nails. Straight nail joists wherever possible. A spacing strip, made of a long narrow piece of stock with markings every 16" may be used to help hold the joists in place. All headers, stair
wells and any irregular framing are framed according to the special details
worked out in the set of plans.

When joists are used over a long span they become quite flexible. In
order to overcome this tendency to bend and to make these carrying members
more rigid a series of braces are inserted at regular intervals. These
braces are known as bridging, which is inserted in rows about 8' cc. If
bridging is made of wood stock it is usually 1" x 3" material. Obtain a
pattern of bridging stock by placing a piece of material in position as
shown in the following details. The saw cut will form the correct angle.
Nail the top of the bridging with 6 or 8 d. nails but do not nail the bottom of the bridging until the rough floor has been laid. This is done in
order to keep the bridging from pushing up any joist which would cause an
uneveness in the floor.

Joists placed in a bathroom may have to be braced to carry the extra
load of fixtures.

Structural steel joists are braced with metal bridging.

Practical jobs. Study the details in the set of plans and erect the
type of joist required. Insert the bridging in the joists. Refer to the
details that follow and the details as shown in the preceding chapter dealing with girders.

Showing Cross Bridging between wooden joists.

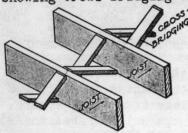

Showing bridging loose at lower end until sub-floor is nailed into position.

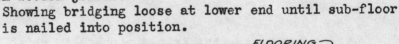
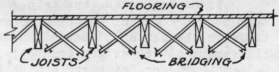

Piece let in joist which supports bathroom floor and conveniences.

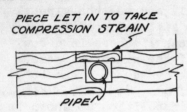

Showing use of trimmer and header joists. Tail beams or short joists may be larger.

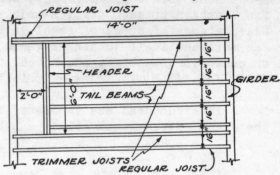

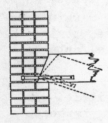

Trimmer

Header

Showing joist anchored in brick wall by use of iron anchor. Left is correct use and right is incorrect. This decreases hazard of falling walls during fire from within a structure.

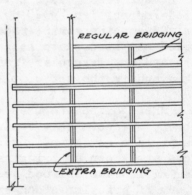

Showing use of extra bridging to support trimmer when it is placed more than two ft. from regular bridging.

Stirrup for Joist Support

AN idea for use in remodeling a house is that of using sheet iron for stirrups, made as shown in the accompanying illustration. Strips of sheet iron are quickly cold bent to the shape shown, and, with a nail punch, all holes are made for nailing. While this stirrup does not differ much from the usual iron hanger, it is simpler. The main strength difference rests in the increased bearing at the edge of the header and the bottom of the beam, and the iron does not break into wood nearly like the iron hanger of smaller width. As many nails can be inserted as desired, as other holes are made quickly with a punch.—B. S. LUERS, 2355 Ashmead Pl., N. W., Washington, D. C.

To Cut Floor Bridging

A GOOD way to find the right cut for floor bridging is to lay a piece of a floor joist timber from floor joist to floor joist and mark as shown. Now lay a piece of bridging across as shown and mark. You will then have the right cut for your bridging.

H. E. JENKINS, Sutherland, Neb.

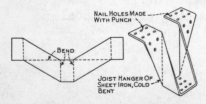

How Homemade Sheet-iron Hangers Are Designed.

H. E. Jenkins Describes This Method of Figuring Cut for Floor Bridging.

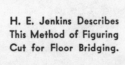
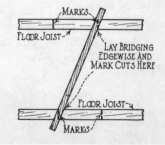

Related Studies

Drawing

In foregoing chapters the salient points in freehand perspective sketching, angular and parallel perspective sketching were discussed. In order to further acquaint oneself with these methods of shape representation, sketch the following listed illustrations in freehand, angular and parallel perspective sketches without the use of a ruler or straight edge. Use a pencil and eraser only. The illustrations to be sketched are: 8" Stran-steel joist on page 74 , inside door jamb with double rabbet on page 65, girder construction for braced and western framing on page 64 and joist lapped on top of girder on same page.

In continuing further the study of methods in shape representation there has been devised a very excellent method known as isometric (equal angle) drawing or sketching. It is quite similar to angular or two point sketching with this one important exception, all lines are parallel, in groups, which does away with vanishing lines. Isometric drawing or sketching may be said to be a system of representing shapes by the use of three groups of parallel lines. The first group are the vertical lines, the second the 30 degree lines to the left hand and the third the 30 degree lines to the right hand.

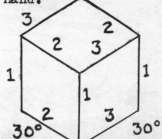

Showing a block in angular or two point perspective drawing. Note the absence of parallel lines and the presence of vanishing lines.

Showing a block in isometric drawing or sketching. Note the absence of vanishing lines and the presence of parallel lines. #1 lines are parallel one with another, also #2 lines and #3 lines.

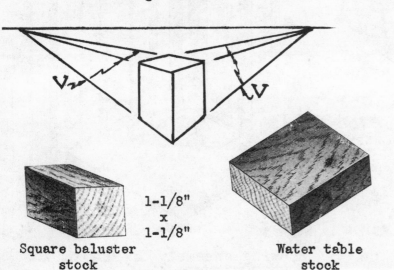

Square baluster stock

1-1/8" x 1-1/8"

Water table stock

Lattice Stock

1-3/4" x 2-3/4"

5/16" x 1-3/8"

Sketch, with the aid of a rule or straight edge and a pencil and eraser, the above illustrations of building material in isometric.

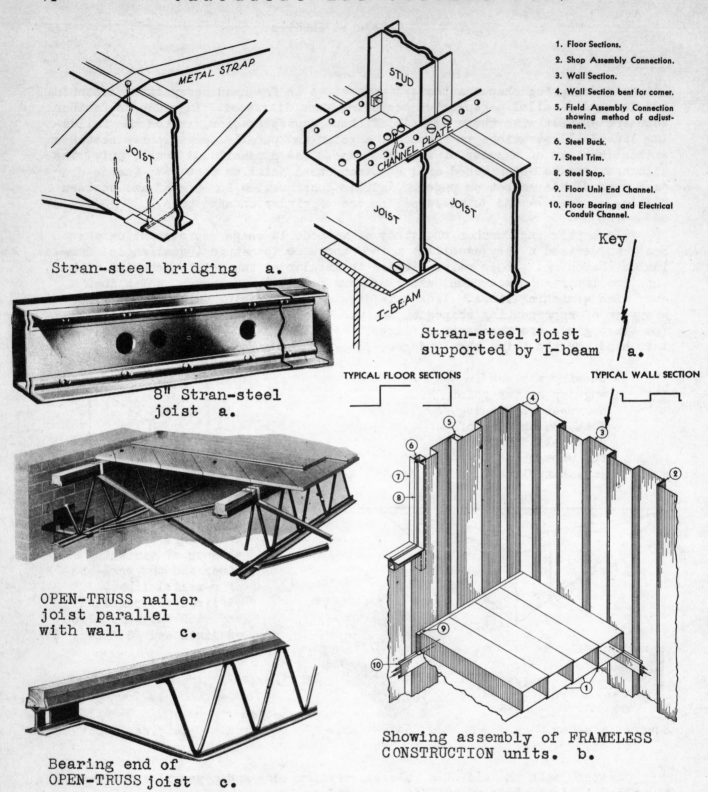

METAL STRAP

JOIST

Stran-steel bridging   a.

STUD

CHANNEL PLATE

JOIST   JOIST

I-BEAM

Stran-steel joist supported by I-beam   a.

1. Floor Sections.

2. Shop Assembly Connection.

3. Wall Section.

4. Wall Section bent for corner.

5. Field Assembly Connection showing method of adjustment.

6. Steel Buck.

7. Steel Trim.

8. Steel Stop.

9. Floor Unit End Channel.

10. Floor Bearing and Electrical Conduit Channel.

Key

8" Stran-steel joist   a.

OPEN-TRUSS nailer joist parallel with wall   c.

Bearing end of OPEN-TRUSS joist   c.

TYPICAL FLOOR SECTIONS   TYPICAL WALL SECTION

Showing assembly of FRAMELESS CONSTRUCTION units.   b.

a. Courtesy STRAN-STEEL CORPORATION, Detroit.

b. Courtesy INSULATED STEEL CONSTRUCTION COMPANY, Cleveland.

c. Courtesy TRUSCON COMPANY, Cleveland.

Mathematics

Floor joists are estimated by the actual count of the number required. To obtain this number one must study the framing plan, as each plan has its individual problem in framing. This applies to wooden joists and steel joists. One might divide the butt side of the sill by the distance the joists are placed on centers and consider this the number of joists to use. To this number, however, must be added the special sizes or additional full lengths for opening headers, trimmers, etc. Estimate the number of first floor joists required in the accompanying set of house plans. Base the estimate for labor on the fact that a good carpenter can erect about 1000 board feet of joists in two eight hour days. The hardware will be about 24 lbs. of spikes, 20 d., for every 1000 board feet. The number of pieces of structural steel fittings can be estimated by the piece. The amount of labor for structural steel joists erection will be about half that of steel joist erection.

The carpenter's steel framing square has two parts, the body, which is the longer, wider part and the tongue, which is the shorter, narrower part. The steel square is an accurate right angle. It bears a very definite relation to the circle. A circle is a plane figure (section of a cone) bounded by a curved line called a circumference, which is everywhere equally distant from a point within it called the center. The easiest subdivision of a circumference is six equal parts, due to the fact that the chord of the arcs is equal to the radius.

The Babylonians divided one of these arcs into 60 equal parts and obtained the degree. The degree is divided into 60 equal parts called minutes and the minutes into 60 equal parts called seconds. By this method was produced the sexagesimal (founded on the number 60) scale. This scale or method of dividing allows 90 degrees in a right angle, 180 degrees in a semi-circle and 360 degrees in a circle. The supposed number of days in the year led to the division of the circle into 360 equal parts for use in instruments of astronomy.

Bridging is estimated by the linear feet of stock used. Each set of cross bridging takes about 4' of 1" x 3" stock. A man can cut and nail about 1000 lineal feet of bridging stock in an hour. 8 d. common nails are used. Add this bridging estimate to the other estimates of the quantity estimate of the house. Structural steel bridging is estimated by the piece. This bridging requires no nailing as each piece is bent over the joist. A man can work this bridging up at about twice the speed of wood bridging.

What is a circle? How many degrees in it? What is the relation of a right angle to a circle? Is a set of bridging at right angles to the floor joists?

Showing a circle which has been divided into six equal parts on the circumference (8).

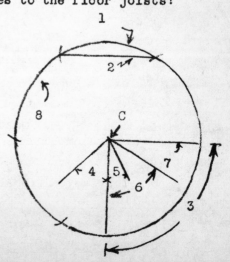

#1 is the arc created by 2.
   2 is the chord.
   3 is $\frac{1}{4}$ of the circumference which is $\frac{1}{4}$ of 360 degrees which is 90 degrees which is a right angle.
   4 contains 45 degrees
   5 contains 30 degrees
   6 contains 60 degrees
   7 is the radius
   C is the center of the circle

Science

Approximately 22,000,000 cubic feet of timber are cut annually from the forests of the United States and about 3,000,000 cubic feet are destroyed by forest fires and insects. There are about 850 species of trees in the United States and of all these but a few have commercial value. There are, in addition, approximately 350 species occuring in isolated localities. This group is not included in the 850 species.

The builder is concerned with woods used in building and construction work. The following species are known as commercially important woods. This list is a courtesy of the American Forest Products Industries, of Washington.

1.   EASTERN (Aromatic) RED CEDAR
(Juniperus virginiana)

SOURCE: Eastern U. S., principally Tennessee and adjacent States.
ANNUAL PRODUCTION: Lumber 17,000,000 bd. ft.   All purposes 36,000,000 bd. ft.
PROPERTIES: Soft, light in weight, fine uniform grain, easily worked, heartwood red in color, thin nearly white sapwood.   Has a pronounced aromatic odor.   Weight, air-dry: 33 lbs. per cu. ft.
USES: Chests, closet lining, pencils, fence posts.
PRODUCED BY MEMBERS OF: Hardwood Manufacturers Institute, Memphis, Tenn.

2.   INCENSE CEDAR
(Libocedrus decurrens)

SOURCE: California and southern Oregon.
ANNUAL PRODUCTION: 35,000,000 bd. ft.
PROPERTIES: Light in weight, soft, durable, aromatic, shrinks very little, light brown to red in color.   Weight, air-dry: 26 lbs. per cu. ft.
USES: Pencils, sheathing, sub-sills, posts, grape trellises, closet lining, etc.
PRODUCED BY MEMBERS OF: Western Pine Association, Portland, Ore.

3.   NORTHERN WHITE CEDAR
(Thuja occidentalis)

SOURCE: Northeastern and Lake States.
ANNUAL PRODUCTION: Total of 340,000,000 bd. ft., including poles, posts, shingles, lumber, ties.
PROPERTIES: Light in weight, soft, splits easily, fragrant, works easily, durable, shrinks very little, wood light brown.   Weight, air-dry: 22 lbs. per cu. ft.
USES: Posts, ties, poles, shingles, boat construction, canoe ribs, etc.
PRODUCED BY MEMBERS OF: Northern Hemlock and Hardwood Manufacturers Association, Oshkosh, Wis., and Northern Pine Manufacturers Association, Minneapolis, Minn.

4.   PORT ORFORD CEDAR
(Chamaecyparis lawsoniana)

SOURCE: Coastal region of Oregon and Northern California.
ANNUAL PRODUCTION: 40,000,000 bd. ft.
PROPERTIES: Light in weight, fairly hard, strong, durable, fine textured, easily worked, has a spicy, fragrant odor, wood yellowish white.   Weight, air-dry: 29 lbs. per cu. ft.
USES: Sash and doors, interior finish, storage battery separators, ties, matches, shipbuilding, airplane construction, moth-proof chests, etc.
PRODUCED BY MEMBERS OF: West Coast Lumbermen's Association, Seattle, Washington.

Courtesy NATIONAL LUMBER MANUFACTURERS ASSOCIATION, Washington.

5. WESTERN RED CEDAR

(Thuja plicata)

SOURCE: Washington, Oregon and Idaho.
ANNUAL PRODUCTION: Lumber, 225,000,000 bd. ft., Shingles, 800,000,000 bd. ft.
PROPERTIES: Light in weight, very soft, easily worked, durable, shrinks very little, dark reddish brown in color. Weight air-dry: 23 lbs. per cu. ft.
USES: Shingles, siding, planing mill products, poles, tanks, caskets, small boats, etc.
PRODUCED BY MEMBERS OF: West Coast Lumbermen's Association, Seattle, Washington, and Western Pine Association, Portland, Ore.

6. TIDEWATER RED CYPRESS

(Southern Cypress—Coast Type) *(Taxodium distichum)*

SOURCE: Gulf and South Atlantic States.
ANNUAL PRODUCTION: 800,000,000 bd. ft.
PROPERTIES: Moderately light in weight, fairly soft, easily worked, very durable, shrinks little, reddish brown in color. Weight, air-dry: 32 lbs. per cu. ft.
USES: Millwork, tanks, silos, coffins, exterior finish, interior finish and trim, laundry appliances, porch flooring, machine construction, agricultural supplies, boxes, crates, etc.
PRODUCED BY MEMBERS OF: Southern Cypress Manufacturers Association, Jacksonville, Fla.

7. DOUGLAS FIR

(Pseudotsuga taxifolia)

SOURCE: Washington, Oregon, California, Idaho, Montana.
ANNUAL PRODUCTION: 9,000,000,000 bd. ft.
PROPERTIES: Moderately heavy, strong, fairly hard, stiff, heartwood light red to yellow. Weight, air-dry: 34 lbs. per cu. ft.
USES: Heavy timber construction, car construction, shipbuilding, tanks, silos, wood pipe, furniture, millwork, etc.
PRODUCED BY MEMBERS OF: West Coast Lumbermen's Association, Seattle, Wash., and Western Pine Association, Portland, Ore.

8. WHITE FIR

(Abies concolor and Abies grandis)

SOURCE: California, Idaho, Washington and Oregon.
ANNUAL PRODUCTION: 350,000,000 bd. ft.
PROPERTIES: Light in weight, soft, odorless, grayish brown in color. Weight, air-dry: 26 lbs. per cu. ft.
USES: Butter boxes, crates, sheathing, false flooring, house framing, planing mill products, etc.
PRODUCED BY MEMBERS OF: Western Pine Association, Portland, Ore.

9. EASTERN HEMLOCK

(Tsuga canadensis)

SOURCE: Lake States, Northeastern U. S. and Appalachian Region.
ANNUAL PRODUCTION: 900,000,000 bd. ft.
PROPERTIES: Light in weight, fairly hard, retains nails firmly, light brown in color. Weight, air-dry: 28 lbs. per cu. ft.
USES: Planing mill products, general construction, boxes, crates, refrigerators, trunks, etc.
PRODUCED BY MEMBERS OF: Northern Hemlock and Hardwood Manufacturers Association, Oshkosh, Wis.

10. WEST COAST HEMLOCK

(Tsuga heterophylla)

SOURCE: Washington, Oregon.
ANNUAL PRODUCTION: 1,300,000,000 bd. ft.
PROPERTIES: Light in weight, strong and stiff, retains nails firmly, light yellowish brown in color. Weight, air-dry: 28 lbs. per cu. ft.
USES: Planing mill products, house construction, boxes and crates, car construction, furniture, refrigerators, trunks, gates and fencing, ship and boat building, etc.
PRODUCED BY MEMBERS OF: West Coast Lumbermen's Association, Seattle, Wash.

11. LARCH

(Larix occidentalis)

SOURCE: Montana, Idaho, Washington, Oregon.
ANNUAL PRODUCTION: 300,000,000 bd. ft.
PROPERTIES: Hard, stiff, strong, moderately heavy, narrow growth rings, durable, russet to yellowish brown. Weight, air-dry: 36 lbs. per cu. ft.
USES: House framing, flooring, drop siding, rustic finish trim, railroad car material, ties, bridge planks, etc.
PRODUCED BY MEMBERS OF: Western Pine Association, Portland, Ore.

12. ARKANSAS SOFT PINE

(Pinus echinata)

SOURCE: Uplands, of south central and south western Arkansas.
ANNUAL PRODUCTION: 500,000,000 bd. ft.
PROPERTIES: Soft-textured, moderate weight, free from hard streaks and pitch, easily worked, heartwood pale yellow. Weight, air-dry: 38 lbs. per cu. ft.
USES: Interior trim, structural dimension for buildings, planing mill products, boxes, car construction, toy stock, wood specialties.
PRODUCED BY MEMBERS OF: Arkansas Soft Pine Bureau, Little Rock, Ark.

Continued on page 88

Obtain a map of the United States. See that each state is in outline.
Check over each of the 48 woods as listed. Place the proper number within the
border of each state so as to locate the source of the lumber. For example,
number one would be put in Tennessee, North Carolina, South Carolina, Georgia,
Alabama, Mississippi and Kentucky.

English

A clear expression of thought is the goal to be reached in all sentence
construction. Sentences, as has been explained, are made up of words. Words
are thoughts. Often words mean two or even three different thoughts. An English dictionary is a book giving the spelling and meaning, pronunciation, usage, etc. of words. Often not every meaning of each word is given, because the
particular meaning is confined to certain sections, peoples or trades. Words
which have a distinct meaning in certain trades are known as technical words or
trade terms. There are three important phases of trade terms: First, the knowing
and recognizing of a trade term; Second, knowing the spelling of the term; Third,
knowing the meaning of the term. The following is an alphabetical list of trade
terms used in house construction. Study the spelling of each word, copy the list,
designate the nouns and find an illustration in this text, placing the page where
found.

Abutment	air tight	anchor bolts	angle post	apron
adjustable	aisle	anchor iron	annealed wire	apron (window)
adz	alcove	anchoring	apartment	arch
air pockets	altitude	angle	apprentice	architecture

architect	area	ash pit	auger bit
architectural	arris	astragal	awning
architrave	asbestos	attic	axis
arc-light	ashlar	authorize	

Civics

Mankind has always measured objects. It would be impossible to trace the
origin of length standards. It might be safe, however, to assume that length
standards had a definite relation to some parts of the human body.

Nearly all civilized nations have at some time employed a unit of length the
name of which bore the same significance as does the foot unit of measure. This
unit, no doubt has been derived from the length of the human foot. In England, the
yard was chosen as standard and was supposed to represent the length of the arm of
King Henry I. The foot was then chosen as one-third of a yard.

In different countries units of length have been derived either from the
lengths of different members of the human body or from equally unrelated magnitudes,
and in consequence have been connected with one another by different and often very
awkward multiples.

A similar and even worse complexity exists in the relations of the units of
length to those of area, capacity and mass. In Egypt the unit of length is called
PIC, in Greece PIKE, in China CHIK, in France METER, in Mexico VARA, in Siam, NUI.

Angles deal with the measuring of certain space. This measuring of space is a science, the science of mathematics called Geometry. Mention has been made in this text of the thickness, width and length of objects. The geometry of three dimensions is called Solid Geometry.

Geometry has a division or art called Descriptive Geometry. Descriptive geometry represents, by projection on a plane, the form and position in space of objects having three dimensions. Orthographic projection, a system of shape description dealt with in a succeeding chapter, is a form of descriptive geometry.

Tradition ascribes the origin of geometry to the Egyptians, but the history of geometry as a science begins with Thales of Miletus, who lived during the years 640-542 B. C. Miletus was an ancient city of Ionia in Asia Minor. The study of geometry lagged from 640 B. C. to 1600 A. D. Due to the influence of the Renaissance, in 1800 A. D. there was a renewed interest in the subject. Present day geometry can be traced back to this revival.

Industry uses solid, plane, descriptive, analytical, topographical, graphical and metrical geometry constantly, especially in large construction projects.

What is the origin of the following: measuring, the meter, metric system, table of linear measure, square measure, cubic measure, angular measure, geometry and the foot measure?

What is the building code requirement for bridging? For floor joists?

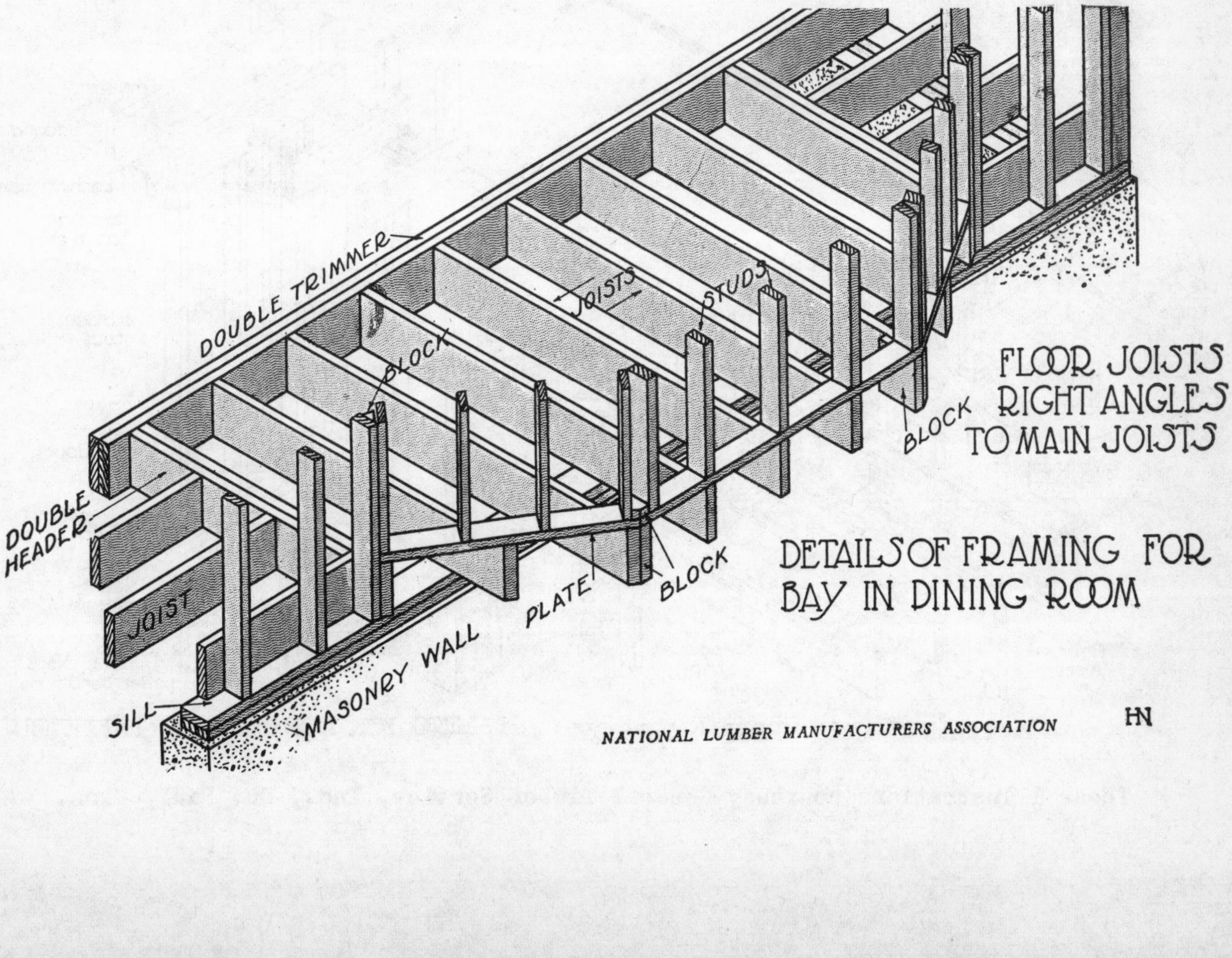

DOUBLE TRIMMER
JOISTS
STUDS
BLOCK
FLOOR JOISTS RIGHT ANGLES TO MAIN JOISTS
BLOCK
DOUBLE HEADER
JOIST
SILL
MASONRY WALL
PLATE
BLOCK
DETAILS OF FRAMING FOR BAY IN DINING ROOM

NATIONAL LUMBER MANUFACTURERS ASSOCIATION   HN

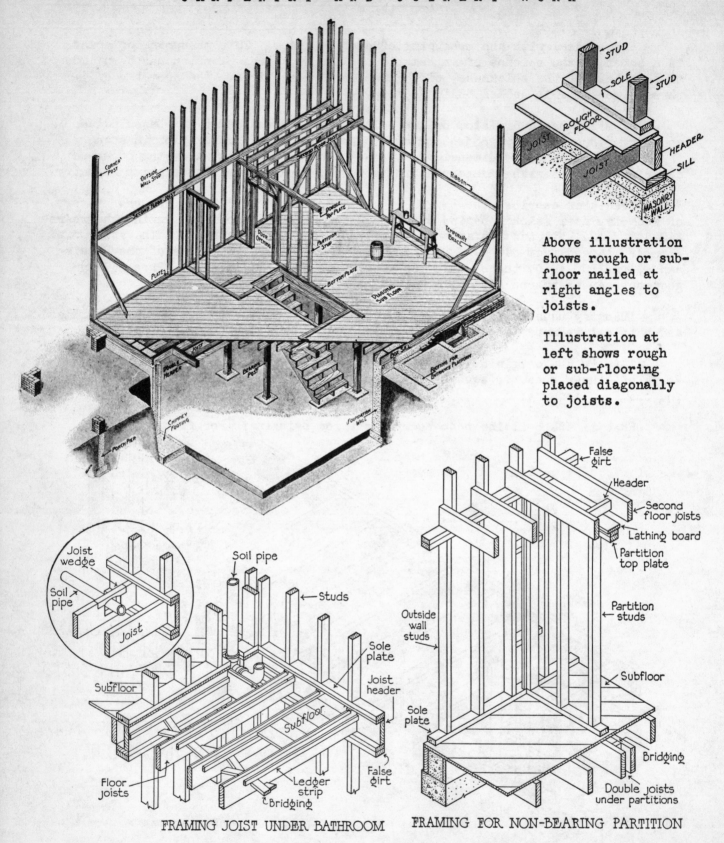

Above illustration shows rough or sub-floor nailed at right angles to joists.

Illustration at left shows rough or sub-flooring placed diagonally to joists.

FRAMING JOIST UNDER BATHROOM

FRAMING FOR NON-BEARING PARTITION

These illustrations courtesy General Timber Service, Inc., St. Paul, Minn.

Chapter X

Sub-Flooring

The floor joists form a frame work for the sub floor. This floor is called the rough floor and may be visioned as a large platform covering the entire width and length area of the building. Two layers or coverings of flooring material are generally placed on the joists. This practice has many advantages. Some are: it makes for better insulation, stronger construction and a finer and more pleasing finish; wood can be used as the finished flooring.

Clear the top of the floor joists of all material save the nailing or spacing strips used to hold joists in place. Check the joists for proper spacing, twist or wind. Place several pieces of rough tongue and groove and flooring stock on the joists in such a manner as to furnish a temporary walk. Do not nail these pieces down on the joists.

Select a sound, straight piece of flooring to begin with and place this piece flush with the edge of the sill header. Nail down with 8 d. common nails. This piece can be held by nails driven vertically, as a piece of shoe stock will hide these nails. All succeeding pieces should be held by nails driven at a slant at the tongue side of the stock. This method is called toe-nailing.

If the specifications require the flooring to be laid diagonally to the floor joists, begin at the extreme edges of two sill headers which form a corner of the house and nail the flooring. Select short pieces of stock at first, nail in place and saw off flush with the outside face of the sill header. Place each additional piece of flooring, fitting the groove over the tongue and toe-nail in place. Nail at each joist.

Study the framing details carefully as the work progresses. Allow for any openings such as stair wells, chimney openings or clothes chute, as designated.

Check all joists for uniformity of level surface. Sight from width side of joists for any joist having excessive crown or upward bulge. Use a long straight edge to test levelness and remove excessive crown by chopping with a hatchet. Straighten any joist having excessive wind.

Floors laid on structural steel joists may be nailed directly to the joists in the same manner as wooden floors are nailed to wooden joists. Join all floor-ing over joists, never without a support.

Practical jobs. Study the details in the set of plans and lay the type of flooring required. This job is the sub-flooring only. The foregoing illustrations show the sub-flooring laid in several ways.

Related Studies

Drawing.

In continuing the study of methods in shape representation there is also devised a very excellent method known as oblique drawing. Oblique drawing bears a very close resemblance to parallel perspective drawing with the one all important difference, which is, the use of series of parallel lines and the absence of vanishing lines.

Oblique drawing has some of the characteristics of isometric drawing in that three groups of parallel lines are used. The first group of lines are horizontal ones, the second are vertical ones and the third group are lines to the right at 30 degrees.

Showing a block in parallel or one point perspective drawing. Note the vanishing lines and the two groups of parallel lines.

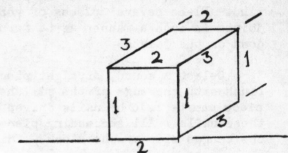

Showing a block in oblique drawing or sketching. Note the absence of vanishing lines and the presence of parallel lines. #1 lines are parallel one with another, #2 lines parallel one with another and #3 lines parallel one with another.

Sketch, with the aid of a rule or straight edge and a pencil and eraser, the following illustrations of building material.

Door casing 3/4" x 4½"

Door casing 3/4" x 3½"

Mold casing 1" x 1¼" and 3/4" x 3½"

Mullion casing 5/8" x 3-3/4"

Mathematics.

In light frame construction there is no need to use sub-floor thicker than 25/32ds. This is the thickness of dressed 1" lumber, according to American Lumber Standards.

Sub-floor may be placed in either of two ways, squarely across the joists or diagonally across the joists. The sub-floor laid squarely across the joists is much more economical in labor with all except end-matched material. It has the disadvantage, however, that the finished floor can be laid only at right angles to the sub-floor and parallel with the joists. Diagonal subfloor is troublesome to lay, with the exception of the end matched type, because of the necessity

of cutting all ends to fit diagonally over the joists, which requires two or
more cuts for every board, each of which is longer than a square cut. With end
matched lumber this is not necessary, as the pieces may be butted wherever the
joints occur, whether between joist supports or not. The tongue at the ends
and edges of such joinsts give sufficient strength, according to the tests of
the Forest Products Laboratory, to support any reasonable weight, especially
when supplemented by the finish floor.

A diagonal sub-floor further gives choice of laying the finish floor in
either direction, parallel to or at right angles to the joists. It is possible,
therefore, to arrange the finish floor to run in one direction in one room and
in another in the next, should that be desirable.

There should be two 8 d. nails in each piece of subfloor up to 6 inches in
width at every joist, and three or more in every piece over 6" in width. (Courtesy Forest Products Laboratory, Madison, Wis.)

Flooring is sold by the board measure and comes in designated thicknesses
and widths but often in random lengths. Calculate the actual area to be covered
and for the following widths add the corresponding percentage for waste:

For 6" flooring add 15% for waste.   Add 30 lbs. of 8 d. common
  " 4"   "   " 20% "   "   nails for every 1000 B. M.
  " 3"   "   " 25% "   "   of flooring. For diagonal
For right angle flooring figure   flooring figure 12 hours of
10 hours of labor for every 1000   labor for every 1000 B. M.
B. M. of flooring.

Using the above information estimate and place with other estimates the
amount of flooring stock, hardware and labor required to place the sub-flooring
in the house in the accompanying set of plans.

Science.

The belief that a timber with a so-called 'factor of safety' of 3 or 4
will carry three or four times the load for which it is designed is erroneous
and has been the cause of failure through the overloading of structures. Only
a small part of the usual 'factor of safety' for wood is available for taking
care of overloading; most of it is required to adjust for the known variability
in the strength of clear wood, the effect of defects, the moisture conditions of
service and the duration of the load.

Some of the working stresses assigned by the Forest Products Laboratory to
structural timbers, when compared with laboratory test data on small clear spec-
imens, have an apparent 'factor of safety' as high as 10, but in reality such factors make an allowance for an accidental overload of only 50%. A general explanation of how this 'factor of safety' is taken up largely in adjusting laboratory
test data to service conditions is given as follows:

Variations in the strength of clear wood. The strength of clear wood varies
a great deal within a species. It is not uncommon to find one piece of wood twice
as strong as another piece of the same species, although both pieces may be clear,
straight grained and sound. It is evident, therefore, that part of the 'factor of
safety' as measured by comparison of working stresses with average strength values
for a species would be used in making the working stresses safe for the weaker

Reference can be made to illustrations
of sub-flooring on wooden joists on pages
54, 74 and 80.

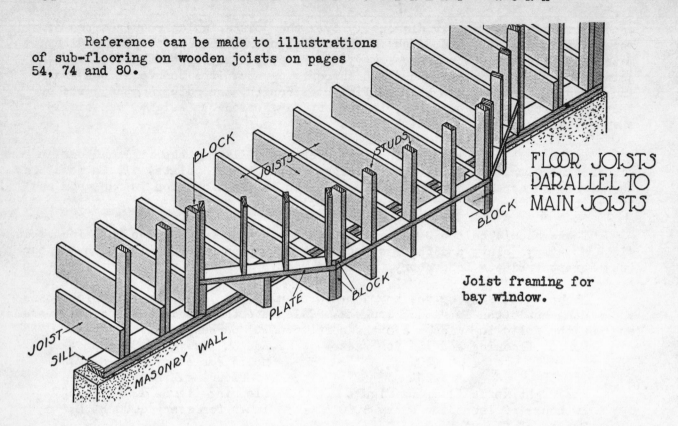

FLOOR JOISTS PARALLEL TO MAIN JOISTS

Joist framing for bay window.

FLOOR MEMBERS are lightweight.

SECOND FLOOR construction detail.

ERECTED like lumber.

Showing Structural Steel Joists and House Framing

timbers. If a builder could sort over his timbers and cull out those that fall below a prescribed minimum strength, he could, by rejection of relatively few timbers, assign his structure considerably higher working stresses without reducing his true factor of safety. The dense, strong timbers of Douglas fir and southern yellow pine, for example, can be selected by inspection and they can be assigned stresses 1/6 higher than unclassified timbers of the same species.

Effects of defects. Defects have about the same effect on strength in all species; that is, a given defect in a given location in a given timber reduces the strength of the timber from the strength of clear wood by about the same percentage, whatever the species. Grading rules applicable to all classes and species have been formulated by the Forest Products Laboratory limiting the size and location of defects in timbers for the various grades and provisions have been made in the permitted stress for loss of strength resulting from the defects allowable in each grade.

Moisture conditions of service. Dry wood fibers are stronger than wet wood fibers. Because of the checking that accompanies drying, however, many large timbers are no stronger after drying than when green; hence the stresses permitted in the dry timbers are based on green strength values. For large timbers in damp locations the working stresses must be decreased to make allowance for some deterioration which in such timbers is not offset by any gain in strength due to the dryness of the fibers. In small high grade timbers checking is not serious; dry 2 x 4's, for example, are actually somewhat stronger than green 2 x 4's. In order to avoid the inconvenience, however, of having two working stresses for timbers in dry locations - one for large timbers and one for small timbers - the size of defects permissible in each grade for small dimension timbers has been increased.

Duration of load. Part of the 'factor of safety' is necessary to make timbers safe for loads that may be left on for a long time. Laboratory tests indicate that if a certain load will cause failure in a structure if it is left off for a given time, nine-tenths of that load would cause failure if left on ten times as long. If a builder could be sure that his structure would never be subjected to the design load for long periods, he could safely use higher stresses. It is for this reason that in designing for combined live, dead and wind loads, stresses 50% higher than those permissible if the load were made up of live and dead loads alone may be used, provided the resulting sections are not less than those required for the actual live and dead loads alone.

Overloading. Part of the 'factor of safety' plays the role of a true factor of safety; that is, it makes allowance for small accidental overloads that may be left on a structure for a short time. This factor is not designed to take care of large overloads. In good construction occasional timbers might be expected to fail if such loads were applied for a long time. It is evident, therefore, that timbers should not be deliberately subjected to long-time loads much greater than the design load.

What is meant by factor of safety? List the main items of thought in each of the foregoing paragraphs.

English.

There are some magazines devoted to the interests of the carpenter. Some of them are: THE CARPENTER, THE AMERICAN BUILDER, THE AMERICAN HOME, HOUSE BEAU-

Cincinnati's Steel Frame Demonstration Home

An Ultra-Modern Home at LaGrange, Illinois

BETTER HOMES AND GARDENS, PENCIL POINTS, ARCHITECTURAL FORUM and the
COUNTRY HOME.

Obtain copies of these magazines from the school or public library and
try to find an article dealing with wood, its uses or a topic of technical information. From the selected article, jot down the main points of each paragraph. The following article, taken from the July, 1933 issue of the CARPENTER,
is a typical article on wood and its uses:

OTHING that comes out of
the earth or grows above
it has surpassed wood in
its adaptability to man's
needs. Nothing, except
fire, air and water, is so
indispensable to man's life and comfor

Wood combines strength and stiffness
with lightness, an important factor in
buildings of all descriptions. Weight for
weight it is stronger than steel. It is
resilient and shock-absorbing. It is
easily sawed, carved, planed and lathed
to any desired pattern; it may be bent
or twisted, and is readily shaved to
paper-like veneers and plywood. It can
be quickly and firmly glued, doweled,
or jointed into place.

Wood has beautiful natural textures,
grain and figures. Its color is varied and
pleasing; it may be easily stained and
painted, thus affording much variety of
appearance from a single species. It is
easily applicable in large units, and yet
those units are not rigid, being capable
of facile alteration on the job with hand
tools. A board may be reduced to many
pieces of many shapes.

Wood is the principal raw material
of some seventy groups of woodworking industries, and of many thousand
plants, besides being the chief source of
paper and yielding many industrial
chemicals. There is scarcely any industry that does not use wood incidentally
if not depending entirely on wood as its
raw material. Ten years ago but 2,000

uses of wood could be enumerated. Now
there are more than 4,500 uses.

One architect said of wood: "There
has never yet been found or invented a
substitute which, combining economy,
durability and ease of handling, can
take the place of wood. Even in localities where there is no timber, wood is
still cheaper and easier to transport
than any one of the heavier substitutes,
and in places where stone, cement, and
brick are not available, there is no al-
ternative.

"Except for nails, glass and whatever
masonry is necessary for chimneys, a
house can be completely built of wood
alone, which cannot be said of any
other material."

Wood is durable. Chariots used by
the ancients have come down to us
with their wood parts still sound. In
Japan there is a wood temple erected
thirteen centuries ago. A wood church
built in Oslo, Norway, 800 years ago is
sound and is still in use. Wood, when
properly cared for, can be preserved in-
definitely.

Wood is plentiful, inexpensive and
capable of perpetual replacement. The
forests are the only basic natural re-
source that is eternally renewable. Forests have been replenishing themselves
since the dawn of time on earth and
will, doubtless, continue to go on in
their immortality when mineral de-
posits are exhausted for all time. Forests can be grown like crops.

Wood is the most humanly intimate
of all materials. Because it is a product
of life, man has always felt for wood
a close kinship. Trees take their food
from soil, the same as man does; their
water from the rains and breathe the
same air. Man finds wood friendly. He
loves his association with it, likes to
feel it under his hand sympathetic to
his touch and to his eye. Wood is uni-
versally beautiful to man. All ages of
history have recorded this close friend-
ship.

There is a charm and a dignity about
a well-built wood house that cannot be
successfully imitated. Wood is also
most desirable for house building because it is a natural insulator against
heat and cold. This gives it a great
advantage over the mineral building
materials and assures greater comfort
the year around.

Civics.

In floor laying the carpenter is working at somewhat of a disadvantage
as compared with sill and girder erection. While due precautions must be taken
in sill and girder work, added precautions must be taken in floor laying. The
worker should watch the following points when laying floors: a. Position of
feet for secure standing; b. Splinters from tongue or groove or edge of stock;
c. Position of feet in kneeling and the placing of knees; d. Placing of legs in
sawing and position of back; e. Care in nailing.

The following items, taken from a leaflet issued by the American National
Red Cross, give practical information about first aid help in case of hemorrhage,
open wound, burn, fracture, eye injury and the use of a stretcher:

First Aid Suggestions

HEMORRHAGE.—Bleeding can usually be stopped by applying a pad of sterile gauze and a tight bandage over wound; or by pressure with fingers on main blood vessel between wound and heart; also elevate the limb. Points for hand pressure are—(1) just in front of ear for bleeding from temple; (2) inner side of arm below armpit, about where inside sleeve of coat comes; (3) fingers against the side of windpipe, thumb around the back of the neck pressing cut vessels of throat against the spinal column; (4) in the middle of the groin pressing against the pelvis bone. Failing by pressure, apply tourniquet hand's breadth below armpit or groin as needed. Place firm pad over artery and tie a bandage or handkerchief loosely over this around the limb. Insert stick and twist until bleeding stops. **LOOSEN EVERY FIFTEEN MINUTES.** Let remain loosened if bleeding has stopped; watch closely and tighten tourniquet or bandage if necessary.

OPEN WOUNDS.—Apply half-strength tincture of iodine; let dry; then cover with sterile gauze, or freshly laundered cloth, and bandage. Do not allow fingers to touch the wound, or that part of the gauze that comes in contact with the wound. Never wash a wound with water. Grease may be removed with benzine, naphtha, or turpentine. Other dirt may be removed with "rubbing alcohol" such as may be purchased at any drug store. Never use cobwebs, tobacco, waste, or oil, as infection may result.

BURNS.—Apply sterile gauze, or freshly laundered cloth, wet with one of the following: baking soda, 2 tablespoonsful to a quart of water that has been boiled, or Epsom Salts, 6 tablespoonsful to a quart. Or a good burn ointment may be used. This is especially useful on small burns. Picric acid gauze moistened with clean water is good if at hand.

FRACTURES (Broken Bones).—DO NOT MOVE PATIENT UNLESS ABSOLUTELY NECESSARY. Call physician to scene of accident. If necessary to move patient, always apply splints before moving. Handle carefully to prevent sharp ends cutting through flesh. With a little pull on the end of the limb and carefully supporting it under the break, move it VERY gently into normal position. Apply splints well padded made from narrow boards, heavy cardboard, umbrellas, etc. Splints must be long enough to reach beyond the joints above and below fracture. Treat for shock.

STRETCHER.—Three persons are necessary to place an injured person properly on stretcher, one to lift head and shoulders, another the hips, and a third the legs. The stretcher should be placed alongside the injured, and the helpers should kneel on one knee on the side of the patient away from the stretcher lifting him in unison, first to their bended knees and then lay him gently on the stretcher.

EYE INJURIES.—Loose particles may be removed from the eyelid with a clean handkerchief, or a bit of clean cotton rolled on a toothpick or a match stick. If not easily removed in this way, make no further attempt. Particles embedded in the lid or eye ball should be left to the surgeon. Never violate this rule. Blindness may result. In case of serious eye injury, cover with clean cloth compress wrung out in ice cold water and send patient to surgeon or hospital.

Continued from page 77

13. IDAHO WHITE PINE
(Pinus monticola)

SOURCE: Northern Idaho, and bordering territory in Washington and Montana.

ANNUAL PRODUCTION: 500,000,000 bd. ft.

PROPERTIES: Very soft uniform texture, straight grain, light weight, easily worked, moderate shrinkage, white to pink in color. Weight, air-dry: 27 lbs. per cu. ft.

USES: Matches, toys, siding, knotty paneling, mouldings, millwork, wood carvings, etc.

PRODUCED BY MEMBERS OF: Western Pine Association, Portland, Ore.

14. LONGLEAF PINE
(Pinus palustris)

SOURCE: Gulf States from Florida and Georgia west to Texas.

ANNUAL PRODUCTION: All species Southern Yellow Pine: 13,000,000,000 bd. ft.

PROPERTIES: Hard, heavy, tough, durable, resinous, narrow ring growth, orange to yellowish brown. Weight, air-dry: 41 lbs. per cu. ft.

USES: Heavy timber construction, flooring, boxes and crates, railroad cars, general construction, planing-mill products, ship and boat building, paving material, tanks, etc.

PRODUCED BY MEMBERS OF: Southern Pine Association, New Orleans, La.

15. NORTHERN WHITE PINE
(Pinus strobus)

SOURCE: Lake States, Northeastern U. S.

ANNUAL PRODUCTION: 825,000,000 bd. ft.

PROPERTIES: Soft, light in weight, easily worked, straight grain, durable, shrinks and swells very little, pale reddish brown to white. Weight, air-dry: 25 lbs. per cu. ft.

USES: Millwork, sash, patterns, boxes, matches, building construction.

PRODUCED BY MEMBERS OF: Northern Pine Manufacturers Association, Minneapolis, Minn.

Continued on page 114

Chapter XI

Outside Framed Walls

The foundation walls of a building form bearing walls for the upper structure and an enclosure for the basement. The outside walls, which rest directly on
the foundation walls (sills acting as anchors for them) form bearing walls for
the roof, as well as the upper story walls and an enclosure for the entire inner
construction.

From the set of house plans obtain the requirements for the framing of the
outside walls. If the corner posts are not assembled and raised with the outside studded walls they should be assembled and erected by finding the length
of the corner posts from the framing details and cut the stock to proper lengths.
Nail pieces together with 12 d. or 16 d. nails, using the method required.
Erect the post at the corner of sill, plumb and brace securely.

The corner posts may be framed with outside studded walls before the wall
is raised in place. Plumb and brace the entire wall after it is raised. Use
the spirit level and plumb bob to test corner post and plate.

Individual members of the studded wall may be raised one at a time. If
this method is used note the length of studs, cut and place ready for nailing.
Find the distance the studs are to be placed on centers and mark this distance
on extreme edge of the flooring above the sill. If a shoe plate is placed on
the flooring before the studs are in place, nail this shoe plate down and nail
each stud to the shoe plate. Brace the studs temporarily and nail plate member
to top of studs. If a shoe plate is not used nail studs to flooring by toe-
nailing and place plate on top of studs.

If the studded wall is assembled on the sub-floor or away from the structure, space each stud 16" cc, nail shoe, ribband strip and top plate to the studs
and raise in section and nail securely to sill or sub-floor.

Brace all erected walls securely, keeping in mind always that framing
timber is quite heavy and that wind exerts considerable pressure on open frame
work.

If the framing details of the set of house plans do not give the information regarding the size of the window and door openings the following general rules can be used. Obtain the width of the glass used in the sash and add
11" to this as an over all width of the rough window opening. Obtain the
length of the glass (if two sash are used double this amount) used in the
sash and add $10\frac{1}{2}$" to this as an over all height of the rough window opening.

In allowing an opening for a casement sash or window opening an allowance
of 8" must be added to the width of the glass size and 10" added to the height
of the glass size.

In allowing an opening for a door add 3" to the width of the door and 3"
to the height of the door. This rule applies to both outside and inside doors,
French doors or any other type of door not having a side light sash.   Doors or
sash with special side lights or framing must be dealt with as special cases,

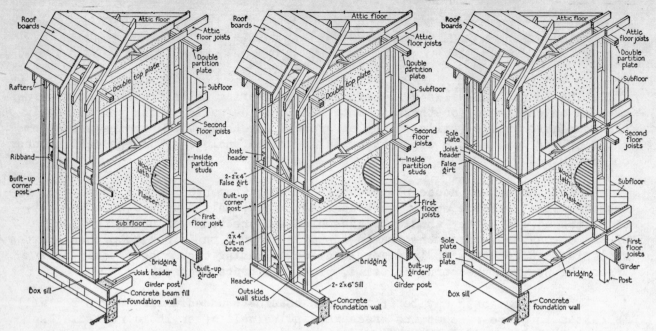

THE BALLOON FRAME

This type of frame has many things to recommend it. The one piece studs, extending the full height of the wall and tied together by the ribband at the second floor line reduce to a minimum the shrinkage factor. It is strong and rigid but requires careful fire stopping.

This frame is more efficient when the interior studding is set directly on top of girders or bearing partitions.

THE MODERN BRACED FRAME

This type of frame is an outgrowth of New England solid timber post and girth construction. Built-up members are used today very largely and with equal satisfaction. Instead of heavy posts set eight or ten feet apart, walls are built with 2x4 in. studs set 16 in. on centers. The second floor is carried on a double 2x4 in. girt. Diagonal bracing is inserted at the corners. This type has several commendable features. It is simple to build and has good provision for fire stopping both at sill and second floor line. 2x4 in. cut-in bracing, as illustrated, may also be used with other types.

~

THE FRAME provides the network to which the other materials are fastened and the strength and rigidity required to support the loads put upon it and preserve the materials with which it is built. Three distinct types of frames are shown by Figs. 1, 2 and 3. Numerous combinations of these types are frequently employed.

BALANCED SHRINKAGE

The total thickness of horizontal lumber in the framing of outside and inside walls on each floor should be equalized as nearly as possible to eliminate uneven shrinkage.

FIRE STOPPING

Fire safety in a dwelling is increased by preventing the circulation of air in the walls between floors or between rooms. An effective method is shown in the drawing to the right. (Fig 5)

THE PLATFORM FRAME

The Platform Frame is extensively used. It is similar in principle to Braced Frame but has boxed sill construction at each floor line. This makes for greater shrinkage but it is equalized on each floor when a similar type of construction is used under bearing partitions.

This frame is more efficient when the interior studding is set directly on top of girders or bearing partitions.

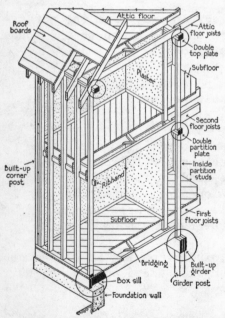

DETAIL OF METHOD FOR SECURING BALANCED SHRINKAGE

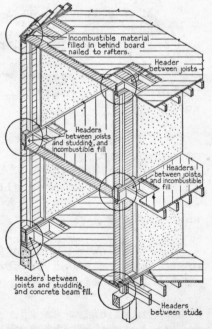

FRAMING FOR FIRE STOPPING

Several Standard Methods of Framing, with Important Facts and Suggestions

using the general rules above as a help in figuring out the special framing to allow for openings. Methods used in framing porches, bay windows and other types of attached construction will be dealt with in Chapter 20.

In framing structural steel walls one must refer to the plans, note the location of the studs and erect them individually. Allowances for door and window openings are made according to the details occuring in the following several illustrations. See pages 102, 103 and 104.

Practical jobs. Frame up all outside wooden walls. Allow for window and door openings or any special openings. Frame up all outside walls of structural steel. Allow for window and door openings or any special openings.

Related Studies

Drawing.

In oblique, isometric, parallel and angular perspective sketching will be found three facts or conditions that are common to one another. The common conditions are: a. There is a portion or face of the object which could be termed the front view; b. There is a face of the object which could be termed the side view; c. There is a face of the object which could be termed the top view.

When these common conditions or points of similarity are seen in these four systems of drawing they will help to introduce a system of drawing in which these faces or views are separated in such a way as to bear a distinct mechanical relation one to another. If, for instance, the isometric figure would have hinges placed on it as shown in the drawing below and the figure unfolded as indicated in the drawing following it, it would form the TOP, FRONT and END views of a system of drawing known as orthographic projection.

This system always has the top, front and end views in relation one to another as shown in the isometric figure unfolded. One good way to remember the relation of the three views of an orthographic drawing is to have an imaginary capital letter L placed over the views. The center of the top view of the drawing will rest at the heel or corner of the capital letter L, and the center of the end or side view will rest at the extreme right hand end of the horizontal bar of the capital letter L.

Drawing related to building construction is not Architectural Drawing but is drawing for builders and mechanics. The approach to architectural drawing should be made from the historical point of view. This need not be done for the type of drawing required by builders or mechanics. Many study architectural drawing to enable themselves to read a complete set of house plans, not necessarily to draw house plans. Architectural drawing is an end in itself. Builders drawing is a means for more efficient work as a mechanic for workers in the house construction field of endeavor.

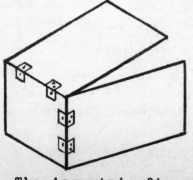

The isometric figure with 'hinges'.

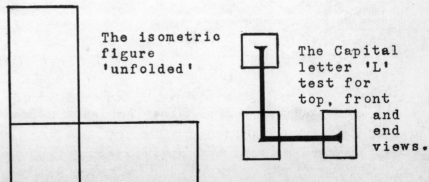

The isometric figure 'unfolded'

The Capital letter 'L' test for top, front and end views.

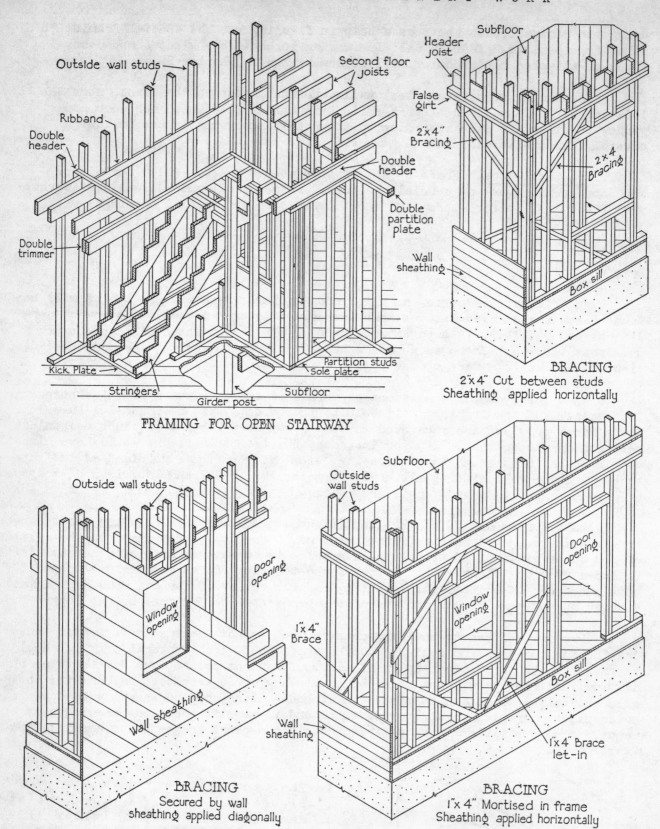

Outside wall studs

Second floor joists

Ribband

Double header

Double header

Double partition plate

Double trimmer

Double partition plate

Subfloor

Header joist

False girt

2"x4" Bracing

2 x 4 Bracing

Wall sheathing

Box sill

Kick Plate

Stringers

Partition studs

Sole plate

Girder post

Subfloor

FRAMING FOR OPEN STAIRWAY

BRACING
2"x4" Cut between studs
Sheathing applied horizontally

Outside wall studs

Door opening

Window opening

Wall sheathing

BRACING
Secured by wall
sheathing applied diagonally

Subfloor

Outside wall studs

Door opening

Window opening

1"x 4" Brace

Wall sheathing

Box sill

1"x 4" Brace let-in

BRACING
1"x 4" Mortised in frame
Sheathing applied horizontally

Showing Several Standard Methods of Framing.
Courtesy General Timber Service, Incorporated, Saint Paul, Minnesota.

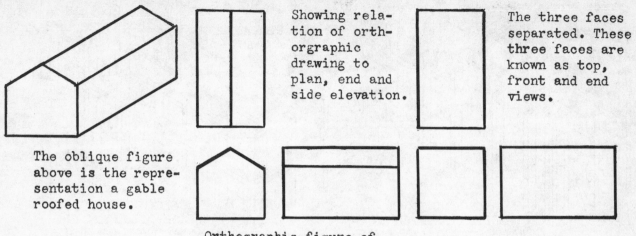

The oblique figure above is the representation a gable roofed house.

Showing relation of orthorgraphic drawing to plan, end and side elevation.

The three faces separated. These three faces are known as top, front and end views.

Orthographic figure of a gable roofed house.

Sketch, with the aid of a rule or straight edge, pencil and eraser the following illustrations of building material. Make them full size or half or quarter size as the space will permit. Make a small capital letter L and test the sketches. Sketch three views each.

Actual lengths 8' - 10' - 12' etc.

Length varies. Use 6" to 12".

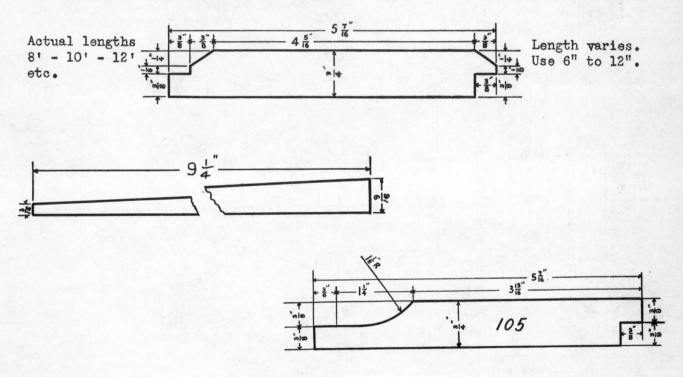

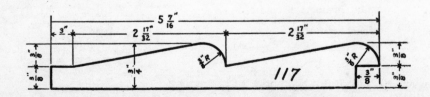

Courtesy QUEEN CITY LUMBER COMPANY, Cincinnati.

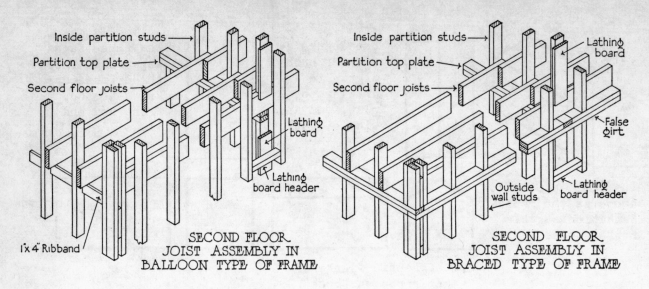

Inside partition studs
Partition top plate
Second floor joists
Lathing board
Lathing board header
1 x 4" Ribband

SECOND FLOOR
JOIST ASSEMBLY IN
BALLOON TYPE OF FRAME

Inside partition studs
Partition top plate
Second floor joists
Lathing board
False girt
Outside wall studs
Lathing board header

SECOND FLOOR
JOIST ASSEMBLY IN
BRACED TYPE OF FRAME

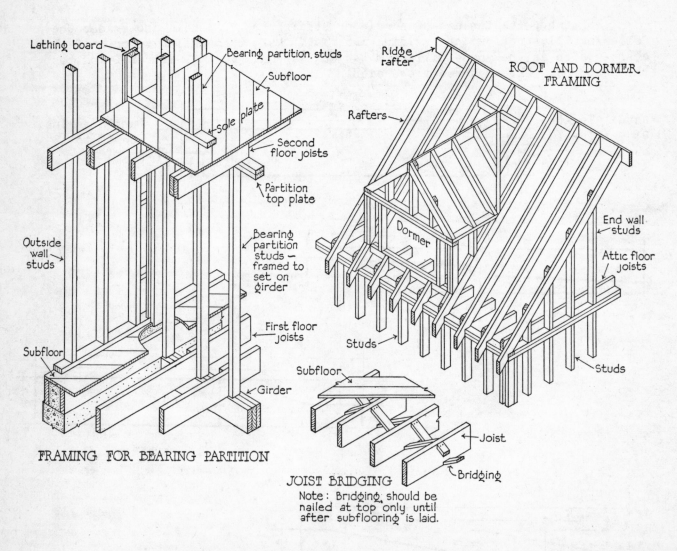

Lathing board
Bearing partition studs
Subfloor
Sole plate
Second floor joists
Partition top plate
Bearing partition studs — framed to set on girder
Outside wall studs
First floor joists
Subfloor
Girder

FRAMING FOR BEARING PARTITION

Ridge rafter
ROOF AND DORMER FRAMING
Rafters
End wall studs
Attic floor joists
Dormer
Studs
Studs

Subfloor
Joist
Bridging

JOIST BRIDGING
Note: Bridging should be
nailed at top only until
after subflooring is laid.

Showing Several Standard Methods of Framing

Mathematics.

The Carpenter or Joiner frames the wood or metal parts of a house together. These parts consist in the main, of wood or steel and hardware. Such items as nails screws, glue, bolts and fastenings may be included in hardware. In addition to the wood or metal parts and the hardware there is an item entering into all construction work known as labor. Labor is known as the money paid the skilled mechancs for their services in erecting the building. Labor is also known as the money paid unskilled mechanics for their hire.

In previous assignments instructions were given to keep the several estimates in record form. There are very many suggested forms to use in estimating construction costs. The following form is only a suggestion which might be used for all types of estimates in house construction.

MATERIAL LISTS AND LABOR COSTS
FOR

DWELLING

Items	Stock #	T- W- L	#pcs.	B.M.	@	Sub.Tot	Hardware	Sub.Tot	Time	Sub.Tot	G.T.

This form may be made up and spaces ruled for as many items as needed in the house. The following is a partial list, according to the place in erection of individual items in the construction of a dwelling.

This form may be made up and spaces ruled for as many items as needed in the construction of the house. The following is a partial list, according to the place in erection of individual items in the construction of a dwelling:

Excavating	purlins	garage siding
trench excavating	braces	ground for plaster
fill	wall plates	building paper
cinders	second floor joists	corner boards
waterproofing	second floor studs	cornice boards
grading	second floor shoe	cornice soffit
trench forms	second floor plate	crown mold
wall forms	outside sheathing	window frames
concrete footings	common rafters	coal chute
concrete walls	hip rafters	window sash
garage forms and footings	dormer rafters	outside door frames
basement floor	cripple rafters	outside doors
sill bolts	bay window rafters	inside door frames
sill header	bay window shoe	inside doors
girder posts	bay window studs	screens
first floor joists	bay window plate	screen doors

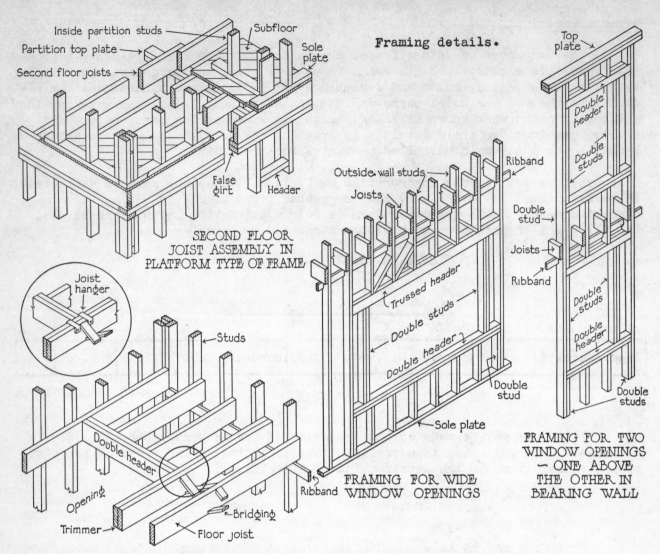

Inside partition studs
Partition top plate
Second floor joists
Subfloor
Sole plate
False girt
Header

SECOND FLOOR
JOIST ASSEMBLY IN
PLATFORM TYPE OF FRAME

Joist hanger

Studs
Double header
Opening
Trimmer
Bridging
Floor joist
Ribband

FRAMING AROUND FLOOR OPENING

Framing details.

Top plate

Double header
Double studs
Double stud
Joists
Ribband
Double studs
Double header
Double studs

FRAMING FOR TWO
WINDOW OPENINGS
— ONE ABOVE
THE OTHER IN
BEARING WALL

Outside wall studs
Joists
Ribband
Trussed header
Double studs
Double header
Double stud
Sole plate

FRAMING FOR WIDE
WINDOW OPENINGS

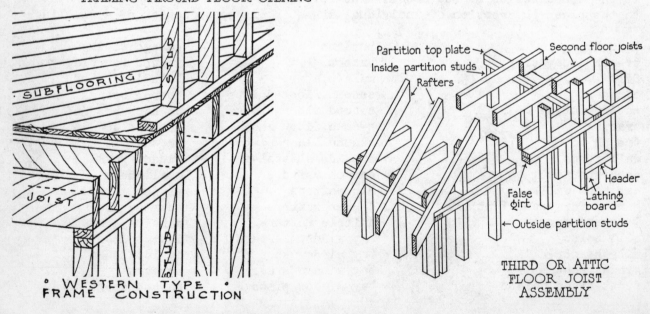

SUBFLOORING
STUD
JOIST

WESTERN TYPE
FRAME CONSTRUCTION

Partition top plate
Inside partition studs
Rafters
Second floor joists
False girt
Outside partition studs
Header
Lathing board

THIRD OR ATTIC
FLOOR JOIST
ASSEMBLY

joist headers, trimmers
stair horses, steps
bridging
first floor sub floor
shoe
porch framing
partition studs
outside wall studs
carpet strip
breakfast nook units
porch columns

ridge board
garage sill, shoe
studs, plates, rafters,
second floor sub floor
ridge
roof sheathing
shingles
beveled siding
finish flooring
casement work
porch trim

window trim
door trim
stairway
medicine cabinet
kitchen cupboards
closet shelving
picture mold
base mold
porch ceiling
porch sheathing
etc., etc., etc.

The cost of studded walls may be estimated by the count. Allow one stud for every 12" of length of wall, either outside or inside. In this way, if studs are placed 16" cc, this will allow a sufficient number to be used at corners, windows and doors. It will take about 32 hours to frame 1,000 B. M. of studding. Steel studs are estimated by count, taking off the count from the set of plans. Hardware and fastenings according to plans. The time is the same as for wood framing.

Estimate the material and time required to erect the outside walls of the house in the accompanying set of house plans. Keep this in a permanent record form.

Science.

There are several ways to drive a nail into a piece of stock. The most common way is called 'straight nailing', that is, the nail is always 90 degrees to the surface of the stock. Another way to drive nails is just like straight nailing but the nail is not driven clear through the stock. This is called 'draw nailing'. This allows for a small part of the nail to extend above the surface for pulling back with the claw of the hammer.

Still another way to drive nails is the method called 'toe nailing'. In this method the nail is driven into the stock at about 45 degrees to the surface of the stock. Nail setting is the sinking of nails below the surface of the stock by use of a small tool called the nail set.

Obtain a piece of 1" x 2" x 6" stock of wood and produce the four systems or methods of nailing as shown in the following sketch:

Straight nailing   Draw nailing   Nail setting   Toe nailing

The properties of wood may be divided into two general classes, the physical and the mechanical. Physical properties deal with the structural phases while the mechanical properties deal with such factors as loads, shocks, forces, or deformations.

In very few cases do two or more species of wood have the same degree of

SHOWING, at left, a dwelling having two stories, combined hip and gable roof, which is almost entirely framed and ready for sheathing.

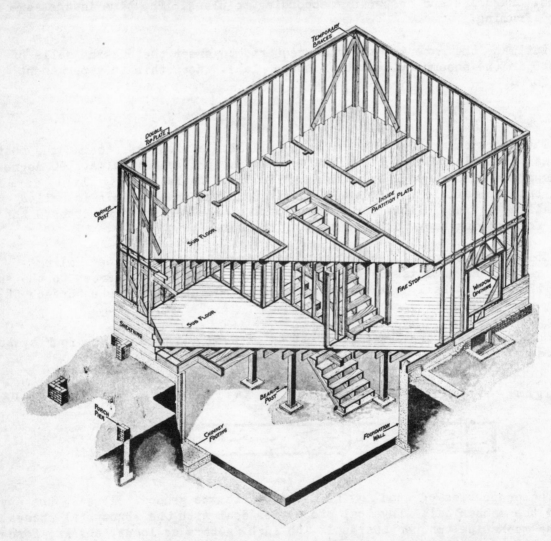

The illustration above shows a two-story dwelling, with sheathing partly applied and ready for placing of roof timbers. Note construction details.

various physical or mechanical properties. This is the reason for the demand for certain species in certain uses. Physical properties may be said to be those facts about wood as it comes to our use and mechanical properties may be said to be those facts about wood as we use it in construction.

Large sized timbers are best used in giving dependable results in wood property findings. Results from small pieces are proportioned down from results on large stock.

What are two properties of wood? Define them. Obtain a piece of $\frac{1}{4}$"x2"x6" stock, any kind, soak this piece in water for 48 hours. Note the weight of the piece before and after soaking. What property does this show, a physical or mechanical change or condition?

A lever is a mechanical device, consisting of a rigid structure, often a straight bar, turning freely on a fixed point or fulcrum and serving to impart pressure or motion from a source of power to a resistance. A lever is one of the six mechanical powers intended to change the direction of motion, as a crow-bar, human jaw, the human arm or an oar of a boat.

Levers are commonly divided into three classes. A first class lever is one in which the fulcrum is between the power and the resistance, as in a pair of scissors.

A second class lever is one in which the resistance is between the power and the fulcrum, as in a lemon squeezer.

A third class lever is one in which the power is between the resistance and the fulcrum, as in the human forearm.

Provide three pieces of wood $\frac{1}{4}$" or $\frac{1}{2}$" x 1" x 3". Provide three pieces of wood $\frac{1}{4}$" or $\frac{1}{2}$" x $\frac{1}{2}$" x 3". Provide three 6 d. finishing or common nails. Provide three bases for these three different levers using $\frac{1}{2}$" x 2" x 4" stock. With this material build up three sets of levers, one each of the first class, second class and third class. Label each and place on each the place of the power, pressure and fulcrum. Refer to the drawings throughout this text and find practical uses of the three types of levers.

Showing below illustrations of first, second and third class levers.

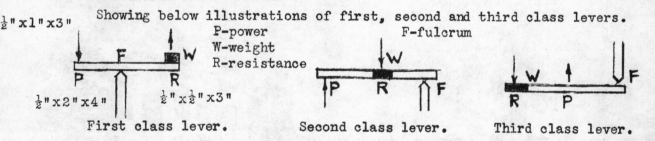

First class lever.   Second class lever.   Third class lever.

English.

It is a good habit to read the advertisements found in trade magazines. Much valuable information can be obtained from some of the advertisements. Refer to the list of magazines given in the previous lesson in English. Obtain a few of these magazines and notice the advertisements. Try to find an advertisement that deals with a product of interest to you. Write a letter to the

Showing the
construction
of a FRAMELESS
STEEL dwelling.
It is a new
building material
having a complete-
ly enclosed metal
structural shell
or chassis.

Below, showing
dwelling of
FRAMELESS STEEL
in various stages
of construction.

Courtesy
Insulated Steel
Construction
Company,
Cleveland. Ohio.

← Wall Unit Erection.

→ Floor Unit (19' 6" Span) in place.

← Sheathing which forms protective covering for steel.

→ Armco-Ferro House—"A Century of Progress" Frameless Steel "Chassis" —Porcelain Enamel Exterior Finish.

Details of the modern framed dwelling, each detail properly titled
will be found on pages 102, 103, 104 and 105.

concern advertising its product. In this letter ask for certain information and sales literature regarding this product or products. See advertisement below.

The following letter will give the correct form in letter writing. It is in answer to an advertisement appearing in a recent issue of THE CARPENTER.

Cincinnati, Ohio.
April 24, 1935

Samuel Cabot, Inc.,
141 Milk Street,
Boston, Mass.

Gentlemen:

Please send, to the address below, a copy of your book, 'Build Warm Homes' as advertised in the March issue of THE CARPENTER.

Raymond Dames,   Very truly,
1046 Stallo Ave.,
Sedamsville,
Cincinnati, Ohio.

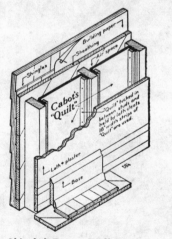

Civics.

The Department of Industrial Relations and the Industrial Commission of the State of Ohio publish the state requirements 'SPECIFIC SAFETY REQUIREMENTS RELATING TO BUILDING AND CONSTRUCTION WORK' in a bulletin #202. Write for this code. Address the State Office Building, Columbus, Ohio.

Read through the entire code. List the sections pertaining to carpentry work. Make sketches of scaffolds that a carpenter would use.

If this code cannot be obtained, write the Industrial Commission of other states or consult a public library for copies of safety codes.

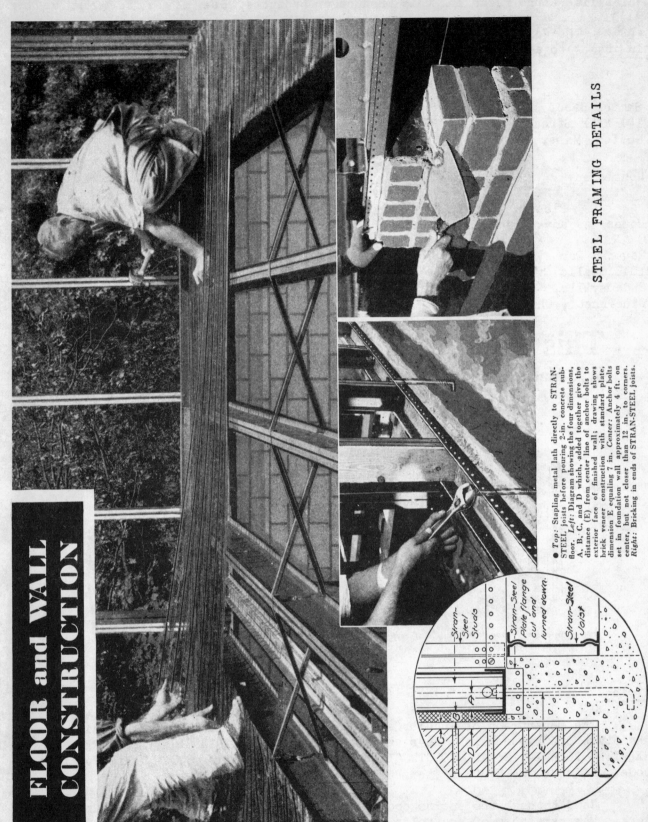

FLOOR and WALL CONSTRUCTION

STEEL FRAMING DETAILS

● *Top:* Stapling metal lath directly to STRAN-STEEL joists before pouring 2-in. concrete sub-floor. *Left:* Diagram showing the four dimensions, A, B, C, and D which, added together give the distance (E) from center line of anchor bolts to exterior face of finished wall; drawing shows brick veneer construction with standard plate, dimension E equaling 7 in. *Center:* Anchor bolts set in foundation wall approximately 4 ft. on center, but not closer than 12 in. to corners. *Right:* Bricking in ends of STRAN-STEEL joists.

Courtesy STRAN-STEEL CORPORATION, Detroit.

ROOF FRAMING

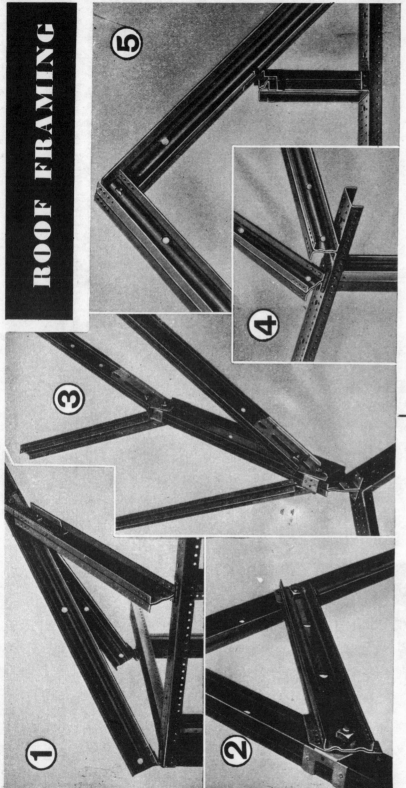

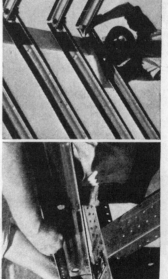

1 Hip roof framed with STRAN-STEEL. Rafter hinges may be attached to rafters and plate before rafters are elevated into position.

2 Collar tie in place. This picture clearly indicates the simplicity of STRAN-STEEL roof connections as well as the rigidity of the entire roof framing.

3 Valley construction; 3⅝-in. STRAN-STEEL rafter rigidly connected to 8-in. STRAN-STEEL joist used as valley rafter. The simplicity of STRAN-STEEL

attachments and the full adjustment which they permit are strikingly evident here.

4 Roof rafter and ceiling joist relationship is shown in this picture. Note alignment of center lines of stud and rafter; ceiling joist is set to one side to facilitate attachment.

5 Details of peak connection and attachment of gable stud to plate and rafter. Note how adjacent lower flanges on rafters are cut and bent at peak. Also note how rafter clip is nailed to rafter.

● All STRAN-STEEL attachments have been carefully designed for strength and simplicity; provision is made for adjustments where necessary.

● Inserting hinge pin in rafter rings; the hinge takes care of any pitch roof and pin is located in place with cotter key.

● Tightening bolts at rafter peak after rafters have been raised and temporarily braced in position.

STEEL FRAMING DETAILS

BUCKS, NAILERS, OTHER MATERIALS

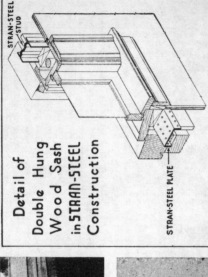

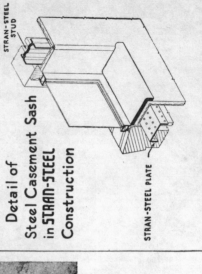

Detail of Double Hung Wood Sash in STRAN-STEEL Construction

STRAN-STEEL STUD

STRAN-STEEL PLATE

Detail of Steel Casement Sash in STRAN-STEEL Construction

STRAN-STEEL STUD

STRAN-STEEL PLATE

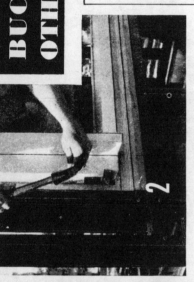

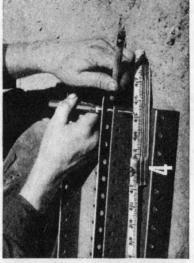

● 1—Reinforcing stud corners with corner bracket. 2—Nailing wood casing to wood bucks, the latter attached with nails through flanges of STRAN-STEEL stud and holes in sill plate. 3—STRAN-STEEL half-stud used as lath backing in ceiling corner between joists. 4—Aligning holes in upper and lower plates before cutting to length. Detail drawings show methods of framing window casings into STRAN-STEEL brick veneer construction.

BUCKS—These are purchased locally. They are ripped to fit between flanges of studs adjacent to openings. Where the standard studs are used the buck is ripped to $3\frac{7}{16}$ in. from a standard wood 2 x 4. Where bucks are to be used with narrow studs for greatest economy these are ripped from a standard wood 2 x 8. Holes for nailing bucks in place are hand-punched in opposite flanges of studs; space holes about four inches from each end of bucks and approximately every 12 in. between end nails. Holes for these nails are hand-punched along center line of plate, one near each end and approximately 1 in. apart between end holes.

FRAMING DOORS AND WINDOWS—Door and window frames are attached to STRAN-STEEL by means of rough wood bucks placed between flanges of jamb studs, under joist headers and over window sill plates where wood stool is used.

STEEL FRAMING DETAILS

Standard Lumber Abbreviations

AD—Air dried.
a.l—All lengths.
av—Average.
av.w.—Average width.
av. l.—Average length.
a.w.—All widths.
B1S—Beaded one side.
B2S—Beaded two sides.
BBS—Box bark strips.
bd.—Board.
bd. ft.—Board foot; that is, an area of 1 square foot by 1 inch thick.
bdl.—Bundle.
bdl. bk. s.—Bundled bark strips.
Bev.—Beveled.
B/L—Bill of lading.
b. m.—Board (foot) measure.
Btr.—Better.
c.&f.—(Named port.) Cost and freight to a named port. Term used when the seller is ready to go farther than the delivery of his goods upon a vessel and is willing to pay transportation to another port.
c.i.f.—(Named port.) Cost, insurance, and freight to a named port. Term used when the seller desires to quote a price covering the cost of the goods, the marine insurance on the goods, and all transportation charges to the point of delivery.
c.i.f.e.—(Named port.) Cost, insurance, freight and exchange to a named port. This is the same as c.i.f. with the additional provision that the seller guarantees the buyer against loss due to a decline in the rate of exchange.
Clg.—Ceiling.
Clr.—Clear.
CM—Center matched; that is, the tongue and groove joints are worked along the center of the edges of the piece.
Com.—Common.
Coop.—Cooperage (stock).
Csg.—Casing.
Ctg.—Crating.
cu. ft.—Cubic foot.
Cust.—Custom (sawed).
D&CM—Dressed (one or two sides) and center matched.
D&H—Dressed and headed; that is, dressed one or two sides and worked to tongue and groove joints on both the edge and the ends.
D2S&SM—Dressed two sides and standard matched.
D&M—Dressed and matched; that is, dressed one or two sides and tongued and grooved on the edges. The match may be center or standard.
D&SM—Dressed (one or two sides) and standard matched.
D2S&CM—Dressed two sides and center matched.
D2S&M—Dressed two sides and (center or standard matched).
Dim.—Dimension.
D.S.—Drop siding.
E.—Edge.
E&CB1S—Edge and center bead one side; surfaced one or two sides and with a longitudinal edge and center bead on a surfaced face.
E&CB2S—Edge and center bead two sides; all four sides surfaced and with a longitudinal edge and center bead on the two faces.
ECM—Ends center matched.
E&CV1S—Edge and center V one side; surfaced one or two sides and with a longitudinal edge and center V-shaped groove on a surfaced face.
E&CV2S—Edge and center V two sides; all four sides surfaced and with a longitudinal edge and center V-shaped groove on each of the two faces.
EM—End matched—either center or standard.
ESM—Ends standard matched.
exp.—Expert (lumber or timber).
FAS—First and seconds—a combined grade of the two upper grades of hardwoods.
f.a.s. vessel—(Named port.)—Free alongside vessel at a named port. Term used when the seller desires to quote a price covering delivery of the goods alongside a vessel and within reach of its loading tackle.
f.b.k.—Flat back.
fcty—Factory (lumber).
F. G.—Flat grain.
Flg.—Flooring.
f.o.b.—(Named shipment point.) Free on board at a named shipping point. Term used when the price quoted applies only to an inland shipping point and the seller merely undertakes to load the goods on or in cars or in lighters furnished by the railroad company serving the industry or most conveniently located to the industry, without other designation as to routing.
f.o.b.—(Named point.) Freight prepaid to (named point). Free on board at a named point and freight prepaid to a named point. Term used when the seller quotes a price including transportation charges to a given point without assuming responsibility for the goods after obtaining a clean bill of lading at point of origin.
f.o.b.—(Named point.) Freight allowed to (named point). Free on board at a named point and freight allowed to a named point. Term used when the seller wishes to quote a price from which the buyer may deduct the cost of transportation to the point of destination, without the seller assuming responsibility for the goods after obtaining a clean bill of lading at the point of origin.
f.o.b. cars—(Named destination point.) Free on board cars at a named destination point. Term used when the seller desires to quote a price covering the transportation of the goods to a given point, assuming responsibility for loss and/or damage up to that point.
f.o.b. cars—(Named point.) Free on board cars at a named point less carload lots. Term used when the goods on which a price is quoted to a given point constitutes less than a carload lot.
f.o.b.—(Named port.) Lighterage free. Free on board at a named port with lighterage free. Term used when seller desires to quote a price which will include the expense of transportation of the goods by rail to the seaboard, including lighterage.

S1S1E—Surfaced one side and one edge.
S2S1E—Surfaced two sides and one edge.
S1S2E—Surfaced one side and two edges.
S4S—Surfaced four sides.
S4SCS—Surfaced four sides with a calking seam on each edge.
S&CM—Surfaced (one or two sides) and center matched.
S&M—Surfaced and matched; that is, surfaced one or two sides and tongued and grooved on the edges. The match may be center or standard.
S&SM—Surfaced (one of two sides) and standard matched.
S2S&CM—Surfaced two sides and center matched.
S2S&M—Surfaced two sides and (center or standard) matched.
S2S&SM—Surfaced two sides and standard matched.
Sap.—Sapwood.
SB—Standard bead.
Sd.—Seasoned.
Sdg.—Siding.
Sel.—Select.
S. E. Sdg.—Square edge siding.
s.f.—Surface foot; that is, an area of one square foot.
Sftwd.—Softwood.
Sh.D.—Shipping dry.
Ship—Shipment or shipments.
Ship.—Shiplap.
s.m.—Surface measure.
SM—Standard matched.
smkd—Smoked (dried).
smk.stnd.—Smoke stained.
s.n.d.—Sap no defect.
snd.—Sound.
sq.—Square.
Sq.E&S—Square edged and sound.
sqrs.—Squares.
Std.—Standard.
stnd.—Stained.
stk.—Stock.
Stp.—Stepping.
S.W.—Sound wormy.
Symbols: "—inch or inches, as 12".
'—foot or feet, as 12'.
x—by, as 6x8 timber.
4/4, 5/4, 6/4, 8/4, etc.=1 inch, 1¼ inches, 1½ inches, 2 inches, etc., when referring to the size of lumber.
T&G—Tongued and grooved.
TB&S—Top, bottom and sides.
Tbrs.—Timbers.
V1S—V one side; that is, a longitudinal V-shaped groove on one face of a piece of lumber.
V2S—V two sides; that is, a longitudinal V-shaped groove on two faces of a piece of lumber.
V.G.—Vertical grain.
wal.—Wider, all lengths.
Wth—Width.
wdr.—Wider.
Wgn.—Wagon (stock).
wt.—Weight.
f.o.b. vessel—(Named port.) Free on board vessel of a named port. Term used when the seller desires to quote a price covering all expenses up to and including delivery of the goods upon a vessel at a named port.
f.o.k.—Free of knots.
f.o.w.—First open water.
Frm.—Framing.
ft.—Foot or feet. Also one accent ('). See symbols.
ft.b.m.—Feet board measure.
ft.s.m.—Feet surface measure.
Furn.—Furniture (stock).
G. R.—Grooved roofing.
H.bk.—Hollow back.
Hdl.—Handle (stock).
hdwd.—Hardwood.
Hrt.—Heart.
Hrtwd.—Heartwood.
1s&2s—Ones and twos—a combined grade of the hardwood grades of first and seconds.
Impl.—Implement (stock)
in.—inch or inches. Also two accent marks ("). See Symbols.
KD—Kiln-dried.
k.d.—Knocked down.
lbr.—Lumber.
l.c.l.—Less carload lots.
lgth.—Length.
lgr.—Longer.
lin. ft.—Lineal foot; that is, 12 inches.
Lng.—Lining.
LR—Log run.
LR, MCO—Log run, mill culls out.
Lth.—Lath.
M.—Thousand.
M.b.m.—Thousand (feet) board measure.
MCO—Mill culls out.
Merch.—Merchantable.
m.l.—Mixed lengths.
Mldg.—Moulding.
MR—Mill run.
M.s.m.—Thousand (feet) surface measure.
Pn.—Partition.
m.w.—Mixed widths.
No.—Number.
Ord.—Order.
P.—Planed.
Pat.—Pattern.
Pky.—Pecky.
Pln.—Plain, as plain sawed.
Prod.—Production.
Qtd.—Quartered—When referring to hardwoods.
rdm—Random.
res.—Resawed.
Rfg.—Roofing.
Rfrs.—Roofers.
rip.—Ripped.
r.l.—Random lengths.
rnd.—Round.
R. Sdg.—Rustic siding.
r.w.—Random widths.
S&E—Surfaced one side and one edge.
S1E—Surfaced one edge.
S2E—Surfaced two edges.
S1S—Surfaced one side.
S2S—Surfaced two sides.

from 1936 YEARBOOK Material Men's Club, Inc., Red Bank, N. J.

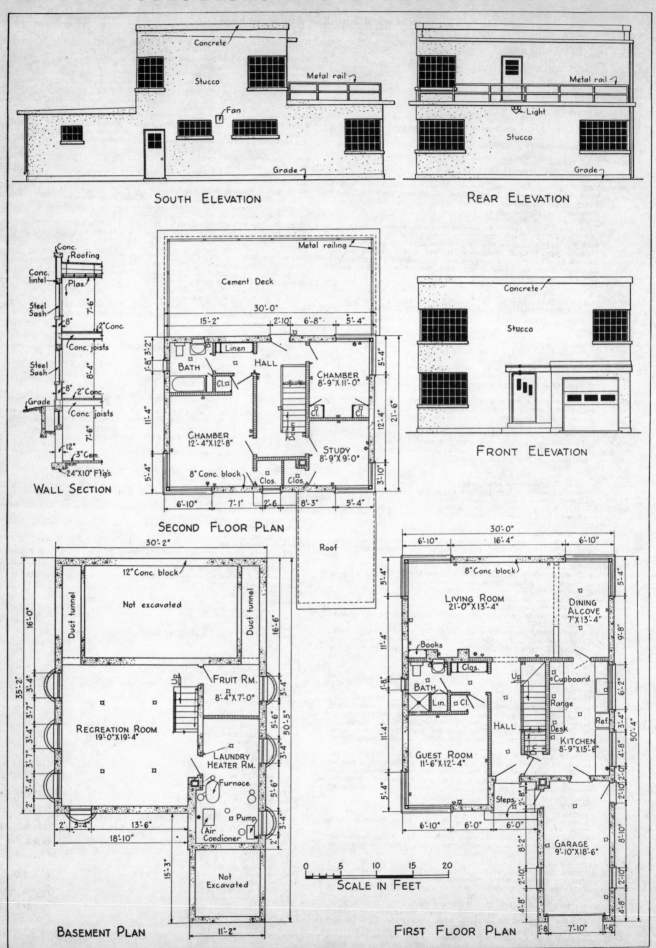

SOUTH ELEVATION

REAR ELEVATION

WALL SECTION

SECOND FLOOR PLAN

FRONT ELEVATION

BASEMENT PLAN

SCALE IN FEET

FIRST FLOOR PLAN

THE "Home of Tomorrow" is constructed of Haydite cinder blocks finished with "Colorcrete," a water proof glazed covering, which will not absorb dirt. The blocks have acoustical and insulation qualities not found in ordinary cement blocks. The joists are of pre-cast Haydite concrete reinforced with steel; and both floors and roof are made with pre-cast cement floor slabs, over which is poured a smooth coat of cement. Kalamazoo Haydite Tile Co. furnished these products. The roof is of built-up asphalt under which is a double thickness of Insulite insulating board. The roof is by Cooper Hoekstra Roofing Co. The G. E. air conditioning and oil burning unit was installed by the Fred J. Hotop Co. The oil fuel tank is underground and the oil is fed into the combustion chamber of the furnace from above, through a new designed burner. Air ducts overhead carry warmed air to the rooms, and a secondary line returns cooled air to a reconditioning unit where the air is washed, filtered, reheated and recirculated.

See pg. 106.

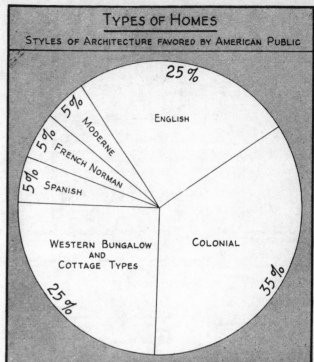

TYPES OF HOMES

STYLES OF ARCHITECTURE FAVORED BY AMERICAN PUBLIC

25%

ENGLISH

5% MODERNE

5% FRENCH NORMAN

5% SPANISH

WESTERN BUNGALOW AND COTTAGE TYPES

COLONIAL

25%

35%

Splendid porch and entrance detail; Randolph Evans, architect.

A COLONIAL ENTRANCE DETAIL

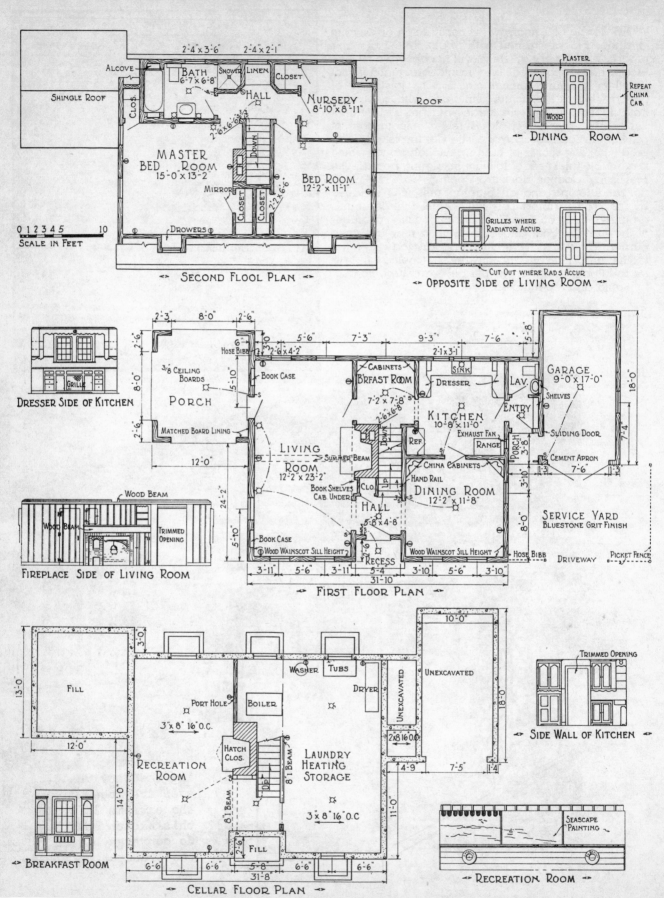

SECOND FLOOR PLAN

DINING ROOM

OPPOSITE SIDE OF LIVING ROOM

DRESSER SIDE OF KITCHEN

FIREPLACE SIDE OF LIVING ROOM

FIRST FLOOR PLAN

SIDE WALL OF KITCHEN

BREAKFAST ROOM

CELLAR FLOOR PLAN

RECREATION ROOM

Working Plans

Chapter XII

Inside Framed Walls

The outside walls of a house serve as a support for the roof and an enclosure for the entire inner construction. The inside walls serve as partitions or divisions for the several rooms inside the house. Inside walls may or may not support other parts of the structure.

Studded partition walls are framed on the floor and raised in place in much the same manner as the outside studded walls. Walls may be framed piece by piece too. However, in any case great care must be taken to allow for all door, entry or special openings in the walls. See that the free or lower end of all bridging is nailed in place before any walls are erected. Inside walls of structural steel are set in place piece by piece, each piece bolted in place following the cc specifications on the plans.

Refer to the illustrations in the previous chapters, particularly on pages 80, 84 and 92.

Practical jobs. Frame up all inside wooden walls. Allow for window and door openings or any special openings. The illustrations show typical methods of framing inside walls.

Related Studies

Drawing.

A picture of a house gives an excellent idea of the whole house in its completeness. In order to have drawings from which things can be made engineers have devised a definite system of shape representation known as orthographic projection. Orthographic projection ignores the use of vanishing lines and assumes that all points project at right angles of any surface whose outline shape is to be represented.

The plan of right angled projection at all points is illustrated in the following diagram:

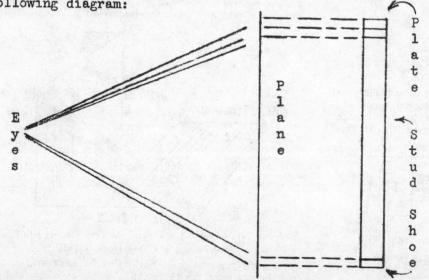

In the figure at the left is a detail of an inside framed wall as projected or drawn against a drawing paper or transparent plane such as a plate of glass. The lines do not come together notwithstanding the fact that the eyes are located at the extreme left, in this sketch and they do converge beyond the transparent plane.

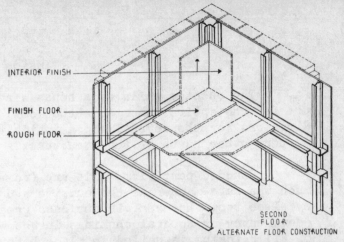

INTERIOR FINISH

FINISH FLOOR

ROUGH FLOOR

SECOND FLOOR
ALTERNATE FLOOR CONSTRUCTION

Details of Stran-Steel construction

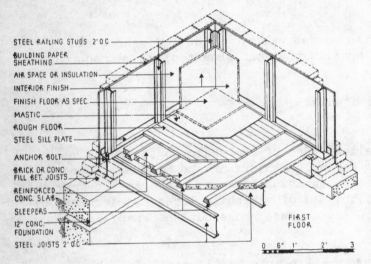

STEEL RAILING STUDS 2' O C
BUILDING PAPER SHEATHING
AIR SPACE OR INSULATION
INTERIOR FINISH
FINISH FLOOR AS SPEC.
MASTIC
ROUGH FLOOR
STEEL SILL PLATE
ANCHOR BOLT
BRICK OR CONC FILL BET. JOISTS
REINFORCED CONC. SLAB
SLEEPERS
12" CONC. FOUNDATION
STEEL JOISTS 2' O C

FIRST FLOOR

0 6" 1'   2'   3

To Lay Warped Flooring

IN laying flooring, pieces that are badly bent can be used satisfactorily by the following method: Take two short pieces of waste material. Place one of them against the wall, as shown in the sketch. The other piece should be about two inches longer than the distance from the bent piece of flooring to be laid to the wall. Place this piece with one end against the bent flooring and the other against the upright piece as a pry, and drive the bent flooring into place, ham-

To Cut Through Flooring

TO simplify sawing through a floor, or board wall, file your saw as shown in the sketch. By rounding off point and filing teeth in the curved part it is possible to saw through a board without boring a hole and using a compass saw. This not only saves time but also makes a neater job.

A. E. EVELAND, Balsam Lake, Wis.

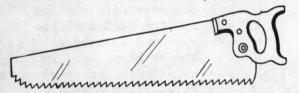

This Saw, with the Point Rounded Will Cut Through a Floor Neatly and Quickly.

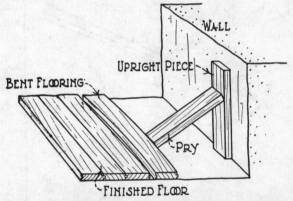

WALL

UPRIGHT PIECE

BENT FLOORING

PRY

FINISHED FLOOR

A Few Taps on the Pry Will Force the Bent Flooring into Place for Nailing and Save Much Material.

mering the pry, and nail. For laying the next strip of flooring the pry piece can be cut off a couple of inches and used again.

If the transparent plane or drawing paper is turned around so one can view the entire flat surface of it the following view or views of the inside framed wall will be seen.

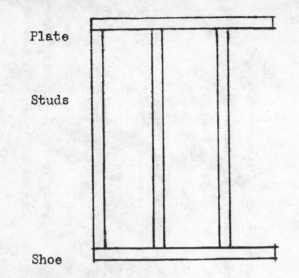

Plate

Studs

Shoe

In the figure at the left one sees the view that is, in orthographic projection, termed the front view. Note how the various lines are parallel one with another. Note the presence of right angles. Note the mechanical appearance of the lines. Note the marked absence of converging lines or of vanishing lines. This front view is but one side of the framed wall.
Call to mind a square block of wood. The block has a base, a top, a front, a back and left and right sides.

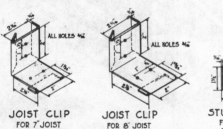
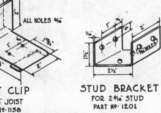
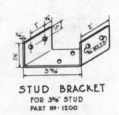

JOIST CLIP
FOR 7" JOIST
PART Nº 1157

JOIST CLIP
FOR 8" JOIST
PART Nº 1158

STUD BRACKET
FOR 2⅝" STUD
PART Nº 1201

STUD BRACKET
FOR 3⅞" STUD
PART Nº 1200

STUD CLIP
FOR 7" JOIST
PART Nº 1207

STUD CLIP
FOR 8" JOIST
PART Nº 1208

The above oblique and isometric views of attachments for structural framing steel members are to be sketched in orthographic projection views. The top, front and end views only to be shown. A pencil, eraser, straight edge and paper to be used. The use of mechanical methods will come a bit later in the text.

Mathematics.

All framed walls, either outside or partition, have openings allowed for doors, windows and other types of passages. The size of the openings is estimated or calculated from the size of the door or window, etc. to be housed in the opening. In allowing for an opening in the framed studded wall to house a door the following items are considered. List and add the widths.

a. Width of door - 3' outside doors, 2'6" inside doors.
b. Twice width of outside casing trim = 2 x 4½"
c. This equals 3' plus 9" or 3'9" between studs for opening.
d. There is, however, one extra stud placed on each side of the single stud opening which will reduce the width of the opening by 2 x 1-3/8" and give a clear distance between doubled studs of 3'6¼" for the door and frame.
e. Length of door - 7' outside doors, 6'8" inside doors.
f. Add 3/4" for rough floor, 3/4" for finish floor, 3/4" for threshold, 1-3/8" for door jamb and 1" for lugs. This will be 4-5/8" in all.
g. Add the 4-5/8" to 7' which will give the total clear space from floor joist to bottom of door header.

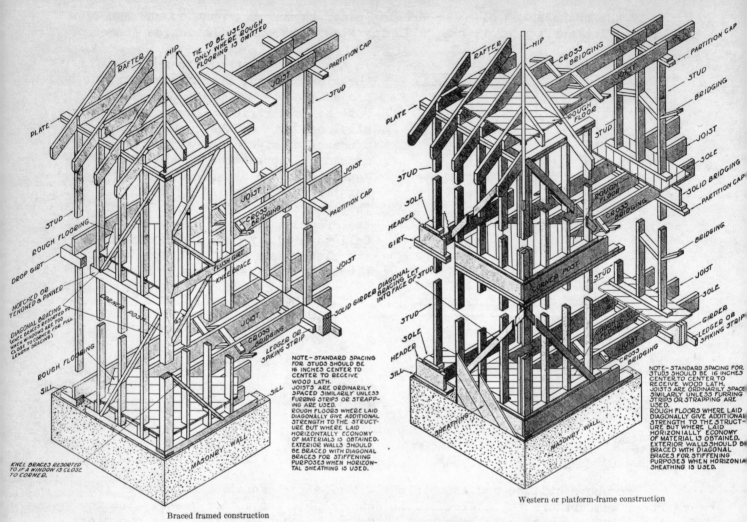

Braced framed construction

Western or platform-frame construction

Courtesy FEDERAL BOARD for VOCATIONAL EDUCATION, Washington.

This picture could be used by an artist to make a pencil or pen sketch. The sketch would convey an idea of the exterior shape of the building but would be useless to use for construction purposes.

In other words, add 9" to width of door and 4-5/8" to height of door in order to obtain the inside width and height of framed opening.

In allowing for an opening in the framed studded wall to house a window the following items are considered. List and add the widths.
    a. Width of glass in sash = a two light window or sash having each light of glass 28" x 34" in size.
    b. 28" plus 2" plus 2" is 32" (two inches for stiles of sash).
    c. Add to this the width of outside casings = 2 x 4" is 8".
    d. This totals (32" plus 8") 40". This is the distance from center to center of the single studs.
    e. Two studs are placed on each side which will reduce the width by the thickness of one stud since the distance is from center to center.
    f. This will be 40" less $\frac{1}{2}$ of 2-3/4" (1-3/8") which is 38 5/8"
    g. Twice length of glass for a double hung sash - 34" x 2 is 68".
    h. To this add thickness of window frame sill 2", window frame head jamb 2", space for lugs 2", plus 6" for lower and upper sash rails and meeting rails, total addition 12".
    i. 68" plus 12" equals 80".
    j. If muntins in sash add $\frac{1}{4}$" for each one.
In other words, add 10 5/8" to width of glass and 6" to each single height of glass to obtain clear space to allow for a sash and window fram

In estimating inside and outside studded walls no allowances are made for openings.   The studs are estimated by count, allowing one for every 16" of length to be walled.   Corners are counted as two or three, depending on the type of corner post used.

Bay window framing is estimated as any outside studded wall. Openings for windows are estimated as any ordinary window.

Make a diagram of a window and of a door opening as described above. Place all necessary dimensions on each sketch. The illustrations on page 92 will help to make clear the foregoing discussions.

Estimate the material and labor costs in the erection of all inside framed walls of the accompanying set of plans.

Science.

The following has been taken verbatim from a technical note published by the Forest Products Laboratory of Madison, Wisconsin.

THE STRUCTURE OF A SOFTWOOD. This drawing of the cell structure of a minute block of softwood - white pine - was made by a wood technologist at the Forest Products Laboratory. The microscope cannot bring several planes into sharp focus at the same time as does this drawing, but it was by means of studies of various thin sections with the microscope that the drawing was accomplished. The drawing here shows a cube about 1/32 inch on a side.

Wood, instead of being a relatively solid material like steel or concrete, is seen to be composed of many tubular fiber units or cells cemented together. The top of the block represents a plane parallel to the top surface of a stump or the end surface of a log. The rectangular units which make up this surface are sections through vertical cells, mostly tracheids or water carriers, TR, the

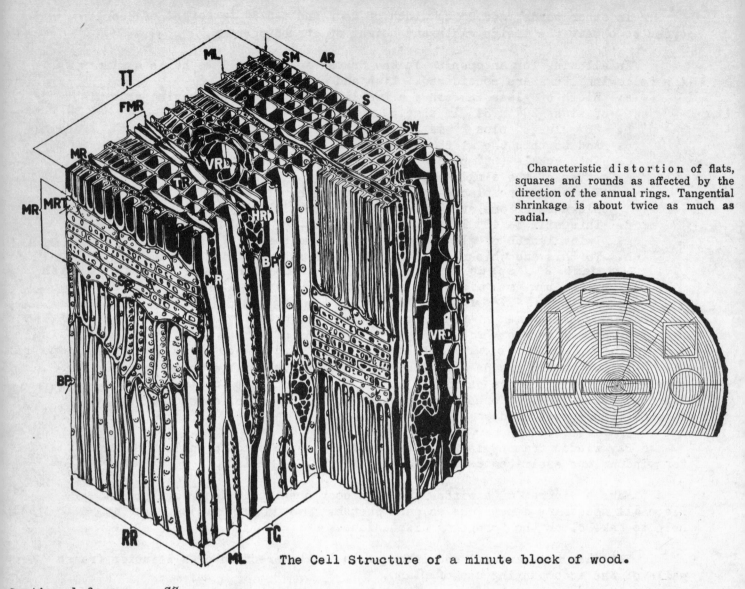

Characteristic distortion of flats, squares and rounds as affected by the direction of the annual rings. Tangential shrinkage is about twice as much as radial.

The Cell Structure of a minute block of wood.

Continued from page 88

16.   **NORWAY PINE**
(Pinus resinosa)
SOURCE: Northern U. S. from Maine to Minnesota.
ANNUAL PRODUCTION: Included with Northern White Pine (825,-
000,000 bd. ft.)
PROPERTIES: Moderately heavy, hard, fairly strong, heartwood pale
red. Weight, air-dry: 33 lbs. per cu. ft.
USES: Millwork, boxes, poles, general construction, etc.
PRODUCED BY MEMBERS OF: Northern Pine Manufacturers Asso-
ciation, Minneapolis, Minn.

17.   **PONDEROSA PINE**
(Pinus ponderosa)
SOURCE: Oregon, California, Washington, Idaho, Montana, New
Mexico and Arizona.
ANNUAL PRODUCTION: 3,500,000,000 bd. ft.
PROPERTIES: Soft, easily worked, finished smoothly, seldom splits,
shrinks very little, creamy white to pale red in color. Weight, air-dry:
28 lbs. per cu. ft.
USES: Sash, doors, mouldings, knotty paneling, shelving, millwork,
boxes and crates, wood novelties, etc.
PRODUCED BY MEMBERS OF: Western Pine Association, Portland,
Ore.

Continued on page 117

walls of which form the bulk of the wood substance. Between the various cell
units is a cementing substance called the middle lamella, ML. Springwood cells
S, distinguishable by their greater size and summerwood cells SM, are formed
during the early part and the later part of a year's growing period, respectively. The growth of the springwood is the more rapid. Together the springwood
and the summerwood cells make up the annual ring AR. One such ring is added to
the outside of the tree each year.

The function of the medullary rays MR is to store and to distribute horizontally the food material of the tree. These rays - including the fusiform
medullary rays FMR, or rays having horizontal resin ducts HRD, at their centers,
are found on end surfaces as fine white lines radiating from the growth center.
The large hole VRD in the center of the top surface is a vertical resin duct.

The left side surface RR represents a vertical plane along the radius of
the trunk. This surface - commonly called 'edge grain' in softwoods and 'quartersawed' in hardwoods - is not so distinctively marked in the quartered surface
with its large lustrous 'flakes' formed by medullary rays entering and leaving
the plane of the saw is valued for use in furniture because of its attractive
figure.

The symbol SP indicates a simple pit, an unthickened portion of the cell
wall through which sap passes from ray cells to fibers or vice versa. The bord-
ered pits BP, seen in section on surface TG, have their margins overhung by the
surrounding cell walls. The surface TG, at right angles to the flat grain or
plain sawed surface of lumber.

English.

It is necessary to carry on a telephone conversation without hesitation.
Perhaps a good way to begin a telephone conversation is to study the important
items in a telephone directory or 'book'. Telephone directories are generally
divided into two sections, an alphabetical classifaction of telephone subscrib-
ers and a trade classification of business houses, merchants, professional men,
manufacturers, services, etc.

Turn to the classified advertisement or business section of the directory.
Find the section LUMBER DEALERS. Note the names, addresses and telephone numbers
of three or four lumber dealers. At some convenient time, in school or at home,
call one or two of these dealers and ask the price of 2" x 4" framing stock.
Find the price of some other items of framing stock, such as 2" x 8" and 2" x 10"
stock, all of course in yellow pine lumber.

In using the manual type of telephone remove the receiver from its hook
and ask for the number in a clear manner when the operator says 'NUMBER PLEASE'.
Give the number in the following manner - (Canal 1012) Canal one-oh-one-two.
Do not say 'Canal ten-twelve'.

In using the dial type of telephone remove the receiver from its hook.
If someone is talking over the line place the receiver on the hook at once. If
no one is talking wait until a buzz is heard which is known as the dial tone.
When the dial tone is heard begin to dial the number. Place the finger in the C
opening and turn the dial to the right until the hook stop is reached. Do this
for the A and for the 1, 0, 1 and 2 in quick succession. Directions for dialing

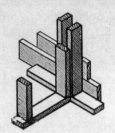
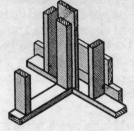
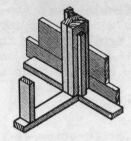

METHODS OF FRAMING STUDS AT PARTITION CORNERS

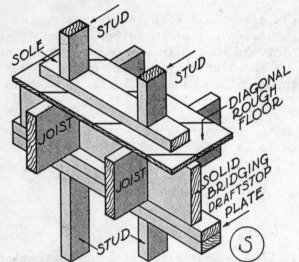

PARTITION AT RIGHT ANGLES TO JOISTS
WESTERN FRAME

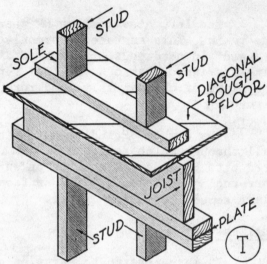

PARTITION PARALLEL WITH JOISTS
WESTERN FRAME

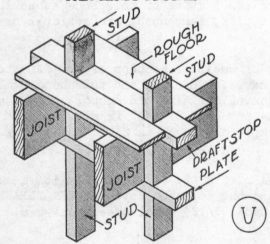

PARTITION AT RIGHT ANGLES TO JOISTS
BALLOON AND
BRACED FRAME

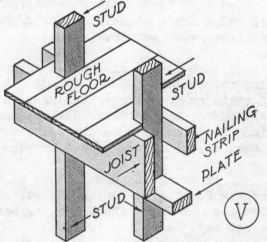

PARTITION PARALLEL WITH JOISTS
BALLOON AND
BRACED FRAME

are generally placed on a small card in the center of the dial.

Write down the information as it is obtained from the dealer and keep for future reference.

Refer to page 78 and read again the introduction to the trade terms. Carry out the same method in the following group of words.

back bone	backing	balcony	balloon frame	baluster
band	banister	balustrade	barge board	barge
barrel roof	base block	base board	basement	base
base shoe	bass wood	batch	bath room	bath tub
batten	batten board	batter	batter boards	bay window
bead	beaded ceiling	bed moulding	bearing surface	beam
bearing	bearing partition		bed	bed plate
bearing wall	bed in	belt	bench bracket	bevel
bed room	beech	beveled off	beveled siding	binding
bevel out	bevel jack	bisect	bit	blade
birch	bird's mouth	blind	black and white prints	
blind stop	blinds	blue prints	boarding	board
block plane	blocks	border	bore	boring
bolts	bond	bow compass	bow dividers	box
box cornice	boxed	box gutter	box sill	box stairs
box up	box wood	braced	braced framing	bracing
bracket	breadth	breakfast room	brick	bridging
broken joints	bruise	buckle up	buckling	build
built	built in	built on	bull nose	building
building lot	building paper	bundle	burnt	burrs
butt	butt gauge	butted	buttress	bit

Civics.

Information about the value of health is very important to all, regardless of the occupation or place in life. Obtain a text, TEXT-BOOK IN CITIZENSHIP, written by Mr. R. O. Hughes, published by Allyn & Bacon Co., New York, N. Y. Refer to Chapter IX of this text and read the discussion on HEALTH, Refer to other texts or reference books and report on the following topics: The most common diseases of today; The Public Health Service of our state and community; What sanitation did for the Canal Zone; The fight against yellow fever; The white plague and how to combat it; The hospitals of our community; My experience in a hospital; The safety first movement; The water supply of our community; Housing conditions in our town; Our grocery stores and meat markets; The National Bureau of Chemistry; The milk supply of our community; Getting rid of yellow fever and the care of the insane and the feeble minded.

18. **SHORTLEAF PINE**
(Pinus echinata)

SOURCE: Southeastern and southern states, from Virginia to south and west to Texas.

ANNUAL PRODUCTION: All species Southern Yellow Pine: 13,000,-000,000 bd. ft.

PROPERTIES: Soft-textured, moderate weight, free from hard streaks and pitch, easily worked, heartwood pale yellow. Weight, air-dry: 38 lbs. per cu. ft.

USES: Interior trim, structural dimension for buildings, planing mill products, boxes, car construction, toy stock, wood specialties.

PRODUCED BY MEMBERS OF: Southern Pine Association, New Orleans, La.

Continued on page 118

19. SUGAR PINE
(Pinus lambertiana)

SOURCE: California and southern Oregon.
ANNUAL PRODUCTION: 300,000,000 bd. ft.
PROPERTIES: Very soft even texture, satiny finish, shrinks little, works easily, light in weight, white to pink in color. Weight, air-dry: 25 lbs. per cu. ft.
USES: Foundry patterns, piano keys, organs, drawing boards, wood carvings, sidings, screens, millwork, etc.
PRODUCED BY MEMBERS OF: Western Pine Association, Portland, Ore.

20. REDWOOD
(Sequoia sempervirens)

SOURCE: Coastal region of Northern California extending into Southern Oregon.
ANNUAL PRODUCTION: 500,000,000 bd. ft.
PROPERTIES: Moderately light in weight, strong, very durable, easily worked, shrinks very little, red in color. Weight, air-dry: 30 lbs. per cu. ft.
USES: Planing-mill products, wood pipe, tanks and silos, agricultural supplies, heavy duty (bridges, trestles, etc.) construction, caskets, patterns, boxes, fixtures, etc.
PRODUCED BY MEMBERS OF: California Redwood Association, San Francisco, Calif.

21. EASTERN SPRUCE
(Picea glauca, Picea rubra and Picea mariana)

SOURCE: Northeastern and Lake States and Appalachian region.
ANNUAL PRODUCTION: Including White, Red, and Black Spruce: 310,000,000 bd. ft.
PROPERTIES: Light, soft, strong, elastic, resonant, light yellow to white in color. Weight, air-dry: 27 lbs. per cu. ft.
USES: Planing-mill products, general construction, boxes and crates, pulp, musical instruments, wooden-ware, tanks, etc.
PRODUCED BY MEMBERS OF: Northern Pine Manufacturers Association, Minneapolis, Minn.

22. ENGELMANN SPRUCE
(Picea engelmannii)

SOURCE: Montana, Colorado, Idaho and eastern Washington.
ANNUAL PRODUCTION: 50,000,000 bd. ft.
PROPERTIES: Light, soft, workable, strong, white to light grayish brown. Weight, air-dry: 27 lbs. per cu. ft.
USES: Planing-mill products, siding, general construction, etc.
PRODUCED BY MEMBERS OF: Western Pine Association, Portland, Oreg.

23. SITKA SPRUCE
(Picea sitchensis)

SOURCE: Oregon, Washington.
ANNUAL PRODUCTION: 380,000,000 bd. ft.
PROPERTIES: Light, soft, strong, stiff, satiny, heartwood light reddish brown. Weight, air-dry: 27 lbs. per cu. ft.
USES: Millwork, boxes, crates, woodenware, car construction, musical instruments tanks, boat building, airplanes, laundry appliances, cooperage, ladders, etc.
PRODUCED BY MEMBERS OF: West Coast Lumberman's Association, Seattle, Wash.

24. TAMARACK
(Larix laricina)

SOURCE: Northeastern U. S., westward to Minnesota.
ANNUAL PRODUCTION: 20,000,000 bd. ft.
PROPERTIES: Heavy, hard, strong, durable, light brown. Weight, air-dry: 27 lbs. per cu. ft.
USES: Ties, posts, poles, ship timbers, boxes, millwork, tanks, paving materials, etc.
PRODUCED BY MEMBERS OF: Northern Hemlock and Hardwood Manufacturers Association, Oshkosh, Wis, and Northern Pine Manufacturers Association. Minneapolis, Minn.

25. WHITE ASH
(Fraxinus americana)

SOURCE: Central States, Ohio River and lower Mississippi River Valley.
ANNUAL PRODUCTION: 150,000,000 bd. ft.
PROPERTIES: Heavy, hard, strong, close grained, tough, elastic, heartwood brown with pale sapwood. Weight, air-dry: 41 lbs. per cu. ft.
USES: Handles, woodenware, automobile bodies, millwork, car construction, agricultural implements, refrigerators, furniture, sporting goods, etc.
PRODUCED BY MEMBERS OF: Hardwood Manufacturers Institute, Memphis, Tenn., Northern Hemlock and Hardwood Manufacturers Association, Oshkosh, Wis., and Appalachian Hardwood Manufacturers, Inc., Cincinnati, Ohio.

26. BASSWOOD
(Tilia glabra)

SOURCE: Eastern United States, south to Georgia and west to Nebraska.
ANNUAL PRODUCTION: 150,000,000 bd. ft.
PROPERTIES: Light, soft, easily worked, moderately strong, even grained, light brown to nearly white. Weight, air-dry: 26 lbs. per cu. ft.
USES: Boxes and crates, planing-mill products, woodenware, mouldings, trunks, musical instruments, matches, toys, etc.
PRODUCED BY MEMBERS OF: Northern Hemlock and Hardwood Manufacturers Association, Oshkosh, Wis., Hardwood Manufacturers Institute, Memphis, Tenn., and Appalachian Hardwood Manufacturers, Inc, Cincinnati, Ohio.

Continued on page 125

Chapter XIII

Plumbing Framed Work

Outside and inside framed walls, whether of steel or wood, should be checked for horizontal and vertical positions. This checking is known as plumbing and leveling.

Each wall should be temporarily braced and securely held in place as erected. In checking over this bracing the steel square will suffice to check the squareness of the corners formed by the shoe, corner posts and plate.

The corners can be checked too, by use of the 6-8-10 method. A very handy method to use in checking the vertical position or plumb of studs or posts is the use of the plumb rule. It is illustrated on page 124.

After corner posts are plumbed and squared and braced securely, the studs can be lined up with the corner posts by stretching a chalk line from one corner post to another and pulling in or pushing out any stud member that does not line up with the vertical positions of the corner posts.

Check all framed openings in all walls for position and squareness. See that all members are securely nailed. Replace any member that will not come up to good standards.

<u>Practical jobs</u>. Check all outside and inside framed walls whether of wood or steel. Construct a plumb rule as illustrated on following page. Use this tool, together with the plumb bob on a free line, a spirit level and steel square.

Related Studies

<u>Drawing.</u>

In Chapters XI and XII emphases are placed on two methods of obtaining the three views of any object. One way is the suggestion of the use of the capital letter L, the other way is the suggestion of the use of three planes or the orthographic projection box. These ways, although not having the geometrical basis or theory of projection as their development, are excellent methods.

Two additional ways or methods can be suggested that have an appeal and connection with common knowledge. The first might be called the street intersection method. An illustration is as follows:

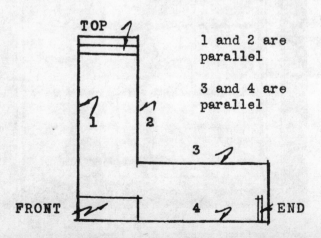

TOP

1 and 2 are
parallel

3 and 4 are
parallel

1
2
3
4

FRONT   END

Showing how objects having straight lines at right angles one to another are placed in the relation of top, front and end views.

You will notice the top 'street' intersects the end 'street' at right angles.

You will notice the various lines or faces of the object intersect parallel to the sides of the 'streets'.

RIGIDITY OF LUMBER CONSTRUCTION

BASED ON A
2-NAIL PANEL HORIZONTALLY SHEATHED WITH 1-INCH SEASONED LUMBER TAKEN AS 100 PER CENT
RESULTS OF TESTS AT
FOREST PRODUCTS LABORATORY
ON FRAMED PANELS 9X14 FEET

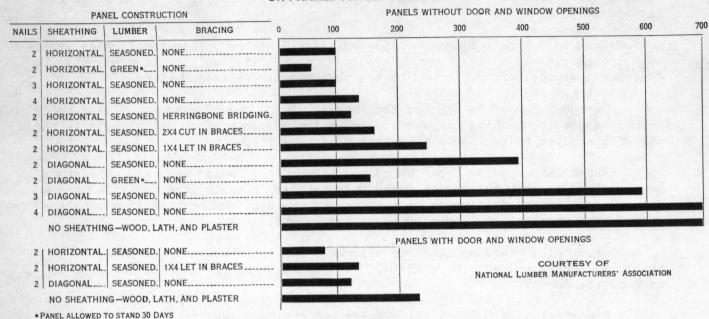

NAILS	SHEATHING	LUMBER	BRACING
2	HORIZONTAL	SEASONED	NONE
2	HORIZONTAL	GREEN ▪	NONE
3	HORIZONTAL	SEASONED	NONE
4	HORIZONTAL	SEASONED	NONE
2	HORIZONTAL	SEASONED	HERRINGBONE BRIDGING
2	HORIZONTAL	SEASONED	2X4 CUT IN BRACES
2	HORIZONTAL	SEASONED	1X4 LET IN BRACES
2	DIAGONAL	SEASONED	NONE
2	DIAGONAL	GREEN ▪	NONE
3	DIAGONAL	SEASONED	NONE
4	DIAGONAL	SEASONED	NONE

NO SHEATHING—WOOD, LATH, AND PLASTER

PANELS WITH DOOR AND WINDOW OPENINGS

2	HORIZONTAL	SEASONED	NONE
2	HORIZONTAL	SEASONED	1X4 LET IN BRACES
2	DIAGONAL	SEASONED	NONE

NO SHEATHING—WOOD, LATH, AND PLASTER

▪ PANEL ALLOWED TO STAND 30 DAYS

PANEL CONSTRUCTION — PANELS WITHOUT DOOR AND WINDOW OPENINGS (scale 0, 100, 200, 300, 400, 500, 600, 700)

COURTESY OF
NATIONAL LUMBER MANUFACTURERS' ASSOCIATION

A panel representing an ordinary stud and plate wall, sheathed diagonally, tested from four to seven times as stiff, and seven times as strong, as a similar panel sheathed horizontally. Three or four nails in place of two added from 30 to 100 per cent to the stiffness. Larger nails (tenpenny in place of eights) do not improve diagonal sheathing

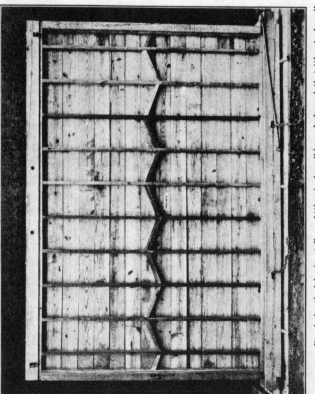

Panel sheathed horizontally and "herringbone" braced showed that "herringbone" bracing has little value

The second method or way might be called the intersecting of two parallel horizontal and two parallel vertical lines method. An illustration is as follows:

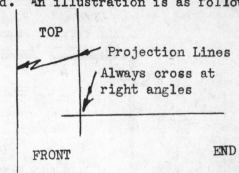

Showing how objects line up when certain faces or points run parallel to groups of parallel lines.

The parallel lines might be termed projection lines on which the various faces of the object project or extend one view to another.

On another page are illustrated several attachments for structural steel framing members. With the use of a pencil, eraser, rule, paper and straight edge draw these members in orthographic projection views. Draw the top, front and end views only. Follow the method last described and test with the capital letter L test. One should learn to make this kind of drawing without the aid of drawing case instruments. It is well to learn the theory of shape representation without the use and hindrance of case instruments. STRAIGHT EDGE sketching is of far more value to the building apprentice than mechanical drafting. Let it be said again that the term mechanical drafting means drawing by the exclusive use of case instruments, angles, irregular curves, scale, etc.

Mathematics.

Geometry is a study of the properties, construction and measurement of of lines, surfaces and solids. There are several definitions of facts and items which will prove of value to the builder. These interesting facts are as follows:
1. A point has no dimensions, merely position.
2. A line has but one dimension, that of length.
3. A straight line is one that does not change its direction.
4. A curved line is one which changes its direction at every point.
5. A surface has two dimensions, length and breadth.
6. A plane surface is one which will wholly contain a straight line no matter in which direction the line is laid in the plane.
7. A curved surface is one which changes its direction in accordance with a given law. The surface of a cylinder or sphere is a curved surface.
8. An angle is formed by two straight lines which meet at a point.
9. A right angle is one in which the two intersecting lines are perpendicular to each other.
10. An acute angle is one in which the lines make less than a right angle.
11. An obtuse angle is one in which the lines make more than a right angle.

Illustrate the above properties by means of freehand sketches. Label each item and number accordingly.

In preceding chapters estimates were designated by the actual count of pieces needed. There are other ways of estimating and one is by the square. A square is the area of 100 square feet or 10' x 10'. Some types of work will not lend themselves to estimating by the square. For example, sill work or any type of linear or 'running work'.

Floor joists, 2" x 8" in size - 16" cc - are estimated at 96 board feet

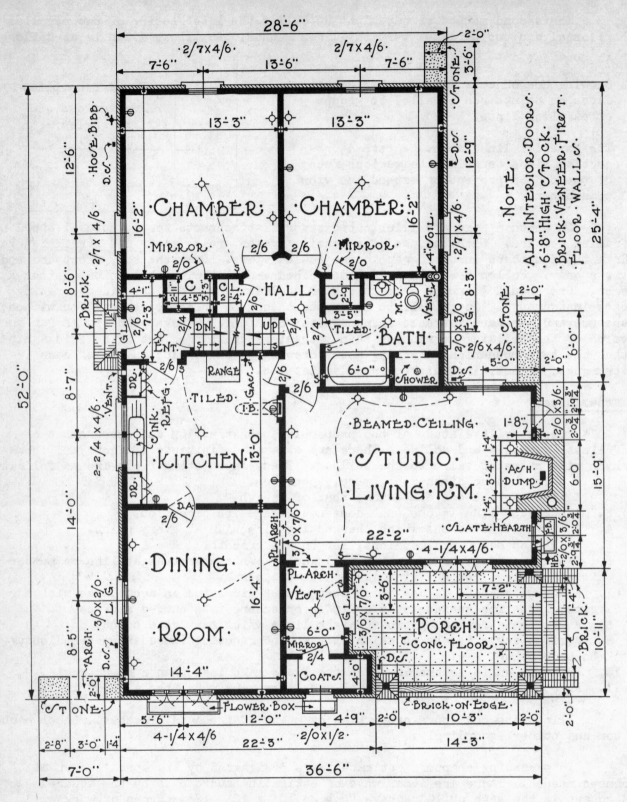

· FIRST · FLOOR · PLAN ·

· SCALE · 1/8" = 1'-0" ·

per square. 2" x 12" joists - 16" cc - at 195 board feet per 100 sequare feet.
about 285 square feet can be laid in an eight hour day and 225 square feet in an
eight hour day of the 8" and 12" joists respectively. An eight hour day of one
man. Sub-floors of 1" x 6" butted pieces require 112 board feet per square and
eight hours to lay about 300 square feet.

With the above explanation the following tables can be used for estimating
by the square.

Floor joists 2" x 8" 16" cc 96 B.F. per 100 Sq. Ft. Lay 285 Sq. Ft. in 8 Hours
   "   "   2" x12" 16" cc 195 B.F. " " "   "   "   " 225 " " "   " " "
Sub-flooring 1" x 6" rl   112 B.F. " " "   "   "   " 300 " " "   " " "
Outside or   2" x 4" 16" cc 65 B.F. " " "   "   "   " 400 " " "   " " "
inside frames walls.
This method may be used instead of the actual count method.

Science.

Bracing is any means taken to stiffen a building against a tendency to
lean or to collapse as the result of high winds or the effect of time. The stiffness and strength in frame house construction will be an asset in preventing plaster cracks and in providing durability and resistance to wind pressures.

Heretofore certain qualities were ascribed to various types of construction
used in bracing frame buildings. The relative value of different methods were not
known. Through the efforts of the Forest Products Laboratory and by cooperation
of the American Forest Products Industries carefully planned tests were conducted.

These tests were carried out in the laboratories of the Forest Products
Laboratory with 9' x 14' framed wooden wall panels, using a 2 x 4 stud 16" cc.
The lower part or shoe of the panels were fastened to the floor and a pressure applied at the top. In order to obtain a standard, 100% was given to a panel which
was sheathed horizontally with dry lumber held with two nails to each stud at
each sheathing piece. All the panels were tested for strength and for rigidity.
Rigidity was measured by the end thrust necessary to cause a given movement of
the end post from upright position.   Strength was tested by the end thrust necessary to cause failure of the whole panel. The graph on another page shows the
results of the rigidity tests on the several types of panels. The strength tests
revealed the following important facts:

a. 1" sheathing nailed with two nails in horizontal position with green boards
    provided only about 70% of the strength of the standard of 100.
b. The addition of one nail in horizontal seasoned boards gave no added strength.
c. When four nails were used instead of two the strength value was increased to
    about 135%.
d. When wooden braces of well seasoned 2x4 stock were used an increased strength
    was noticed to the value of 135%.
e. When braces were 'let-in' an increase of 350% was noted.
f. When diagonal sheathing of seasoned lumber, nailed with two nails was used,
    an increase of 800% in strength was noticed.
g. Wooden lath and lime plaster, without sheathing, gave an increase of 440%
    in strength.
h. The use of herringbone bracing added but little to the strength.
    The above items refer to panels without openings. The four items on the
bar graph on another page reveal the strength of panels with openings let in.

The panel illustrated was covered with 8-inch horizontal, green sheathing, nailed with two eightpenny nails in each board at each stud, given no bracing, and seasoned one month. It showed 50 per cent less stiffness and 30 per cent less strength than if the lumber had been properly seasoned when nailed in place. This test emphasized the value of properly seasoned lumber

(Courtesy of the Forest Products Laboratory.)

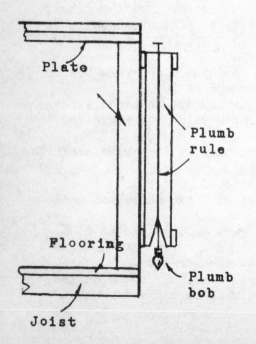

Panels with door and window openings were sheathed diagonally with 1 by 8's and then tested for stiffness and strength under both tension and compression. Results showed that in tension this construction gave about one and one-half times the stiffness and four times the strength of the panel horizontally sheathed without openings for window and door. In compression stiffness was nearly the same and strength nearly one and one-half times that of the horizontally sheathed panel without openings

(Courtesy of the Forest Products Laboratory.)

This panel, with door and window openings, was sheathed horizontally with 1 by 8's and fitted with 1 by 4 let-in braces. It tested one and one-half times as stiff and over twice as strong as the panels without openings and sheathed horizontally

(Courtesy of the Forest Products Laboratory.)

ABOVE - Showing photographs of three 'test panels' made by Forest Products Laboratory.
LEFT - Showing a plumb rule placed on side of stud to test for vertical position. Rule made of straight, clear white pine, 1" x 3" x 6', small blocks, plumb line and bo

English.

Written thoughts have pauses, gestures and changes of voice the same as spoken thoughts. In written thoughts one must use certain symbols to express pause, gesture and voice change. These symbols are commonly known as punctuation marks.

Refer to the portion of this chapter on page 36. Write down the names of two punctuation marks used on this page.

What are the names of the following punctuation marks:

?   '   "   .   ,   -   :   ;

Use the above punctuation marks in the following sentences:

The corner post is made of yellow pine material
How many pieces do you generally find in a corner post
Pine and oak lumber is used in construction work
Sub flooring is made of 1" x 6" boards
 The following pieces of stock were used rafter corner board and carpet strip
We will build this up it will be used for a long time

Civics.

Of the many, many styles and types of household furniture available to the public now on the market there are not many differences in standard sizes. All furniture must meet a certain standard size, otherwise it would have little sales value.

Obtain information relative to standard furniture sizes.

Refer to the set of house plans accompanying this text. List the standard items of furniture which you feel might be used in each room. In freehand sketches, place the furniture in the rooms. What space is left for the occupants of the house? Is this arrangement convenient? Does it make for wholesome living conditions? What are some poor and inconvenient furniture arrangements?

Continued from page 118

27.   **BEECH**
(Fagus grandifolia)
SOURCE: Eastern U. S., westeward to Wisconsin and Texas.
ANNUAL PRODUCTION: 175,000,000 bd. ft.
PROPERTIES: Heavy, strong, hard, stiff, good shock-resisting ability, takes high polish, heartwood light to reddish brown. Weight, air-dry: 44 lbs. per cu. ft.
USES: Boxes, crates, planing-mill products, flooring, furniture, agricultural supplies, handles, laundry appliances, fixtures, etc.
PRODUCED BY MEMBERS OF: Northern Hemlock and Hardwood Manufacturers Association, Oshkosh, Wis., and Hardwood Manufacturers Institute, Memphis, Tenn.

Continued on page 130

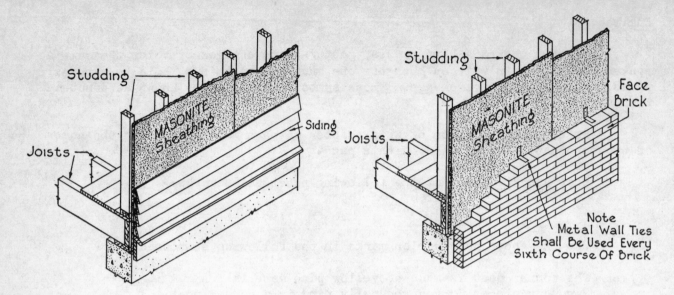

Studding

MASONITE Sheathing

Siding

Joists

Studding

MASONITE Sheathing

Face Brick

Joists

Note
Metal Wall Ties
Shall Be Used Every
Sixth Course Of Brick

SHEATHING DETAILS

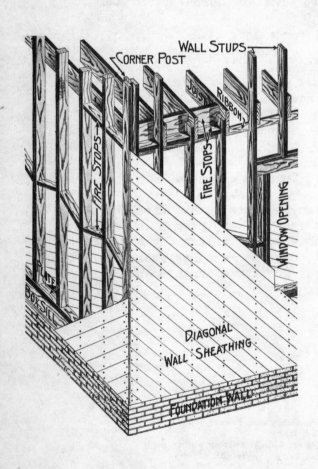

WALL STUDS

CORNER POST

JOISTS

RIBBON

FIRE STOPS

FIRE STOPS

WINDOW OPENING

PLATE

BOX SILL

DIAGONAL WALL SHEATHING

FOUNDATION WALL

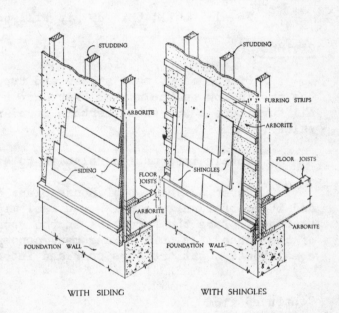

STUDDING

STUDDING

ARBORITE

1" 2" FURRING STRIPS

ARBORITE

SIDING

SHINGLES

FLOOR JOISTS

FLOOR JOISTS

ARBORITE

ARBORITE

FOUNDATION WALL

FOUNDATION WALL

WITH SIDING

WITH SHINGLES

Shingles over
horizontal
wood sheathing

Chapter XIV

Sheathing Walls

With the completion of the outside and inside studded walls, one of the next important jobs in the construction of a house is the boxing up, sheathing or covering of the framed walls.

Previous illustrations shown on pages 92, 102, 106 and 126 illustrate how various types of sheathing boards are placed.

In applying wooden boards or sheathing on studded walls, stack the sheathing stock, tongue and groove, ship-lap or wide board material near the sides of the walls to be covered.

The next step in the application of the sheathing is to select several straight and sound pieces of stock and square one end. Measure from exact corner of corner post along one side of the wall by placing piece of stock in position and mark off on the stock the greatest length that can be used to the center of a stud. Square off and saw stock to size.   This piece can be used for a pattern on all stock that is about the same length as it is.

Place the stock at the bottom of the sill, directly above the foundation wall and nail in place. Use 8 d. nails and face nail the sheathing with two nails at each stud.

Check piece with level for horizontal position and draw the stock down securely at all places. Do not bruise the tongue or groove of the stock. Remember that the sheathing is a tight encasing of wood for the protection of the occupants of the structure and should be placed on the studded walls with this thought in mind at all times.

Continue to place stock in position and face nail each piece with two nails at each stud. Join the stock only in center of stud where joint is required. Sheathe around the studded wall, working up as one goes around the building. When a door or window opening is reached, allow all stock to project slightly, nail stock securely and saw off flush with exact edge of opening.

Sheathing may also be placed on diagonally or in a combination of diagonal and horizontal positions, depending on the specifications and requirements set forth in the set of house plans.

Sheathe the entire outside wall to the very top of the plate. The rafter length is figured to include the thickness of the sheathing stock and it is very necessary that the sheathing stock be placed flush with the top of the plate member at all places.

Steel framed walls are covered with sheathing in much the same manner as wooden framed walls. Illustrations of this type are shown on pages 92, 102, 106, 112, 124 and 126.

If tongue and groove stock is used that has been used in concrete form construction, see that it is clean and free of concrete and earth. Use sound stock free of knots or rot.

Other types of covering for outside walls are wood-fibre board, masonite, gypsum, corkboard, celotex, etc. These types are illustrated elsewhere in this chapter.

<u>Practical jobs</u>. Sheathe up the outside walls. Use a horizontal method, a diagonal method and a combination of the two. Sheathe up outside walls with types of covering other than wood.

Related Studies

<u>Drawing.</u>

Several previous studies in drawing have dealt with two phases of the study, namely, Methods of Shape Description or Sketches of Objects to Draw. This study will deal with sketching from drawings made by instruments. Any drawing made by drawing instruments may be called a mechanical drawing.

Make a complete sketch of the following instrument made drawings. Draw each drawing in two point perspective, one point perspective, oblique drawing, isometric drawing and finally in orthographic projection.

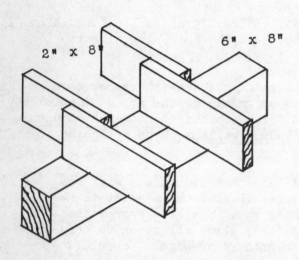

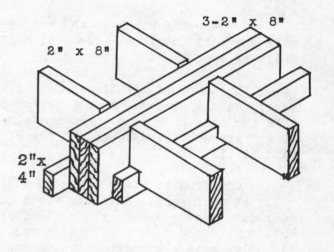

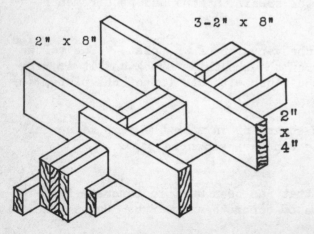

ABOVE AND LEFT - Instrument made
                drawings of girder
                details.
BELOW - Sketch of joists, girder
        and post.

Mathematics.

A very interesting situation arises when one estimates diagonal or horizontal sheathing. The question is, which method will take more stock?

In estimating sheathing the following rules should be observed. In estimating horizontal sheathing find the area of the walls to be covered and add 1/10 th., of this area for waste in cutting. Disregard any openings unless it be a very large one, larger than doors or windows.

In estimating diagonally placed sheathing find the area of the walls to be covered and add 1/6th of the area. Why? The following rules apply to diagonally placed sheathing for the several widths used.

```
          For 6" diagonal sheathing add 1/4 area.
          "  8"      "           "     " 1/6  "      Refer to
          " 10"      "           "     " 1/8  "      page 112-113
          "  6" horizontal       "     " 1/5  "      for other
          "  8"      "           "     " 1/7  "      tables
          " 10"      "           "     " 1/9  "
```

Estimate the quantity of sheathing required for the building in the accompanying set of house plans. Estimate in two or three different types of sheathing such as wood, manufactured wood and synthetic boards.

In quantity estimating by the square method it is found that about 125 board feet of 6" sheathing will cover one square and can be built up in about three and a quarter hours. Refer to pages 112 and 113.

Science.

The following studies have been taken, by permission, from the technical data sheets of the Forest Products Laboratory, Madison, Wisconsin.

"Compression wood can usually be detected by the greater thickness of the annual growth layers or rings in which it occurs, the summerwood layer being especially thickened. Sometimes the compression wood layers are grouped in close succession, in other cases the thickening occurs sporadically. Compression wood soldom or never occupies the complete circuit of a growth ring within the tree; in cross section it is usually found as a scallop or half-moon pattern. Compression summerwood tends to be somewhat paler in color than normal summerwood, but owing to its greater thickness the eara occupied appears darker on the whole than normal wood.

"1. Compression Wood is a hard, heavy, brittle type of wood generally formed on the lower side of branches and leaning trunks of coniferous (softwood) trees. No fixed longitudinal shrinkage value can be assigned to it, but its shrinkage is in general excessive, in extreme cases running as high as 5 to nearly 6 per cent (green to oven-dry), which would mean a shortening of 10 or 11 inches in a 16-foot length; this is more than the average transverse shrinkage for many species. More often its longitudinal shrinkage is less than 1 per cent, but well in excess of ordinary working tolerances.

"The principal effect of compression wood, however, is not direct end shrinkage so much as crooking or bowing of lumber or dimension in drying, owing

Continued from page 125

28. BIRCH

(Betula lutea)

SOURCE: Northeastern and Lake States, and Appalachian region.

ANNUAL PRODUCTION: 360,000,000 bd. ft.

PROPERTIES: Heavy, hard, stiff, strong, close grain, light reddish-brown heartwood. Weight, air-dry: 43 lbs. per cu. ft.

USES: Planing-mill products, interior finish, furniture, veneer and plywood, woodenware, boxes and crates, shuttles, bobbins, fixtures, musical instruments, etc.

PRODUCED BY MEMBERS OF: Northern Hemlock and Hardwood Manufacturers Association, Oshkosh, Wis., and Appalachian Hardwood Manufacturers, Inc., Cincinnati, Ohio.

29. CHERRY

(Prunus serotina)

SOURCE: Eastern United States, principally West Virginia, Pennsylvania, New York and Tennessee.

ANNUAL PRODUCTION: 8,000,000 bd. ft.

PROPERTIES: Moderately heavy, strong, compact, heartwood rich reddish-brown. Weight, air-dry: 35 lbs. per cu. ft.

USES: Printing material, furniture, trim for buildings, electric and railroad cars, instruments.

PRODUCED BY MEMBERS OF: Appalachian Hardwood Manufacturers, Inc., Cincinnati, Ohio, and Hardwood Manufacturers Institute, Memphis, Tenn.

30. CHESTNUT

(Castanea dentata)

SOURCE: Northeastern United States and Appalachian Region.

ANNUAL PRODUCTION: 250,000,000 bd. ft.

PROPERTIES: Rather light in weight, soft but not strong, resists decay, shrinks and swells very little, heartwood brown. Weight, air-dry: 30 lbs. per cu. ft.

USES: Millwork, coffins, furniture, interior finish, core stock, boxes, crates, musical instruments, posts, poles, agricultural supplies, fixtures, etc.

PRODUCED BY MEMBERS OF: Appalachian Hardwood Manufacturers, Inc., Cincinnati, Ohio.

31. COTTONWOOD

(Populus deltoides)

SOURCE: Eastern U. S., principally the Mississippi River Valley.

ANNUAL PRODUCTION: Including several closely related species: 260,000,000 bd. ft. all purposes.

PROPERTIES: Light in weight, soft, easily worked, does not split easily, pale brown to grayish white in color. Weight, air-dry: 24 lbs. per cu. ft.

USES: Boxes, crates, vehicle parts, millwork, laundry appliances, refrigerators, musical instruments, trunks, paper pulp, excelsior, etc.

PRODUCED BY MEMBERS OF: Hardwood Manufacturers Institute, Memphis, Tenn.

32. ROCK ELM

(Ulmus racemosa)

SOURCE: Principally Lake States.

ANNUAL PRODUCTION: All species of Elm: 180,000,000 bd. ft.

PROPERTIES: Heavy, hard, strong, shock resistant. Weight, air-dry: 44 lbs. per cu. ft.

USES: Automobile bodies, boxes and crates, furniture, refrigerators, agricultural implements, millwork, woodenware.

PRODUCED BY MEMBERS OF: Northern Hemlock and Hardwood Manufacturers Association, Oshkosh, Wis.

33. SOFT ELM

(Ulmus americana)

SOURCE: Eastern U. S., principally Lake States and Mississippi Valley.

ANNUAL PRODUCTION: All species of Elm: 180,000,000 bd. ft.

PROPERTIES: Moderately heavy, fairly hard, strong, tough, good wood for bending, difficult to split, heartwood light brown. Weight, air-dry: 35 lbs. per cu. ft.

USES: Boxes and crates, vehicles, automobile bodies, furniture, musical instruments, kitchen cabinets, trunks, agricultural implements, millwork, cooperage, etc.

PRODUCED BY MEMBERS OF: Northern Hemlock and Hardwood Manufacturers Association, Oshkosh, Wis., and Hardwood Manufacturers Institute, Memphis, Tenn.

34. RED GUM (Liquidambar styraciflua)

(Heartwood of the Red Gum Tree)

SOURCE: Southern and southeastern States, principally lower Mississippi Valley.

ANNUAL PRODUCTION: 1,100,000,000 bd. ft. (Red and sap gum.)

PROPERTIES: Moderately heavy, fairly strong, heartwood rich reddish brown, sapwood creamy white. Weight, air-dry: 34 lbs. per cu. ft.

USES: Furniture, millwork, veneer and plywood, vehicles, refrigerators, agricultural implements, coffins, boxes, crates, etc.

PRODUCED BY MEMBERS OF: Hardwood Manufacturers Institute, Memphis, Tenn.

35. SAP GUM (Liquidambar styraciflua)

(Sapwood of the Red Gum Tree)

SOURCE: Southern and southeastern States, principally lower Mississippi Valley.

ANNUAL PRODUCTION: 1,100,000,000 bd. ft. (Red and sap gum.)

PROPERTIES: Moderately heavy, fairly strong, heartwood rich reddish brown, sapwood creamy white. Weight, air-dry: 34 lbs. per cu. ft.

USES: Furniture, millwork, veneer and plywood, vehicles, refrigerators, agricultural implements, coffins, boxes, crates, etc.

PRODUCED BY MEMBERS OF: Hardwood Manufacturers Institute, Memphis, Tenn.

Continued on page 132

to its uneven distribution in the piece. Likewise an occasional streak of compression wood that adjoins normal wood will pull itself apart in drying, so as to form cracks across the grain. Defects of this kind are as a rule well taken care of in grading the material. Sometimes, however, the direct shortening causes trouble, as in the opening up of butt joints in house siding. The prevention of this trouble lies in seeing that the material is thoroughly dry and fully shrunk before it goes into construction.

"Abnormally Light-weight Wood.   Wood below the average weight shrinks lengthwise more than normally dense wood of a given species; this is exactly the reverse of the rule for transverse shrinkage. In lightweight wood the shrinkage is along the grain and may in exceptional cases be as high as 1.5 per cent. In lumber that is graded for density the light-weight material is eliminated from the better grades.

"3. Springwood, the lighter-weight, lighter-colored part of the annual growth layer, invariably shrinks more along the grain in drying than the summerwood. Hence any piece of wood that is markedly excessive in its proportion of springwood will be likely to show a high rate of end shrinkage.

"The difference in lengthwise shrinkage tendency as between springwood and summerwood undoubtedly sets up shearing stresses along the grain, which probably contribute to ease of splitting or slivering. In flat grain flooring the slivering nuisance can be largely avoided by dressing the stock so that the "bark" side forms the face or wearing surface. In that case the summerwood of each annual layer is uppermost, and the tendency of emerging layers is to curve down at the surface instead of up. Rotary-cut veneer, wherever it happens to include a single annual growth ring, will be especially subject to bowing in that area.

"4. Wood taken from near the pith of the tree in some of the softwoods shrinks lengthwise in drying more than the surrounding wood. For this reason short cross breaks are often seen in boards or timbers sawed lengthwise through the pith. For the same reason a narrow piece so cut that the pith runs along an edge will crook as it dries. On the other hand, it has been reported that wood on the bark side of some hardwoods shrinks more than the wood farther in, thereby causing crook or bowing in the reverse direction to the above. This is probably an effect of density decreasing toward the outside of the tree, as frequently happens.

"5. Very fast growing softwoods with wide annual growth rings containing relatively soft and light-colored summerwood bands have been found to yield wood of high longitudinal shrinkage characteristic. Material showing the most pronounced cases of this type has been found in the butt portion of the trunk.

"6. Cross-grained wood. Wood with spiral, diagonal, interlocked, wavy or curly grain may show excessive apparent longitudinal shrinkage on account of having a transverse shrinkage component effective along the length of the piece. Thus, if all the fibers ran through a board at an angle of 45 degrees, it would shrink in the same proportion endwise as edgewise. Even a small knot at the edge of a narrow strip will cause bowing of the strip on account of the cross grain introduced by fibers running around the knot.

"7. Wood in long pieces concentrates all its lengthwise shrinkage effect into large gaps at the ends; the longer the piece the wider the gap. The present-

Continued from page 130

36. HICKORY
(Shagbark Hickory) (*Hicoria ovata*)

SOURCE: Eastern United States, principally Appalachian, Lower Mississippi Valley and central hardwood regions.
ANNUAL PRODUCTION: All species, 80,000,000 bd. ft.
PROPERTIES: Heavy, hard, strong, tough, elastic, close-grained, light brown. Weight, air-dry: 51 lbs. per cu. ft.
USES: Vehicles, handles, agricultural implements, golf shafts, sporting goods, millwork, automobile wheels, screws, etc.
PRODUCED BY MEMBERS OF: Hardwood Manufacturers Institute, Memphis, Tenn., and Appalachian Hardwood Manufacturers, Inc., Cincinnati, Ohio.

37. MAGNOLIA
(*Magnolia grandiflora*)

SOURCE: Southern States, principally Louisiana, Texas and Mississippi.
ANNUAL PRODUCTION: 12,000,000 bd. ft.
PROPERTIES: Moderately heavy, fairly hard, durable, brownish yellow. Weight, air-dry: 35 lbs. per cu. ft.
USES: Boxes, crates, furniture, millwork, tobacco boxes, fixtures, etc.
PRODUCED BY MEMBERS OF: Hardwood Manufacturers Institute, Memphis, Tenn.

38. HARD MAPLE
(*Acer saccharum*)

SOURCE: Eastern United States, principally Michigan, Wisconsin, New York and Appalachian Region.
ANNUAL PRODUCTION: All species of maple: 800,000,000 bd. ft.
PROPERTIES: Tough, heavy, hard, strong, close-grained, takes good polish, wears evenly, pale reddish brown heartwood, sapwood white. Weight, air-dry: 44 lbs. per cu. ft.
USES: Millwork, flooring, furniture, agricultural implements, auto bodies, musical instruments, shoe findings, handles, shuttles, boxes, etc.
PRODUCED BY MEMBERS OF: Northern Hemlock and Hardwood Manufacturers Association, Oshkosh, Wisconsin.

39. SOFT MAPLE
(*Acer saccharinum and Acer rubrum*)

SOURCE: Eastern United States, principally Lake States and Southern States.
ANNUAL PRODUCTION: All species of maple: 800,000,000 bd. ft.
PROPERTIES: Moderately heavy and strong, fairly hard, close-grained, light reddish brown heartwood. Weight, air-dry: 33 lbs. per cu. ft.
USES: Millwork, furniture, automobile bodies, boxes and crates.
PRODUCED BY MEMBERS OF: Northern Hemlock and Hardwood Manufacturers Association, Oshkosh, Wis., and Hardwood Manufacturers Institute, Memphis, Tenn.

40. APPALACHIAN RED OAK
(*Principally Quercus borealis*)

SOURCE: Eastern U. S., principally from the Appalachian Mts.
ANNUAL PRODUCTION: All oaks, red and white groups: 2,100,-000,000 bd. ft.
PROPERTIES: Heavy, hard, strong, heartwood light reddish brown. Weight, air-dry: 44 lbs. per cu. ft.
USES: Furniture, interior finish, flooring, veneers, railroad ties, agricultural implements, construction, shipbuilding, cooperage, etc.
PRODUCED BY MEMBERS OF: Appalachian Hardwood Manufacturers, Inc., Cincinnati, Ohio.

41. SOUTHERN RED OAK
(*Principally Quercus rubra, nigra, and phellos*)

SOURCE: Eastern U. S., principally from the southern States.
ANNUAL PRODUCTION: All oaks, red and white groups, 2,100,-000,000 bd. ft.
PROPERTIES: Heavy, hard, strong, heartwood light reddish brown, prominent quartersawed figure. Weight, air-dry: 45 lbs. per cu. ft.
USES: Furniture, interior finish, flooring, veneers, railroad ties, agricultural implements, construction, shipbuilding, cooperage, etc.
PRODUCED BY MEMBERS OF: Hardwood Manufacturers Institute, Memphis, Tenn.

42. APPALACHIAN WHITE OAK
(*Principally Quercus alba*)

SOURCE: Eastern U. S., principally from the Appalachian Mts.
ANNUAL PRODUCTION: All oaks, red and white oak groups: 2,100,000,000 bd. ft.
PROPERTIES: Hard, heavy, strong, durable, heartwood pale brown, prominent quartersawed figure. Weight, air-dry: 47 lbs. per cu. ft.
USES: Millwork, furniture, interior finish, flooring, car construction, veneers, vehicles, chairs, agricultural implements, fixtures, shipbuilding, etc.
PRODUCED BY MEMBERS OF: Appalachian Hardwood Manufacturers, Inc., Cincinnati, Ohio.

43. SOUTHERN WHITE OAK
(*Principally Quercus alba, prinus and lyrata*)

SOURCE: Eastern U. S., principally from the Southern States.
ANNUAL PRODUCTION: All oaks, red and white oak groups, 2,100,000,000 bd. ft.
PROPERTIES: Hard, heavy, strong, durable, heartwood pale brown, prominent quartersawed figure. Weight, air-dry: 47 lbs. per cu. ft.
USES: Millwork, furniture, agricultural implements, fixtures, shipbuilding, etc.
PRODUCED BY MEMBERS OF: Hardwood Manufacturers Institute, Memphis, Tennessee.

Continued on page 134

tendency toward the use of short lengths will help to break up the longitudinal shrinkage into smaller and less conspicuous units, thereby improving the appearance and service of floors and siding.

"The lengthwise shrinkage of wood in drying from the green to the oven-dry condition is normally somewhere between one-tenth and two-tenths of one per cent. In drying to an average air-dry condition of about 12 per cent moisture content, the normal shrinkage is only about half as much, the amount varying from 1/20 inch to 1/10 inch in a board 8 feet long.

"As a rule, therefore, the user does not need to make any particular allowance for the longitudinal (lengthwise) shrinkage of wood, certainly no such allowance as he must make for transverse shrinkage. Nevertheless, trouble may easily arise of the longitudinal shrinkage becomes abnormally large, as sometimes happens. To prevent such trouble the following information on the main causes of excessive lengthwise shrinkage, their identification and means of avoiding or controlling them will be found useful:

"Two slow but important deteriorating influences against which wood should be guarded in service are weathering and decay. Either of these actions, if permitted, will finally cause complete disintegration of the wood. Weathering and decay should be clearly distinguished from each other because they differ with respect to the causes producing them, the conditions favoring them and the methods effective in combating them.

"Weathering is primarily due to the shrinking and swelling of wood with continual changes in moisture content. The surface layers of a shingle, board or other piece of wood alternately absorb or lose moisture rapidly if exposed to rain and sunshine or to the ever-changing humidity of the atmosphere. Changes in moisture content inside the piece, however, lag behind those in the surface layers because of the relatively slow rate of transfusion of moisture in wood. The lag tends to keep the interior at a relatively uniform moisture content and a constant volume, so that when the outside wood fibers swell and shrink they are alternately squeezed together and pulled apart. This action results in a very slow breaking down and wearing away of the surface fibers and sometimes more noticeably in "raising of the grain," checking, cracking and splitting of the wood. It may be augmented by the action of frost, by the mechanical abrasive effect of rain, hail and wind and by chemical changes in the wood substance brought about by the action of light, moisture and oxygen.

"Decay, on the other hand, is caused by the action of wood-destroying fungi-small living organisms which feed on the wood substance. The visible effect of the attack is familiar to everyone as "rotten" wood. Wood that is rotten, or decayed, is not simply mechanically disintegrated as in weathering, but is actually decomposed.

"Weathering and decay are not usually found in the same place. Wood that is dry will not rot, because the fungi must have water to live on. On the other hand, weathering is usually found where the boards as a whole remain fairly dry. The surface layers of such boards periodically take up moisture, but drying occurs before the water can penetrate to the interior of the wood.

"Typical cases of weathering in wood can be found in old shingles, unpainted house siding, board fences and the tops of posts and poles. Decay is more common

Continued from page 132

44.

SYCAMORE
(Platanus occidentalis)

SOURCE: Central and Southern States.

ANNUAL PRODUCTION: 30,000,000 bd. ft.

PROPERTIES: Hard, fairly heavy, coarse-grained, light brown heart-wood. Weight, air-dry: 35 lbs. per cu. ft.

USES: Crates, millwork, furniture, butchers' blocks, chairs, musical instruments, etc.

PRODUCED BY MEMBERS OF: Hardwood Manufacturers Institute, Memphis, Tenn., and Appalachian Hardwood Manufacturers, Inc., Cincinnati, Ohio.

45.

TUPELO
(Nyssa aquatica)

SOURCE: Virginia, Kentucky, southward and westward to Texas.

ANNUAL PRODUCTION: All species of gum, except red gum: 260,000,000 bd. ft.

PROPERTIES: Medium in weight and hardness, fairly strong, easy to work, does not splinter, interlocked grain, light gray to white. Weight, air-dry: 35 lbs. per cu. ft.

USES: Boxes and crates, millwork, factory flooring, tobacco boxes, agricultural supplies, mine equipment, veneer, etc.

PRODUCED BY MEMBERS OF: Southern Cypress Manufacturers Association, Jacksonville, Fla.. and Hardwood Manufacturers Institute, Memphis, Tenn.

46.

BLACK WALNUT
(Juglans nigra)

SOURCE: Eastern U. S., principally central States.

ANNUAL PRODUCTION: 60,000,000 bd. ft.

PROPERTIES: Hard, heavy, strong, compact, durable, heartwood rich dark brown. Weight, air-dry: 39 lbs. per cu. ft.

USES: Home and office furniture, interior finish and paneling, radios, musical instruments, commercial fixtures, gun stocks, auto trim, steering wheels, caskets, sewing machines, flooring, airplane propellers, clocks, etc.

PRODUCED BY MEMBERS OF: American Walnut Manufacturers Association, Chicago, Ill., and Hardwood Manufacturers Institute, Memphis, Tenn.

47.

WILLOW
(Salix nigra)

SOURCE: Lower Mississippi Valley.

ANNUAL PRODUCTION: 12,000,000 bd. ft.

PROPERTIES: Light in weight, soft, easily worked, shrinks and swells but little, light brown in color. Weight, air-dry: 26 lbs. per cu. ft.

USES: Boxes and crates, furniture, fixtures, artificial limbs, baskets. PRODUCED BY MEMBERS OF: Hardwood Manufacturers Institute, Memphis, Tenn.

48.

YELLOW POPLAR
(Liriodendron tulipifera)

SOURCE: Eastern United States, Appalachian and southern States.

ANNUAL PRODUCTION: 320,000,000 bd. ft.

PROPERTIES: Light, soft, straight-grained, easily worked; shrinks little, greenish to yellow brown in color. Weight, air-dry: 28 lbs. per cu. ft.

USES: Millwork, boxes, crates, furniture, core stock, vehicles, musical instruments, fixtures, etc.

PRODUCED BY MEMBERS OF: Appalachian Hardwood Manufacturers, Inc, Cincinnati, Ohio, and Hardwood Manufacturers Institute, Memphis, Tenn.

(Conclusion)

Pictorial view of framed roof, refer to page 103.

in the bottom steps of porches, the bases of porch and pergola columns, the lowest boards of siding that runs to the ground, the butts of posts and poles and other wood that is used in contact with the ground or in damp, unventilated places.

"Protection against weathering can be obtained by the use of paint or varnish coatings. Such coatings, although not impremeable to moisture, protect the wood enough to prevent rapid changes of moisture content in the surface layers. Paint and varnish do not preserve wood against decay. When wood most be used in places favorable to decay, a naturally durable wood should be selected, or, better yet, the wood should be impregnated with a preservative, such as creosote, zinc chloride, sodium fluoride or other suitable chemical known to be poisonous to the fungi."

English.

It is very important for the apprentice to know what and how to use certain commercial papers, such as checks, deposit slips, time records, signature card, lease, rent bill, bill of sale, contracts, building permit applications, apprentice agreements, numerous AIA contracts and many others.

In order to acquaint the beginner with the papers and their appearance and uses, the author has devised a set of books in which certain business transactions, over a period of several months are carried on. In this set of books a hypothetical business is opened and transactions carried on. Reference should be made to this set of books. It is organized under the title of BUSINESS TRANSACTIONS OF _____ BUILDING COMPANY.

Civics.

One should know, if he would succeed in the building business, certain business practices other than those involved in a set of business books. One should know how to consult an architect, how to obtain a building permit, how to use simple banking laws, how to use simple business laws and how to use the state laws relative to workers.

The way to consult an architect is best explained in a publication of the American Institute of Architects titled THE FUNCTIONS OF AN ARCHITECT. Obtain this publication and read it carefully.

A building permit is obtained from local city cuthorities upon presentation of three set of plat plans, two sets of specifications and three sets of complete house plans. An application is filled out and permits issued. Visit a city building commissioner's office and make inquiry about the methods used to obtain building permits, as they vary greatly in different localities. The method described is applicable, in general, throughout the state of Ohio.

Obtain a book, 'Commercial Law' by S. Williston and one by R. S. Bauer, 'Business Law'. Read these books for items on banking laws and business laws.

Floor plans and elevations.

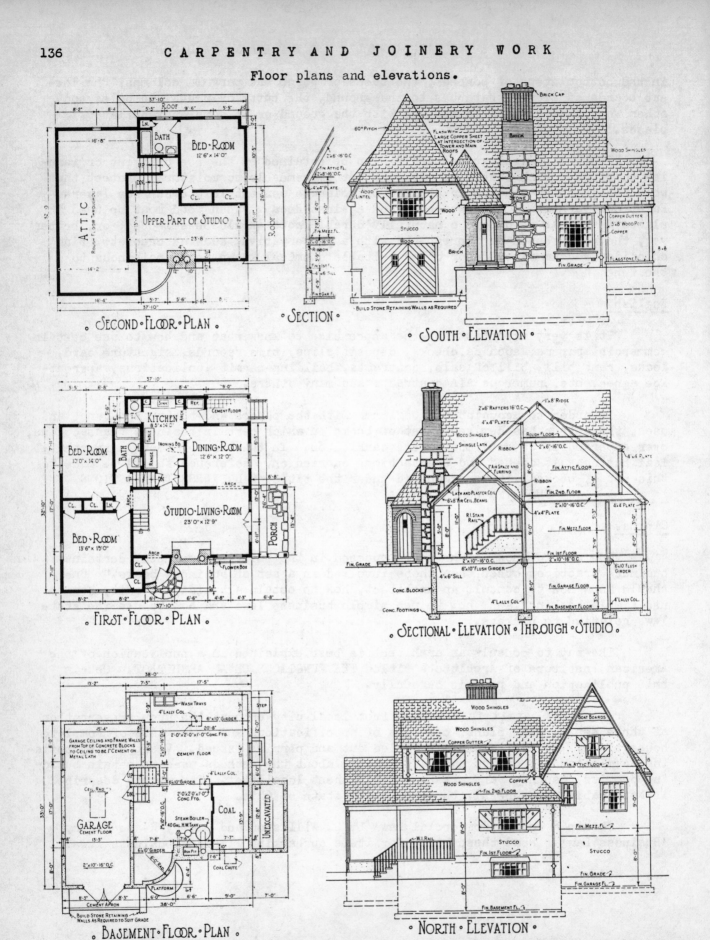

· SECOND · FLOOR · PLAN ·

· SECTION ·

· SOUTH · ELEVATION ·

· FIRST · FLOOR · PLAN ·

· SECTIONAL · ELEVATION · THROUGH · STUDIO ·

· BASEMENT · FLOOR · PLAN ·

· NORTH · ELEVATION ·

Courtesy AMERICAN BUILDER, New York.

Refer to pg. 146 for elevation in perspective.

CHAPTER XV

Ceiling Joists

Ceiling joists are erected in much the same manner as floor joists. In a structure of two or more stories the ceiling joists, of course, become the floor joists of the floor above.

Study the framing details of the set of plans. If the structure is but one story in height the ceiling joists will not be broken in their span from plate to plate or partition plate, depending on the width of the building. It will be necessary, however, to frame in an opening for the chimney scuttle or well hole.

Check over all measurements for accuracy and partition walls for plumb. Determine various lengths of joists to be used. Trim to uniform size all joists resting either on plate or ribband strip. Refer to the illustrations on the following pages.

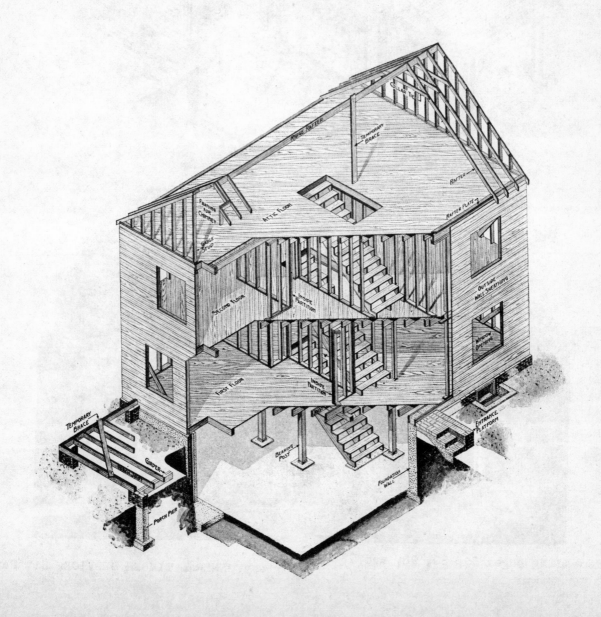

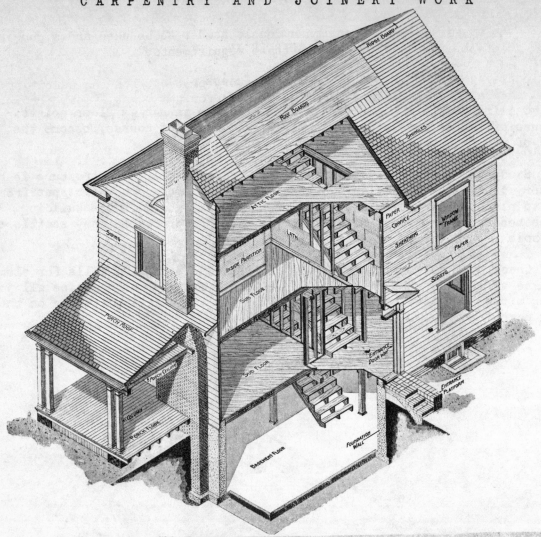

See preceeding pages 56, 80, 98, and 137.
Courtesy GENERAL TIMBER SERVICE, St. Paul.

If the framing details require a double header to be used and a double carrying joist then frame according to these requirements.

If the structure is to have a second story proceed with the partition wall and second floor ceiling joists as directed for the first floor. Provisions must be made for nailing second story flooring along the partition walls that run parallel to the joists.

Practical jobs. Erect ceiling joists as specified in the set of plans. Frame around a chimney. Frame around a stair well. Frame around a scuttle. Frame around a laundry chute.

The accompanying illustrations show special framing details pertinent to the topic of this chapter.

Related Studies

Drawing.

Previous studies in drawing have dealt with assignments in the use of the pencil, straight edge, rule and eraser. This study deals with the drawing or making of drawings with all the mechanical equipment, namely; pencil, scale, eraser, drawing board, T square, case instruments and drawing paper.

The accompanying illustrations show various types of items used in the production of instrument or mechanically made drawings.

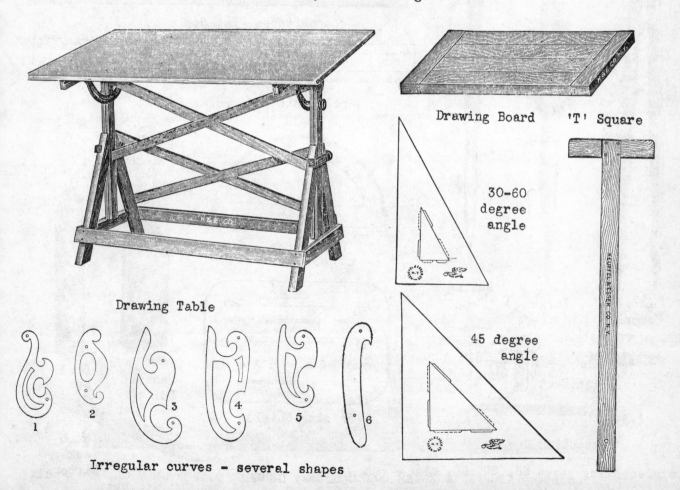

Drawing Table

Drawing Board   'T' Square

30-60 degree angle

45 degree angle

Irregular curves - several shapes

Courtesy KEUFFEL & ESSER COMPANY, New York.

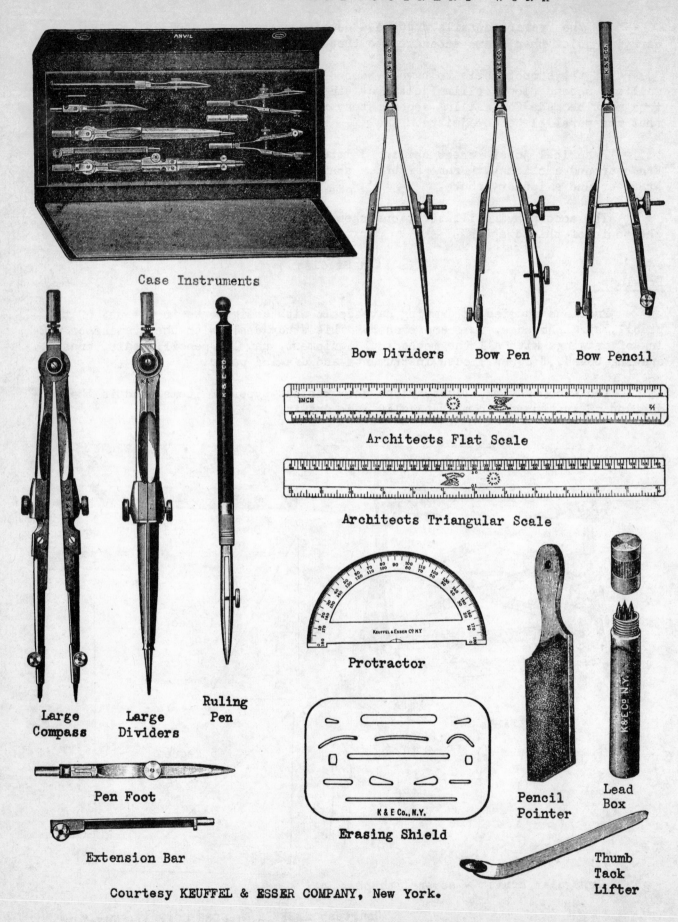

Case Instruments

Bow Dividers   Bow Pen   Bow Pencil

Architects Flat Scale

Architects Triangular Scale

Large Compass   Large Dividers   Ruling Pen

Protractor

Pencil Pointer   Lead Box

Pen Foot

Erasing Shield

Extension Bar

Thumb Tack Lifter

Courtesy KEUFFEL & ESSER COMPANY, New York.

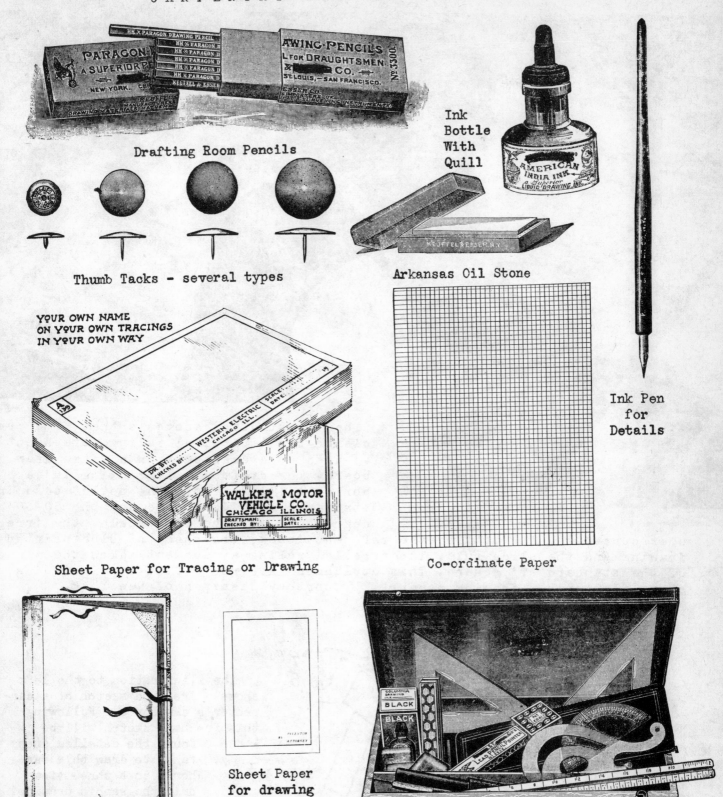

Drafting Room Pencils

Ink Bottle With Quill

Thumb Tacks - several types

Arkansas Oil Stone

Ink Pen for Details

Sheet Paper for Tracing or Drawing

Co-ordinate Paper

Portfolio for Drawings

Sheet Paper for drawing

An outfit of tools in a carrying case

The illustration above is that of a precision-built parallel ruling attachment as used by a draftsman on a large drawing board. The draftsman is 'inking in' a horizontal line. Note the set of case instruments, the 45 degree and the 30-60 degree angles, the flat scale, the irregular curve, the ink bottle, the reference book, the sheet of blue printed drawing and the slide rule. The parallel ruling attachment takes the place of the standard 'T' square. This attachment assures a flat straight-edge that stays flat on the drawing paper.

Courtesy Dietzgen of New York.

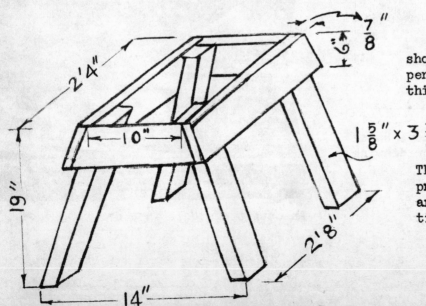

The illustration to the left shows a freehand sketch of a carpenter's saw horse. Following this freehand sketch will be found the detailed steps taken to draw this saw horse in a three view or orthographic drawing. The directions involved in producing these several steps are given with each illustration.

Operation One. Place a sheet of 12" x 18" drawing paper on the drawing board. Hold it down with two or four thumb tacks as desired. The length edge of the paper and the length edge of the drawing board should be parallel.

Operation Two. With a rule or scale measure ½" border around four sides of the paper.

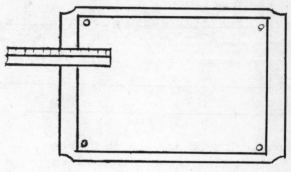

Operation Three. With a T square draw top and bottom border. With a 30 degree angle draw the right and left hand border.

Operation Four. The space inside the border lines is called the working space. Draw lines dividing this space into four equal sections. With any straight edge locate center of each section.

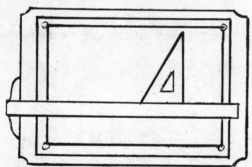

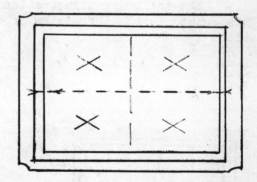

Operation Five. In the upper right hand quadrant sketch the perspective view of the saw horse as shown on page 142

Operation Six. In upper left hand quadrant locate, by mechanical drawing methods, the top view of the saw horse. Likewise place the front view in the lower left hand quadrant and the right hand view in the lower right hand quadrant.

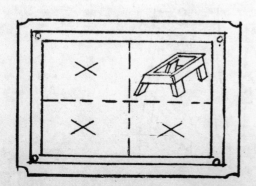

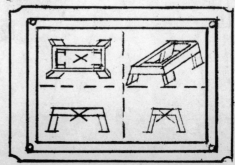

The following illustrations show the way in which a few of the mechanical instruments are used.

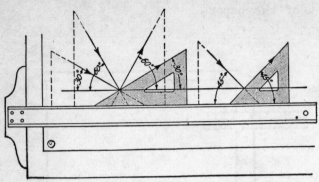

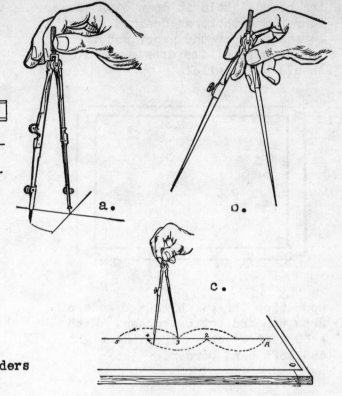

Above. The 30 and the 45 degree
angles used in connection
with a T square.

Right. a. Penciling a circle with
large compass.   Note use
of fingers.
b. Stepping off distance with
large dividers. Note use of
fingers. This tool is never
rammed into the paper or board.
c. Showing swing of large dividers
as distances are stepped off.

The following illustration shows the completed drawing of the saw horse.
This method is the three view or orthographic projection way of shape representation.

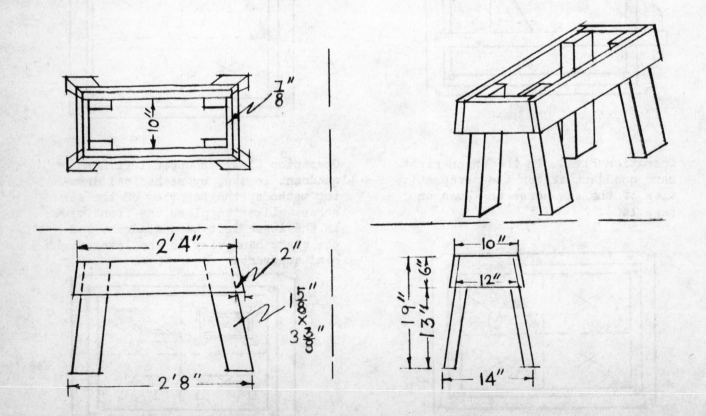

Mathematics.

In the mathematics study of Chapter 13 several important topics were dealt with in practical geometry - that branch of mathematics dealing with the science of two dimensions and one plane. This study is a continuation of practical or plane geometry.

A straight line is bisected in the following manner:
Line AC is the line to be bisected - the middle point to be found.
Place compass at point C and set to a distance of slightly greater than half of AC.
Place compass at A and set to a distance slightly greater than half of AC.
With compass at A swing above and below the line making an arc as at B and F.
With compass at C swing above and below the line making an arc as at B and F.
Where arcs meet above and below AC they form points B and F.
Connect points B and F with a straight line. This bisects or cuts in half line AC at point O.

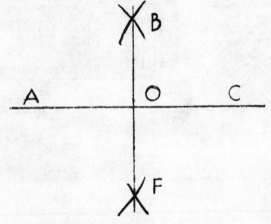

An angle is bisected in the following manner.
AOC is the angle to be bisected.
Place compass at point O and set to distance of slightly greater than half of OA.
Swing compass to cut OA and OC producing points B and D.
Using same distance, placing compass at points B and D produce point directly to right of O at E.
Draw a line through O and E bisecting angle AOC.

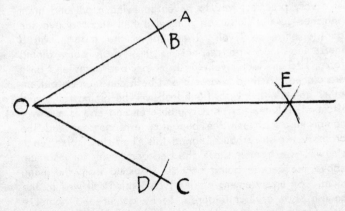

Refer to page 136 for floor plans.

Cottage of Stucco and Stone in English Design Built in Westchester County, New York

WHEREVER the building site is slightly rolling, it works out in a very practical way to have the living room and main entrance to the house on a level a half flight above the garage entrance level. Then above the garage, on a mezzanine floor with respect to the living room, dining room, kitchen floor level, the principal bedrooms and bath are placed. A third bedroom and bath can then be put another half flight up, positioned above the dining room and kitchen. This makes for easy housekeeping and is a clever compromise between the bungalow arrangement and the ordinary two-story house, for in this "half-step" plan, each stairway is extremely short, the bedroom level, for instance, above the garage being only six steps up from the living room. An arrangement of this type lends itself well to the English style of architecture. Many quaint and homelike little places have been built and have found a very ready market arranged on this plan. The accompanying design illustrates a good typical example of this idea and has been classified as one of the most interesting recent designs.

A right angle is constructed in the following manner. This method is the 3-4-5 method. The 6-8-10 method has been explained.

Produce line AB of any length.
Measure OC on AB, three units in length.
Place compass on point O and with radius of four units produce arc at OE.
Likewise produce arc at CF with radius of five units.
Connect point O with intersection of arc at G.
OG then becomes perpendicular to OC and AB.

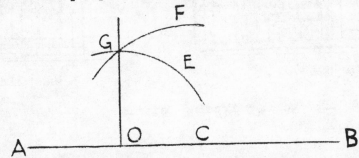

Produce these foregoing figures with drawing instruments.

Science.

Where windows or doors occur in outside walls or partitions, a part of some studs must be cut out. It is necessary, therefore to introduce some form of a header over the doorway to support the lower ends of studs that have been cut. In like manner, there is a similar member which is termed the 'rough sill' at the bottom of window openings.

Headers may be divided into two classes, the nonbearing and the load bearing. The non-bearing headers occur in walls which are parallel to the joists of the floor above and carry only the weight of the framing immediately above. Load bearing headers occur in walls which carry the ends of floor joists, if on plates or ribbands immediately above the opening and must, consequently, support the weight of the floor or floors above.

Header sizes will be determined according to whether they are load bearing or not. Unless the opening in a nonbearing partition is more than 3' wide, a single 2" x 4" is satisfactory as a header. This size is sufficiently strong and eliminates the likelihood of plaster cracks due to expansion or shrinkage. It often happens, however, that trim inside or outside is so wide as to prevent satisfactory nailing over openings with a single 2 by 4. In such cases it will become necessary to double the header merely to provide a nailing base for trim - not for structural strength.

On load bearing partitions or walls the header should be doubled even over narrow openings especially if a short stud occurs near the center of the header. The header rests on the studs.

If the 2 by 4's placed over the opening are one above the other in this construction they should be thoroughly spiked together to properly support the load. If the 2 by 4's used as a header, instead of being laid horizontally, are placed vertically side by side, the spiking will not be quite so important, since each piece will offer greater resistance to bending than when laid flat. It will

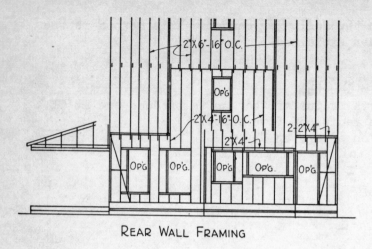

REAR WALL FRAMING

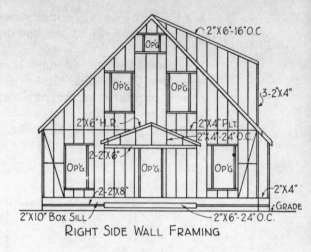

RIGHT SIDE WALL FRAMING

AMERICAN BUILDER Quality Framing Details.

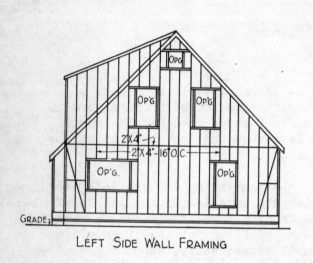

LEFT SIDE WALL FRAMING

FRONT WALL FRAMING

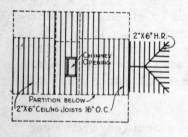

CEILING FRAMING

QUALITY construction calls for complete advance planning and detailing. These quality framing details should be considered the minimum in building long-term financed homes. This is house design No. 754-B of the National Plan Service.

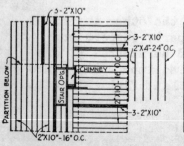

SECOND FLOOR FRAMING

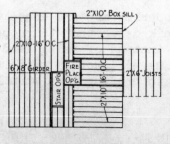

FIRST FLOOR FRAMING

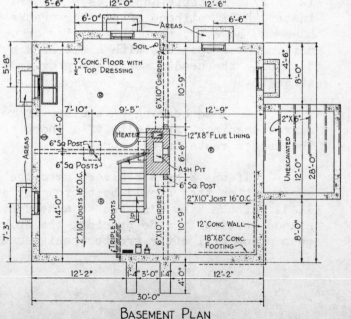

BASEMENT PLAN

be noted, however, that the two 2 by 4's laid on edge will together measure only 3¼" when laid flat, instead of 3-5/8". Consequently, it will be necessary to insert small pieces of lath between the 2 x 4's in order to make the header line up with the studs.

The following illustrations bring out the points given in the preceding paragraphs.

This entire discussion has been by courtesy of the National Committee on Wood Utilization, Washington, D. C.

Produce the following items, as illustrated below, in scaled form. Use a soft wood, working to a one-fourth or one-half size.

All opening stock to be 2" x 4" material.

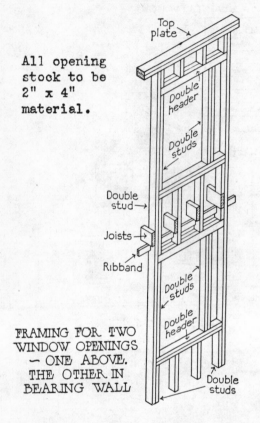

FRAMING FOR TWO WINDOW OPENINGS — ONE ABOVE, THE OTHER IN BEARING WALL

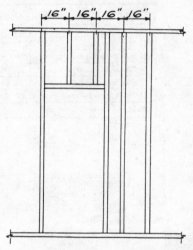

-The header in small openings need not be doubled if they are in nonbearing partitions. The regular studs are spaced 16 inches on centers. An extra stud is introduced to form one side of the opening

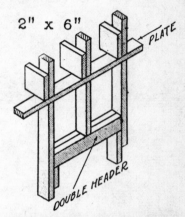

In a bearing partition the header over an opening should always be doubled. If the 2 by 4's are on edge, spacers of lath or other thin pieces of wood should be used to make the header as thick as the studs

Window openings to be for a two light window – 24" x 26" for each light.
Door opening to be for a 3' x 7' door.
Refer to page 111 of this text for method used in obtaining size of openings.

English.

Read again the introduction given to trade terms on page 78 of this text. The following trade terms are those with an initial letter of C.

cabinet	cantilever header	cap plate	carpenter	carpentry
casement doors		casement	carpenter's mouse	
casing	casing up	ceiling joists	center to center	
cellar	cement	cement contractor		cellar steps
centering point		center line	chalk line	centered
cc	center up	chalk	chamfer	check rail
cheek bevel	chimney flashing	chimney	chimney cap	chisel
circle	circle work	circular	claw hammer	clean out door

Plans and Elevations.

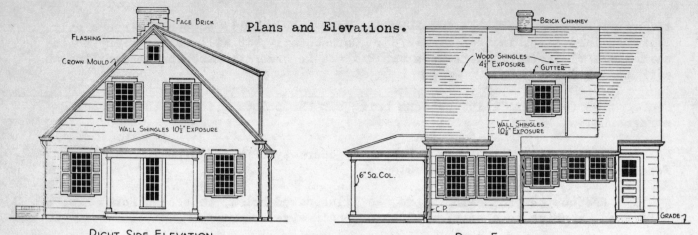

FLASHING

FACE BRICK

CROWN MOULD

WALL SHINGLES 10½" EXPOSURE

RIGHT SIDE ELEVATION

BRICK CHIMNEY

WOOD SHINGLES 4½" EXPOSURE

GUTTER

WALL SHINGLES 10½" EXPOSURE

6" SQ. COL.

C.P.

GRADE

REAR ELEVATION

Electric Wiring Symbols

Symbol	Description	Symbol	Description
	CEILING OUTLET		PANEL BOARD
	WALL BRACKET		METER
	SINGLE CONVENIENCE OUTLET		TRANSFORMER
	DOUBLE CONVENIENCE OUTLET		BUZZER
S	ONE WAY SWITCH		BELL
S³	THREE WAY SWITCH		PUSH BUTTON
	CEILING LAMP RECEPTACLE		

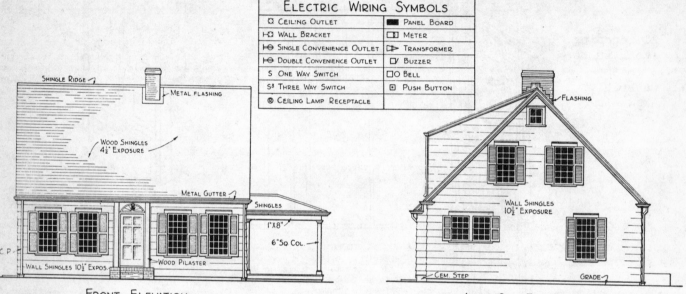

SHINGLE RIDGE

METAL FLASHING

WOOD SHINGLES 4½" EXPOSURE

METAL GUTTER

SHINGLES

1"X8"

6" SQ COL.

C.P.

WALL SHINGLES 10½" EXPOS.

WOOD PILASTER

FRONT ELEVATION

FLASHING

WALL SHINGLES 10½" EXPOSURE

CEM. STEP

GRADE

LEFT SIDE ELEVATION

0   5   10   15   20

SCALE IN FEET

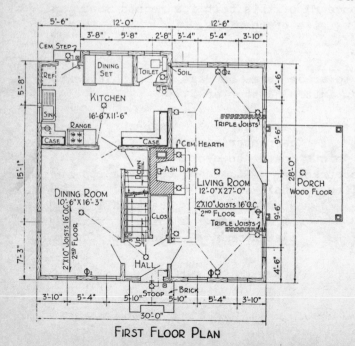

CEM STEP

REF

SIN

CASE

RANGE

CASE

DINING SET

TOILET

SOIL

KITCHEN 16'-6"X11'-6"

TRIPLE JOISTS

CEM HEARTH

ASH DUMP

DOWN

CLOS

LIVING ROOM 12'-0" X 27'-0"

2"X10" JOISTS 16" O.C. 2ND FLOOR

TRIPLE JOISTS

PORCH Wood Floor

DINING ROOM 10'-6"X 16'-3"

2"X10" JOISTS 16" O.C. 2ND FLOOR

HALL

STOOP

BRICK

5'-6"   12'-0"   12'-6"

3'-8"   5'-8"   2'-8" 3'-4"   5'-4"   3'-10"

4'-6"

9'-6"

28'-0"

9'-6"

4'-6"

5'-8"

15'-1"

7'-3"

3'-10"   5'-4"   5'-10"   5'-10"   5'-4"   3'-10"

30'-0"

FIRST FLOOR PLAN

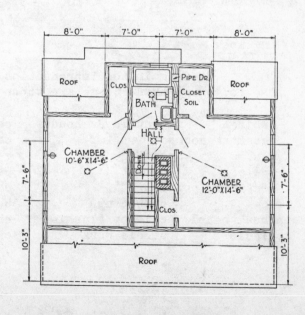

8'-0"   7'-0"   7'-0"   8'-0"

ROOF

CLOS

PIPE DR CLOSET SOIL

ROOF

BATH

HALL

CHAMBER 10'-6"X14'-6"

DOWN

CHAMBER 12'-0"X14'-6"

CLOS.

ROOF

7'-6"

10'-3"

7'-6"

10'-3"

SECOND FLOOR PLAN

clearance	cleat	cloak rail	closed string style	
closet	clothes closet		coal bin	coal chute
coated nails	column	common stock	common nails	common rafter
collar beam	column base	column cap	compass	concave
cone	concrete	conic	convex	coped
coping saw	cord	cornice	corner	corner boards
cornered	corner post	corridor	counter flashing	cove
covered	cripple	cripple jack rafter		cripple studs
cross cut	cross cut saw	crown	crowned	crown edge
crown moulding	cupboard	curved	cut	cut off
cut out	cut up	cut in	cutter	cutting parts
cypress				

Civics.

Refer to several trade magazines and inspect each for technical information. The magazine AMERICAN BUILDER and THE CARPENTER conduct departments in which trade or craft problems are discussed and illustrated.

Make a report on these two magazines in particular. Try to find a discussion relative to floor joists or ceiling joists.

A Colonial Dwelling

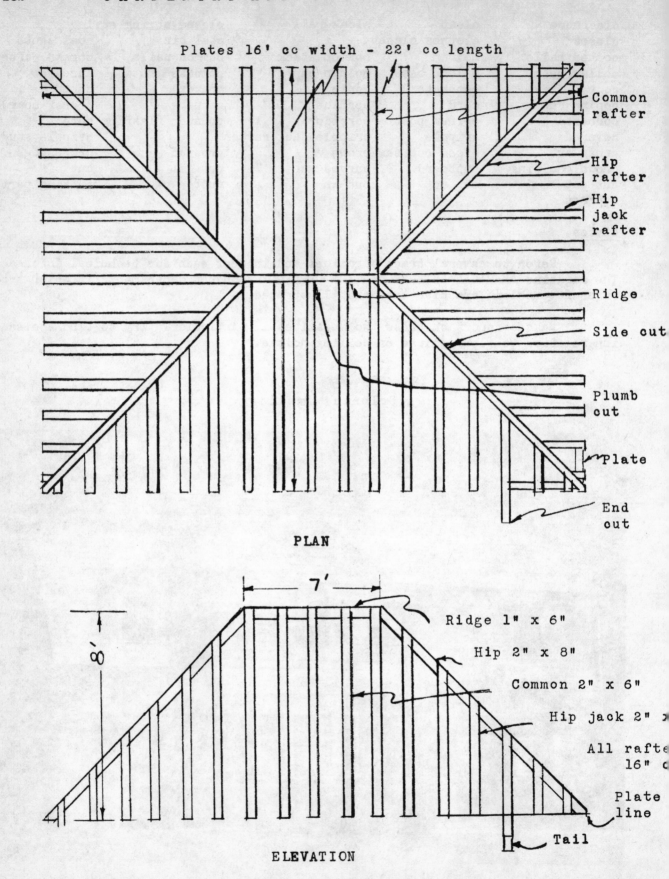

Plates 16' cc width - 22' cc length

Common rafter

Hip rafter

Hip jack rafter

Ridge

Side cut

Plumb cut

Plate

End cut

PLAN

7'

8'

Ridge 1" x 6"

Hip 2" x 8"

Common 2" x 6"

Hip jack 2" x

All rafte
16" c

Plate line

Tail

ELEVATION

Plan and Elevation of a hip roof showing rafter layout.

Chapter XVI

Roof Framing

In dwelling construction roofs serve two purposes, beauty and utility. Both qualities require the most careful efforts on the part of the mechanic if success is to be attained. It can be said that roof framing offers some difficult problems of construction. It is the purpose of this chapter to present typical roof framing problems in a simple, understandable and graphic way.

Refer to the set of house plans and note the type of roof designed for the building. The following illustrations show a gable roof in perspective and in elevation.

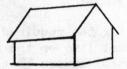
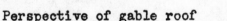
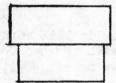

Perspective of gable roof   Side elevation   End elevation

The set of plans usually has one sheet devoted to roof framing details and the following information is placed on this sheet:
a. Width of building from outside edges of plates or sheathing.
b. The size (T & W) of stock to be used as rafters and ridge material.
c. The pitch of the roof.
d. The scale used in making the drawings.
e. The number and different kinds of rafters to be used, such as common, hip, valley, hip jack, valley jack or cripple jack rafters.
f. Type of scuttle, if any, type of chimney and type of dormer framing. Any other detail of construction on or dealing with the roof.

Obtain from the set of plans all possible items of information about the roof. Be certain to know the name and location of each item illustrated in the framing details.

The following steps of procedure deal with the framing of a gable roof. For detailed information about the procedure in framing a hip, gambrel, mansard, etc., type of roof refer to the following study in Science.

Obtain the carpenter's steel framing square and hold it in both hands. Hold the larger part in the left hand and the smaller part in the right hand. The part held in the left hand is called the body or the beam and is the larger and longer part. The part held in the right hand is called the tongue and is the smaller or shorter part.

The two parts, the blade and the tongue, come together or are held in place at a corner or heel or at an angle equal to one-fourth of a circle. This angle is one-fourth of 360 degrees or 90 degrees. It is also a right angle.

Obtain a carpenter's pencil and carefully sharpen it to a flat, wedge shaped point.

Obtain a piece of 2" x 8" or 2" x 10" stock, random length and place it on the saw horse. Lay the stock with the width flat on the horses. Take the steel square in the hands and place the blade against the edge of the stock and the tongue across the width of the stock. Hold the tool firmly in place with one hand and mark a line with the pencil across the face of the width of the stock at the outside edge of the tongue. The following illustration shows the method given.

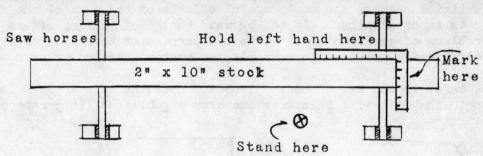

Mark other end of stock in like manner after measuring the required length. The length can be marked off with the two foot rule, the steel line or the steel square. When making successive markings with the rule or steel square be certain to make each marking accurate.

After marking is made, place square carefully to one side, obtain a cross cut saw and cut off the ends of the stock on the outside of the pencil lines. This piece of 2" x 10" stock can be used on a shed roof without additional cuts. The following illustration will show the use of a rafter in shed roof framing.

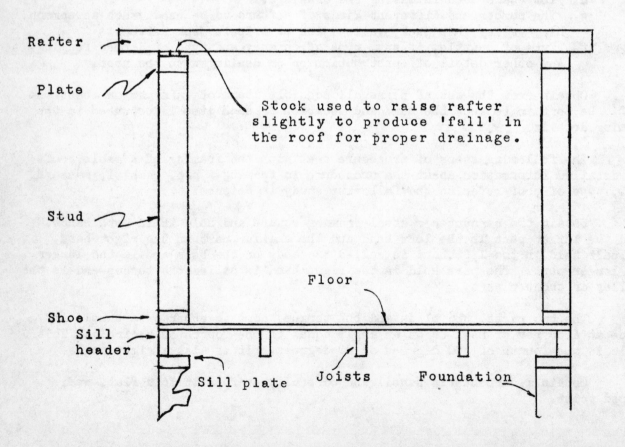

The following illustration shows the result produced when two pieces of stock are placed in position of rafters. Note the stock is without cuts at the plate and the ridge. Note points a, b and c offer very little bearing or nailing surface. This proves the need of a plumb cut and a seat cut for common gable rafters.

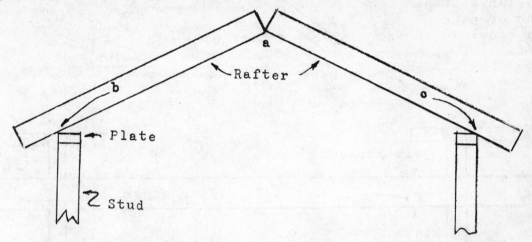

The following sketch illustrates the result produced when two pieces of stock are placed in position of rafters at the extreme outside end of plate members. Note the need of cuts at the plate and the ridge.

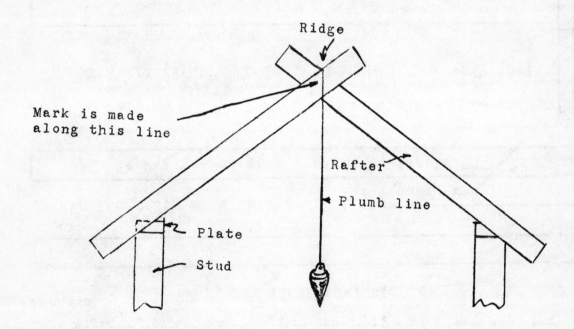

Refer to page 208, for small illustration marked 'Roof Pitch' and note similarity between this small figure and figure formed above at the plate. Note also small figure at top of page 157.

GRAPHIC STEPS TAKEN
TO LAY OFF A COMMON
RAFTER. Follow num-
bered steps as given
at bottom of this
page. Graphic steps
continue of page
158 and conclude on
page 170.

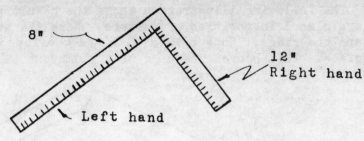

8"

12"
Right hand

Left hand

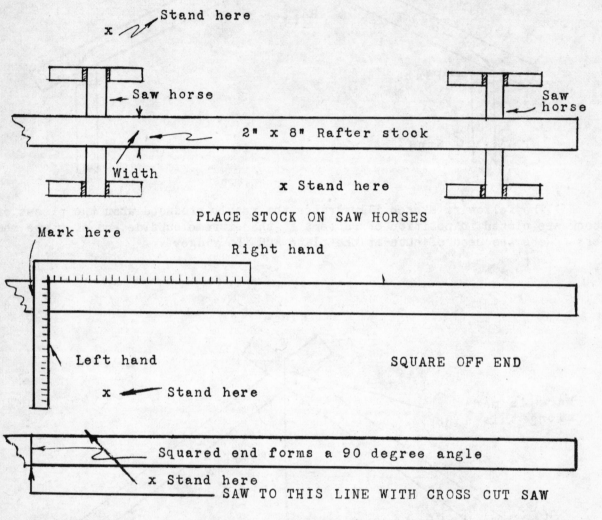

Stand here

x

Saw horse

Saw
horse

2" x 8" Rafter stock

Width

x Stand here

PLACE STOCK ON SAW HORSES

Mark here

Right hand

Left hand

SQUARE OFF END

x   Stand here

Squared end forms a 90 degree angle

x Stand here

SAW TO THIS LINE WITH CROSS CUT SAW

DISCARD UNEVEN END

Cont'd pg. 158.

It has been shown that a plumb and seat cut were needed for rafters. The above a
following steps will show how to produce these cuts:

1. Note in the illustration at bottom of page 154 how the rafter runs from
plate to plate and lies in practically a horizontal position. In other words,
there is a lack of rise to the rafter. It does not go over and up at the same
position.

2. Note in the illustration on page 155 how the rafter runs from plate
to ridge or plumb cut and is no longer in a horizontal position. The rafter has

a rise to it as well as a run. The following figure will show the relation of run to span, to rise and to length of the rafter.

3. Refer to the house plans and note the figure indicating the rise per foot of run. It is generally designated on the plans in the following manner:

4. Hold the steel square as shown below. Place square over the rafter which has been placed on saw horses.

Length of rafter every 12" of run

Rise of 8"

Run of 12"

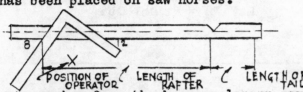

POSITION OF OPERATOR   LENGTH OF RAFTER   LENGTH OF TAIL

Locate number 8 on the beam or longer part of the square. Locate number 12 on the tongue or shorter part. (8 and 12 are taken as an example in this case). Move figures 8 and 12 over width face of rafter until directly over the edge nearest you. Note above illustration. Follow the graphic steps of squaring off a common rafter, marking off plumb cut, seat cut and tail cut. These illustrations begin on page 156, continue on page 158 and are concluded on page 170.

After the rafters have been laid off and cut they should be erected in place in the following manner:

a. Keep the rafter pattern for marking off all like rafters.

b. Obtain length of ridge piece and cut out stock.

c. Place several cut-out rafters on plates, place ridge piece on plates, erect adequate scaffolds or walks, raise rafter members in place against ridge which has been placed in position by temporary vertical members, place each rafter in place above each stud and nail in place.

d. Brace where needed, plumb where needed, place short studs in gables, place on floating rafter and any special tail piece on the tail of the common rafter. The foregoing methods may be used in framing a dormer roof, porch roof and bay window roof in which a common rafter is used.

Practical jobs. Lay out a common rafter and use it for a pattern. Frame a gable roof. Frame a dormer roof, porch roof and bay window roof in which a common rafter is used.

Related Studies

Drawing.

The measuring tool used by the building or architectural draftsman is called a scale. It is a measuring tool and not a guide for a pencil or pen. One type of tool is triangular in shape. It is illustrated below. Another type of tool is flat in shape. It is illustrated on page 140.

A triangular scale used by the architect. Note the 1-½" and 3/4" scales.

Continued from page 156.

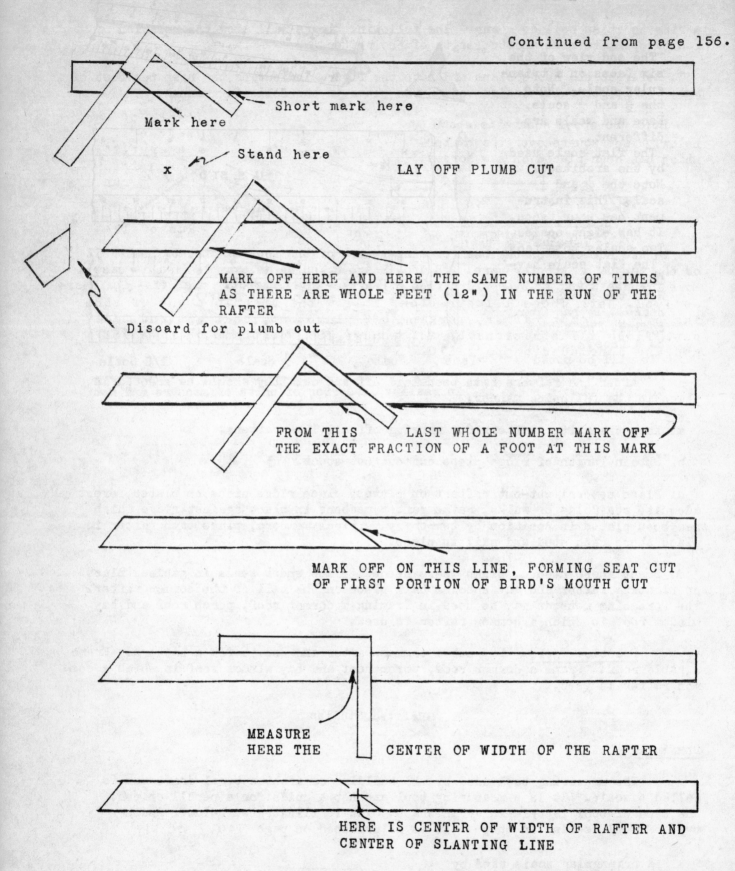

Mark here

Short mark here

Stand here

x

LAY OFF PLUMB CUT

Discard for plumb out

MARK OFF HERE AND HERE THE SAME NUMBER OF TIMES
AS THERE ARE WHOLE FEET (12") IN THE RUN OF THE
RAFTER

FROM THIS   LAST WHOLE NUMBER MARK OFF
THE EXACT FRACTION OF A FOOT AT THIS MARK

MARK OFF ON THIS LINE, FORMING SEAT CUT
OF FIRST PORTION OF BIRD'S MOUTH CUT

MEASURE
HERE THE   CENTER OF WIDTH OF THE RAFTER

HERE IS CENTER OF WIDTH OF RAFTER AND
CENTER OF SLANTING LINE

Continued on pg. 170.

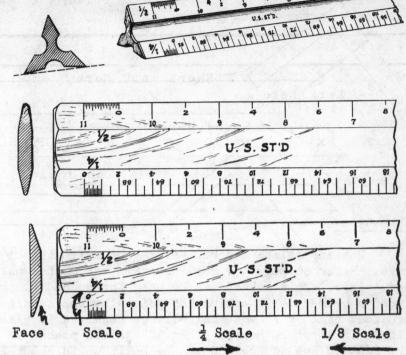

The end view of the six faces on a triangular scale. Note the $\frac{1}{2}$ and $\frac{1}{4}$ scale. Face and scale are different.

The flat scale used by the architect. Note the $\frac{1}{2}$ and $\frac{1}{4}$ scale. This instrument has four faces. It has eight scales. Two scales to a face.

The flat scale having but two faces. Note the $\frac{1}{2}$ and $\frac{1}{4}$ scale. It has four scales. Two scales to a face.

It will be noted from these illustrations that a scale is, in reality, a series of units of measure and not the instrument itself.

Face   Scale $\frac{1}{4}$ Scale   1/8 Scale

Most drawings cannot be made by having the object drawn in full. It is necessary to reduce the size of the object in proportion to properly fit in a working space on a sheet of drawing paper. In order to accomplish this, proportioning scales have been devised to aid the draftsman.

If an object be shown on a drawing half-size, all dimensions are reduced by half. If one-quarter size, all dimensions are reduced to one-fourth. In order to avoid excessive figuring it is much easier to use, in these cases, the half and quarter scales.

Obtain an architectural draftsman's scale. Hold in left hand at center of tool. Turn to face having the 16 scale. This is the same as the ordinary ruler, having 12" divided into inches and each inch into 1/2, 1/4, 1/8 and 1/16ths. Turn the scale again and locate the 1/2 and the 3/8 and 3/4 scales. Turn the scale toward you and locate the 3/8 and 3/4 scales. Turn the scale again and locate the 1/2 and 1 scale. Turn the scale again and locate the 16 scale, now turn the scale end over end and locate the 3/32 and 3/16 scales. Turn the scale and locate the 1/8 and 1/4 scales. Lastly, turn the scale and locate the 1-1/2 and 3 scales.

Having located, on the instrument , the 11 different scales, one can now find the use of each.

Represent one foot of actual length by using the following scales:
3/8" - 1'; 3/32" - 1'; 1-1/2" - 1'; 3/4" - 1'; 3/16" - 1'
3" - 1'; 1/2" - 1'; 1/8" - 1'; 1" - 1'; 1-1/4"- 1'

The illustration below shows the relation of the architectural or drafts-man's scale to the ordinary ruler.

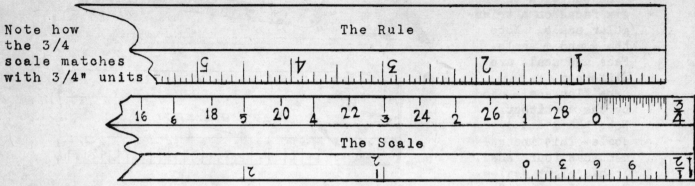

Note how
the 3/4
scale matches
with 3/4" units

Mathematics.

Ceiling joists and rafters may be estimated by actual count or by the square. Refer to page 75 reading again the method used in estimating first floor joists. This method can be used for second floor joists for either steel or wooden members. In estimating joists by the square it is found that 126 board feet of 2" x 8" material will be required if placed 16" cc and can be built up in about 20 hours. 2" x 10" joists placed 16" cc will require 160 board feet to the square and can be built up in about 24 hours.

Rafters for gable roofs can be estimated by the count or square. In es-timating by the count the length of the plate on which the rafters rest can be divided by 16" or the number of inches the rafters are placed cc. In estimating by the square one can use 100 board feet of 2" by 6" stock every square if placed 16" cc. This will take 24 hours to build up.

The rafter layout of a roof can often be made by drawing instruments as well as the steel square. The drawing on page 152 illustrates the plan and ele-vation of a rafter layout of a hip roof.

Estimate the number of rafters and time required to build up the framed roof of either a wooden frame or a steel framed roof.

Draw the illustration on page 152 or the rafter layout of a house in the accompanying set of plans or any other rafter layout.

Science.

In the first part of this chapter detailed steps are given in the framing or laying off of a common rafter by use of the steel square. This study will deal with all other common uses of the steel square.

Section One. Introductory Description of the Steel Square.

The steel square consists of three parts; the body, the tongue and the heel. The body is 24" long and about 2" wide. The tongue is 16" or 18" long and about 1-1/2" wide. The heel is the outside corner formed by the meeting of the body and the tongue.

Project. Obtain a steel square. Hold the square in the hands, body in the left hand and tongue in the right hand. Make a small sketch of the square name the three parts, place of left hand and of right hand and position of standing.

Section Two. The Steel Square, Its Relation to Angles and Degrees.

The steel square (body and tongue) is in the form of a right angle. A right angle is 1/4 of a circle. A circle contains 360 degrees. If the body of the square is placed on a table with the tongue swung above vertically the body would form the base, the tongue the altitude and the line (an imaginary one connecting the ends of the tongue and body) would form the hypotenuse of a right angled triangle.

Project. Obtain a steel square. Place on table as designated above. Locate the base, altitude and hypotenuse. Make a small sketch of the square, name the base, altitude and hypotenuse. Sketch the three remaining right angles and place circle around entire four angles. Designate degrees in entire circle and in each right angle.

Section Three. The Divisions of the Inch Found on the Outer and Inner Edges of the Face and Back of Square.

If the steel square (Stanley 100) is held with the body in the left hand and the tongue in right hand the observer will find the following scales:

Face		
	of	On the body--outside edge--inches and 1/16"
		On the body--inside edge---inches and 1/8"
	square	On the tongue--outside edge--inches and 1/16"
		On the tongue--inside edge--inches and 1/8"

Now if the square is held with the body in the right hand and the tongue in the left hand the following scales will be observed:

Back		
	of	On the body--outside edge--inches and 1/12"
		On the body--inside edge--inches and 1/32"
	square	On the tongue--outside edge--inches and 1/12"
		On the tongue---inside edge--inches and 1/10"

Project. Obtain a steel square. Place in hands as described so that the face is toward you. Observe scales on body and tongue. Make a sketch of the square and indicate the scales found on the face. Likewise make another sketch and indicate the scales found on the back of the square. All measurements begin, on the outer edge at the heel; on the inner edge, at the interior angle.

Section Four. The Hundredth Scale.

There is, most generally, on the back of the square, a small table showing the inch divided into 100 equal parts. This enables the user to obtain any part of an inch, such as 1/100. 1/50. 3/100, 1/25, 1/20, 3/50, 7/100, etc.

Project. Obtain a steel square. Place hands, body in right hand and tongue in left hand. In the corner of the heel there is a scale, 1", divided into equal parts. Obtain a dividers, take off spaces or units of measure from this scale and draw lines, one each, the following lengths: 1/25", 1/2", 4/100", 76/100", 98/100", 13/100", 10/100", 35/100" and 1/50".

Section Five. The Essex Board Measure.

There is, most generally, on the back of the square, a large series of tables, the use of which will enable one to obtain the number of board feet in any given piece of stock. These tables are called the Essex board measure. The inch markings along the outer edge of the square which are above the board measure tables are used with the tables. Calculations are begun with a board 1" thick and 12" wide.

Project. Obtain a steel square. Place tongue in left hand and body in right hand. Locate series of board measure tables along entire length of body. Follow these steps to use the tables:

a. Locate 12" mark on outer edge of body.
b. Under this mark locate figure representing the length of the board for which the board measure is desired.
c. Along the outer edge on the same scale of inch graduations locate the figure representing width of the board.
d. Drop down from this figure to line having the length figure under 12" mark and this figure will give board measure of the stock.

Project. Find the board measure of the following pieces of stock; 1 pc. 1" x 11" x 8'; 2 pcs. ½" x 5½" x 4'; 1 pc. 1-3/4" x 15" x 22'; 5 pcs. 2-3/4" x 8" x 16' and 1 pc. 2" x 10" x 12'.

Section Six. The Octagon Scale.

There is, most generally, a scale on the center of the face of the tongue. By use of this scale one can construct an eight sided figure. The name of this scale is the octagon scale.

Project. Obtain a steel square. Place tongue in right hand and body in left hand. Locate octagon scale along center of tongue. Follow these steps to use this scale.

a. Draw a square 6" to a side.
b. Produce bisectors through base and sides.
c. By use of dividers, take as many units from the scale on the square as there are inches in the width of the figure.
d. Lay off this length on both sides of the four points of intersection of bisectors passing through four sides of figure.
e. Connect points obtained to form eight sided figure.

Section Seven. The Brace Scale.

There is, most generally, on the back of the tongue of the square, a scale which gives the exact length of common braces.

Project. Obtain a steel square. Place tongue in left hand and body in right hand. Locate brace scale or brace measure along center of tongue. If base and altitude are known the length of the hypotenuse or brace can be found on brace table. Follow these steps to use this scale.

a. What is length and height of brace? Locate these two figures
   on scale.
b. Opposite these two figures is given the length of brace.
c. Lay off brace, on paper or 2" x 6" stock, having the following
   units for each brace; 39-39, 48-48, 18-24, 33-33, 24-24.

Section Eight.   Types of Roofs.

    The gable, gambrel and lean-to roofs are the ones most generally used
in house construction. It is a good plan to be able to illustrate several
types of roof shapes.

    Project. Sketch, in perspective, the several types of roofs shown
below in orthographic.

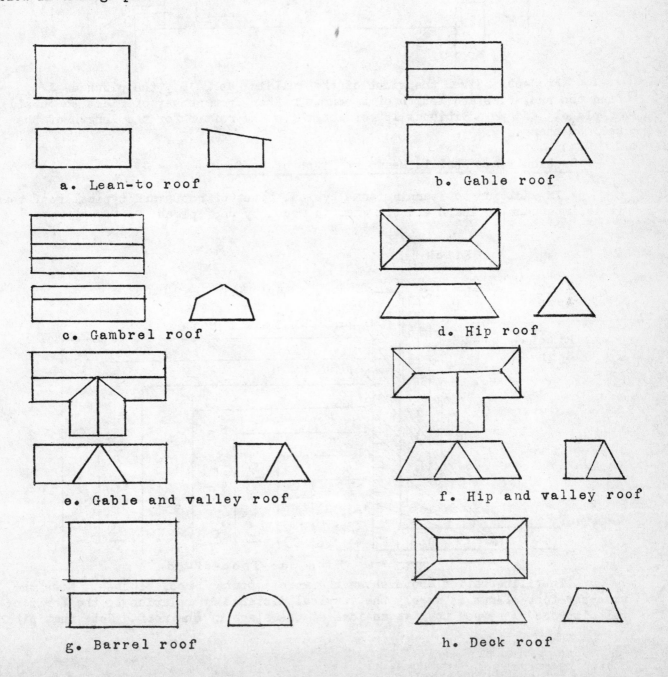

a. Lean-to roof   b. Gable roof

c. Gambrel roof   d. Hip roof

e. Gable and valley roof   f. Hip and valley roof

g. Barrel roof   h. Deck roof

Section Nine. Roof Terms.

A simple gable roof has several very important parts which are mentioned in this roof framing discussion. The parts and terms are illustrated below.

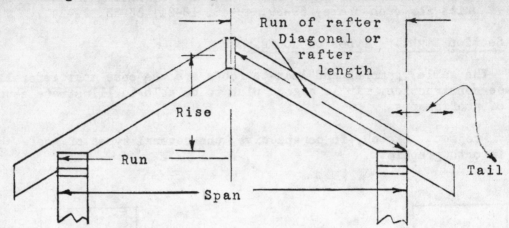

Project. Given the width of the building as 24'6", the pitch as 1/4, find the run, rise and length of a common rafter from center of ridge to outside of plate. Add an additional 18" of length to the rafter for the length of the tail overhang.

Section Ten. What is Meant by Pitch of Roof.

In addition to learning some typical types of roofs and typical roof terms it is important to learn exactly what is meant by roof pitch.

$$\frac{Rise}{Span} = Pitch$$

$$\frac{Pitch}{Span} = Rise$$

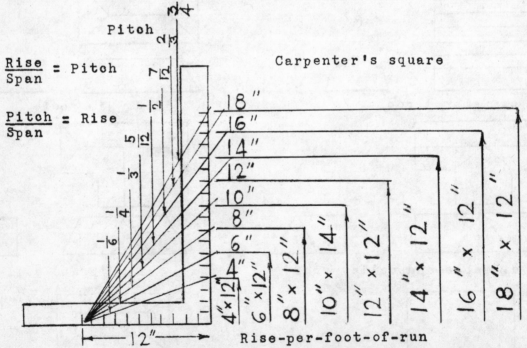

Rise-per-foot-of-run

The illustration above shows the more important roof pitches. Note the rise-per-foot-of-run is merely the vertical distance in relation to the horizontal distance expressed to give an idea of the slant of the roof. Note that 'pitch' means merely dividing the slant height of the roof and is always obtained by dividing the span or building width by the rise.

Project. Illustrate a roof with a span of 24'-0" and having 1/4th pitch. Show the rise of the roof. Draw to center lines. What is meant by pitch, span, rise per foot of run and what are the more common pitches of roofs?

Section Eleven. Types of Rafters.

Before learning how to mark off and cut various types of rafters it is important to learn the names and shapes of several typical roof members. The following illustration shows the types of rafters, namely, the common rafter, the hip rafter, the valley rafter and the three types of jack rafters which are the hip jack, valley jack and cripple jack rafters.

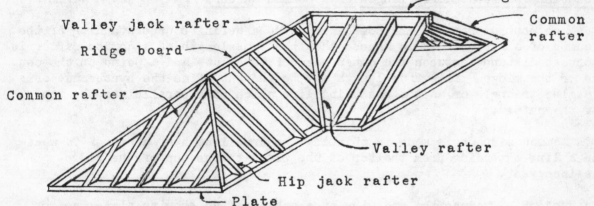

Project. From the above drawing, which is done in oblique, draw the top view (plan) and label each different rafter as shown above.

Section Twelve. Types of Rafter Cuts.

After learning the names and shapes of several typical roof members it is important to learn the typical types of rafter cuts. The following illustration shows shows three types of rafter cuts: heel, plumb and side. These cuts are known by many other names but a little thought will show their basic relations one with another, regardless of name.

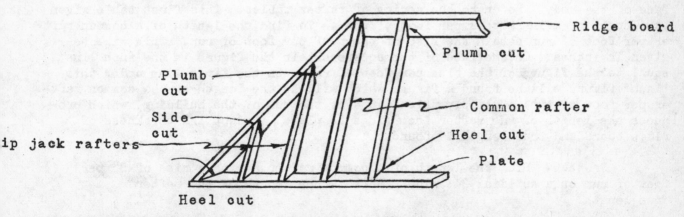

Project. From the above drawing, which is done in oblique, draw the top view (plan) and the side view. Label each different rafter cut.

Section Thirteen. What length-Per-Foot-of-Run Means.

The term "length-per-foot-of-run" means simply this; the slant distance in a combination of horizontal and vertical directions, or the length in space acquired by an over and up movement. If, in the case of the common rafter, we imagine the run to be the base of a right angled triangle, the rise to be the altitude and the length to be the hypotenuse, we can state this: Base is always 1' of run, altitude always rise-per-foot-of-run and hypotenuse always length-per-foot-of-run.

Project. Construct a true right angle triangle, making the base 12" or properly scaled down to fit on drawing paper. Refer to section ten, make the pitch of this triangle 1/3 rd., complete the hypotenuse or length-per-foot-of-run and complete the rise-per-foot-of-run. What is the length of the rafter?

Section Fourteen. True Length of a Common Rafter.

Much controversy can and does arise over a definite understanding of the true length of a rafter. It is agreed that the true length of a common rafter is the shortest distance between the outer edge of the plate and a point on the center line of the ridge. This true length may be thought of as the hypotenuse of a right angled triangle or as the measuring line which runs parallel to the top edge of the rafter.

A common mistake is made in thinking the true length of a rafter is measured on a line extending from the top of the plate to the top of the ridge. This is incorrect.

Project. Produce the end view of a gable rafter showing plate, common rafter and ridge. On this drawing show the correct measuring line for a common rafter.

Section Fifteen. Applying the Square to Find the Length of a Common Rafter.

(This has been explained in full - pages   153-157.

Section Sixteen. Length of Common Rafter as Given on Square.

In addition to the use of the steel square in finding the length of a common rafter the table on the square may be used. Obtain a steel square, find the face of the body. Refer to the series of rafter tables. This first table given is 'length of main rafters per foot of run'. To find the length of a common rafter per foot of run obtain the rise of the roof per foot of run. This will be given in inches. On the face of the square obtain the figure in the inch line equal to the figure of the rise per foot of run. On the first line under this 'inch' figure will be found a figure which will be the length of the common rafter per foot of run. Multiply this figure by the run of the building, which produces the length of the rafter from ridge to plate. Deduct 1/2 thickness of ridge board and true length is found.

Project. Find the length of a common rafter having a rise of 8" per foot of run on a building 24' wide. What is the length of the rafter? True length?

Section Seventeen.   Other Cuts on Common Rafters.

In addition to the plumb cut and seat cut on a full length common rafter there are shortened common rafters or jack rafters taking a bevel or hip cut instead of the usual ridge plumb cut. The heel cut or plate cut or bird's mouth cut of a jack rafter is obtained in the same way as for the full length common rafter.   The plumb cut or ridge cut of jack rafter is obtained the same way as for the full length common rafter.

There are, however, two differences in the cuts on a common rafter and on a jack rafter. One is the side or bevel cut and the other, the length cut, which is shorter than a full length common rafter.

The side or bevel cut is obtained by referring to the rafter table on the face of the square. The line 'side cut of jacks use the marks' will give the figure to use with 12 on the square. If the rise-per-foot-of-run of the roof is 8" refer to the figure in this line under 8. This is 10 and with 10 on outside of square and 12 on outside of square (tongue) lay off bevel cut.

Project.. Lay off the side or bevel cut on a common jack rafter having a rise of 8" per foot of run. Lay off the seat cut. The length of a common jack rafter is found by using the table placed on the steel square. If jack rafters are placed 16" cc use the line 'difference in length of jacks 16" centers'. In the inch line on edge of square find the figure indicating the rise-per-foot-of-run of common rafter and under this figure in the 'difference in length of jacks 16" centers' line find the figure indicating the length of the first jack rafter. For each succeeding jack rafter add this figure once. Lay off the length of the jack rafter. From any length deduct 1/2 the diagonal thickness of the hip or valley rafter.

Note. In the SCIENCE study of Chapter XV11 will be found the
discussion on hip rafters.

English. The following listed books, some of them standard school texts, will be quite an aid in helping the apprentice with his study of House Carpentry.

ROOF FRAMING -- Wilson & Werner -- 1927 -- McGraw-Hill Co., New York.

PROBLEMS IN CARPENTRY -- L. M. Roehl -- 1913 -- Webb & Co., St. Paul, Minn.

PRACTICAL HOUSE FRAMING -- Albert Fair -- 1909 -- Industrial Book Company, New York.

CARPENTRY -- Ira S. Griffith -- 1916 -- The Manual Arts Press, Peoria, Ill.

KING'S WOODWORKER AND CARPENTER -- C. A. King -- 1919 -- American Book Company, New York.

LIGHT FRAME HOUSE CONSTRUCTION -- Federal Board for Vocational Education -- 1930 -- United States Printing Office.

ARCHITECTURAL DETAILS -- U. S. Government -- 1930 -- American Forest Products Industries -- Washington.

Refer to as many of these texts or reference books as possible. See what each text has on the subject of roof framing.

Study the following trade terms:

d. (pwt.)	dead load	deck	definition	degree
den	detail	diagonal	diagram	diameter
dimensions	dining room	dividers	dome	door
door bell	door casing	door frames	door jambs	door key
door knob	door lock	door opening	door sill	dormer
double cap	double course	drain	double face nail	double header
drawing	double hip roof	double hung	draw up	down spout
drafting	draft stop	driving	dressed	dress off
dress up	drip cap	drop board	dropping	dry out
dull	dwelling	earth	eaves	edge
edge tool	eight point	eights	elbows	elevated
elevation	ell	end cut	end tread	entrance
equalize	equal pitch	erecting	escutcheons	excavation
excavator	exit	exposed to weather		exterior
exterior trim	extreme			

__Civics.__ The various styles of architecture virtually demand definite styles of roofs. House roofs, unlike commercial building roofs, afford beauty as well as service to a building. A house roof has four major points; pitch, gable extension, tail or gutter extension and covering. This is from the __artistic point of view.__ From the utilitarian point of view the most important point is strength. Roofs of dwellings must have strength and beauty to be good roofs.

From history we learn of the following styles of roofs as illustrated below.

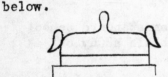

a. Buddhist style

b. Egyptian Style

c. West Asiatic style

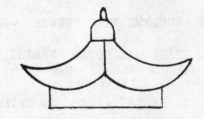

d. Chinese style

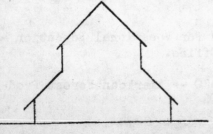

e. Early Roman style

f. Byzantian style

g. Russian style

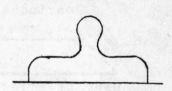

h. Turkish style

i. Roman Renaissance style

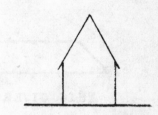

j. Italian style

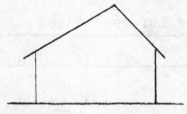

k. Swiss style

l. Early English style

Sketch the above styles of roofs. Refer to page 163 and compare the eight types of roofs used most generally, in America today.

RIDGE

RAFTERS

ROOF BOARDS

In some sections of the country it is considered good practice to use strips for roof boards, spacing them the same distance on centers as the shingles are laid to the weather

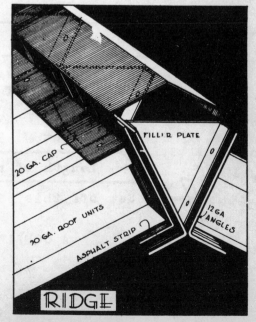

20 GA. CAP

20 GA. ROOF UNITS

ASPHALT STRIP

FILL'R PLATE

12 GA. ANGLES

RIDGE

bove, left - Showing the use of a powered saw in cutting off gable ends of roofing boards.

Center - Showing placing of roofing boards.

Right - Ridge fraiming of STEELOX building.

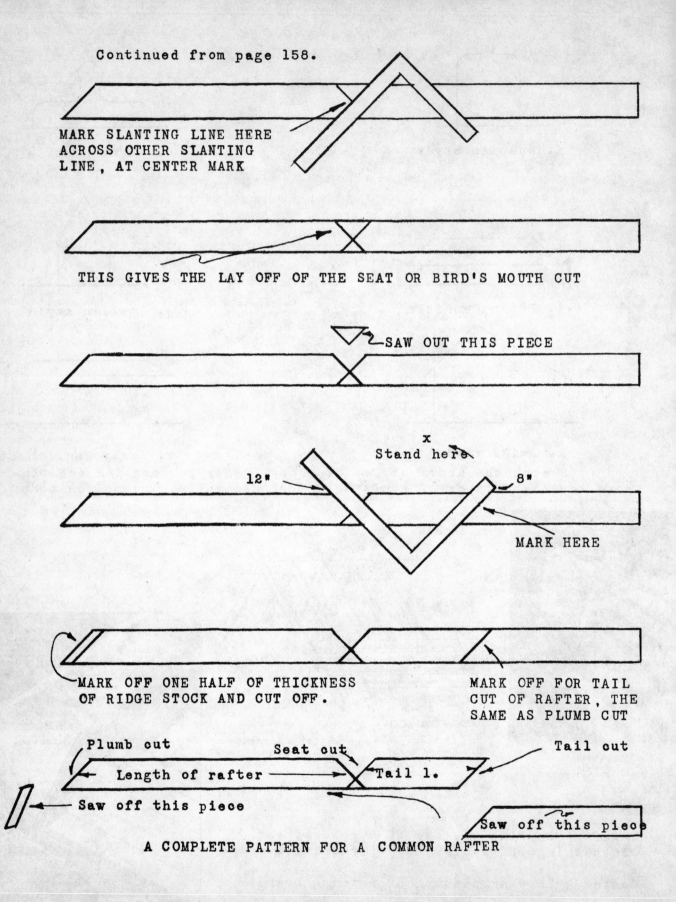

Continued from page 158.

MARK SLANTING LINE HERE
ACROSS OTHER SLANTING
LINE, AT CENTER MARK

THIS GIVES THE LAY OFF OF THE SEAT OR BIRD'S MOUTH CUT

SAW OUT THIS PIECE

x
Stand here

12"   8"

MARK HERE

MARK OFF ONE HALF OF THICKNESS
OF RIDGE STOCK AND CUT OFF.

MARK OFF FOR TAIL
CUT OF RAFTER, THE
SAME AS PLUMB CUT

Plumb cut   Seat out   Tail cut
Length of rafter   Tail l.
Saw off this piece   Saw off this piece

A COMPLETE PATTERN FOR A COMMON RAFTER

Chapter XVII

Roof   Sheathing

Roof sheathing is the first step in covering a roof with wood or composition material as a base for the exposed or finish covering. The sheathing
stock is placed in a convenient place for the worker. Sheathe up the gables by
following the same method as used on side walls.

A roof of wood or steel rafters is sheathed in the same manner. Any
special pre-fabricated sheet roofing should be applied according to the details
in the set of house plans.

In sheathing up the roof proper start at the ends of the rafters and work
toward the ridge. If a wood shingle roofing is used the sheathing stock should be
spaced with an open space of about 2". All sheathing stock should be
spaced with an open space of about 2". All joints of the sheathing stock should
be made at or above the rafters.

Refer to framing details for amount to allow for extension at gable ends.
Most all other types of roofing material require the sheathing stock to be nailed
up solid, that is, all pieces of sheathing stock to be drawn up tightly.

If the cornice is open a good sound grade of sheathing must be used. Allow for proper toe holds for workmen as they nail the sheathing to the rafters.
When roof is sheathed in its entirety, mark off gable ends for desired projection
by use of a chalk line and trim off to this line using a cross cut saw. Double
face nail all pieces at each rafter with at least 8 d. common nails. If the stock
is tongue and groove material handle carefully in order not to bruise the tongue
or groove.

Practical Jobs. Sheathe up the gable ends of the house. Sheathe up the
roof of the house.

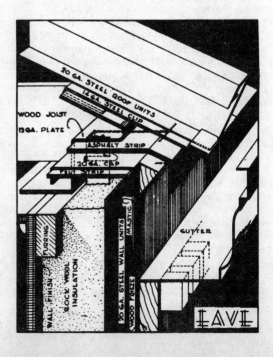

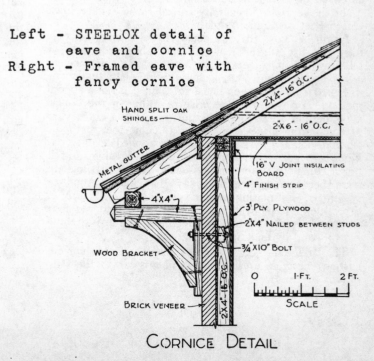

Left - STEELOX detail of
    eave and cornice
Right - Framed eave with
    fancy cornice

CORNICE DETAIL

Estimating "Systems" Analyzed

By L. G. KELLEY

BEFORE we discuss any systems of estimating we will first attempt to define what a "system" is, and what we may expect of it.

Systems of Estimating are largely based on some mathematical or geometrical reasoning. Hence, as mathematics is in no sense really new, very few systems are new. It is doubtful if anyone today can "invent" a system. He can merely collect and arrange data for using one. No system is any more accurate than the mathematics involved.

Estimating Systems Analyzed

By "system" here we refer only to those methods of procedure or mathematical assumptions that can be used for the building as a *whole,* or for *all materials,* or practically all, *that go to make up the building.* For example, the so-called System of Estimating "By the Square" (of 100 square feet) is not a system at all as it cannot be applied to all materials. It is merely part of one of the Unit Systems. This particular Unit System, of course, requires in its application all units of measure, that is, for example, Lineal Feet, Square Feet and Cubic Feet. See outline, Unit Systems, (b) Unit of Construction.

The ordinary Unit Cost System is based usually on a commercial unit of material *as purchased.* Example, 1,000 brick, 1,000 feet B. M. of lumber, etc., but many of the ordinary unit costs are also based on a certain amount of *finished work,* such as 100 square yards of plaster, 100 square feet of flooring, 100 lineal feet of trim, 1 cubic yard of concrete, etc. These last mentioned actually belong to the System we have designated as based on *Units of Construction.* Note that in these cases the terms are generally Lineal Feet, Square Feet, Cubic Feet or Cubic Yards.

Again, suppose that we decide to take a typical cornice and list all the material and labor required for building 100 lineal feet of this cornice. In this case *we are using the Unit System,* but the unit is actually one of *construction* based on lineal feet, but it is not a special method, nor would we be wise in calling it the "lineal foot method." Making up a unit cost for a cubic yard of concrete in place is not using a "cubic foot method."

Any so-called system that can be applied to only one kind or type of building is of doubtful value, and is not a complete system in the sense we wish to use the term here. Also we may say that any method or system of Estimating which is a mixture of two or three methods or systems is not to be considered here as this confusion is one of the things we are attempting to avoid by making this analysis.

The following outline gives about all the various systems used at present that will answer to the definitions given.

Outline of Usual Estimating Methods

Accurate Methods
- (1) DETAILED ESTIMATE.
  - Made up like a grocer's bill—merely a list of materials and their cost. (Labor may or may not be included.)
- (2) UNIT SYSTEMS.
  - (a) Unit of Material.
    - Example—1,000 brick.
  - (b) Unit of Construction.
    - Examples—100 lin. ft. of trim.
    - 100 sq. ft. of wall.
    - 1 cu. yd. of concrete.

Approximate Methods
- (3) GEOMETRICAL.
  - (a) Square Foot Method.
  - (b) Cubic Foot Method.
- (4) PERCENTAGE.
  - (a) Whole Cost = 100%.
    - Example—Foundation = 10% of total cost.
  - (b) Material Cost = 100%.
    - Example—Labor Cost = 60% of material cost.

The Detailed Estimate

In the outline we have listed first the Detailed Estimate. This is the simplest, as far as the reasoning is concerned, of all ordinary estimating methods. Making up a detailed estimate is merely a matter of knowing the construction well enough, and knowing the drawings well enough so that we can visualize all of the various materials which enter into the construction, and proceeding to make a list of these materials. As far as the list itself is concerned, it is nothing more or less than the same sort of list you would obtain from your local general merchant. Hence, we say it is made up like a grocer's bill, and we are sorry to say that in many cases young and inexperienced estimators, who do not use care in grouping their items, may make their estimate look even worse than the bill we receive from a general store.

Here we have the source of one of the most common complaints against this method. For example, in taking off millwork, many young estimators, even where they have a large number of doors of exactly the same size and character, will scatter these through their list in such a way that the entire estimate or list must be made over again when shipment or delivery is made. It is well to remember that for the sake of the man doing the crating at least we must have all similar items grouped, and thereby hangs one of the most important principles of the Unit Cost System of Estimating, which is essentially an attempt to *group items* in such a way that *a number of items can be handled as a single unit.*

Continued on page 174

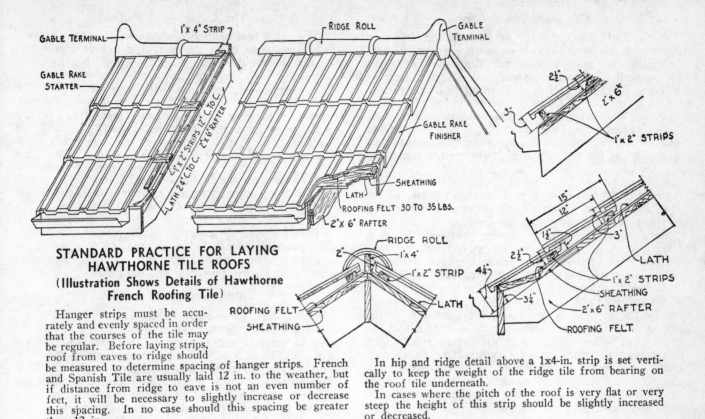

STANDARD PRACTICE FOR LAYING HAWTHORNE TILE ROOFS
(Illustration Shows Details of Hawthorne French Roofing Tile)

Hanger strips must be accurately and evenly spaced in order that the courses of the tile may be regular. Before laying strips, roof from eaves to ridge should be measured to determine spacing of hanger strips. French and Spanish Tile are usually laid 12 in. to the weather, but if distance from ridge to eave is not an even number of feet, it will be necessary to slightly increase or decrease this spacing. In no case should this spacing be greater than 12 in.

In hip and ridge detail above a 1x4-in. strip is set vertically to keep the weight of the ridge tile from bearing on the roof tile underneath.

In cases where the pitch of the roof is very flat or very steep the height of this strip should be slightly increased or decreased.

Courtesy Hawthorne Roofing Tile Company, Cicero, Illinois.

Related Studies

<u>Drawing.</u> In continuing the study of the tools for mechanical drawing one moves on from the scale to the interesting facts about the drawing bench, drawing board, T square and the angles.

The drawing bench may be simple or elaborate in its construction but it must offer a solid and rigid support for the board, etc. The bench and stool should be comfortable to the user.

The drawing board is made in several sizes, preferably of white pine or birch wood. It must offer a true flat surface for the paper. The board should, under ideal conditions, be kept on the bench nearly all the time.

The T square is made in several sizes, of mahogany, maple or a manufactured composition material. The T square is the one instrument receiving the most damage, due to carelessness or the mistaken idea that it can be used for most any purpose such as a hammer or weapon of combat. If the head and blade of a T square become loose the tool is of no value for accurate drawing.

The angles are made in several lengths with one type having 30-60-90 degrees and the other type having 45-90-45 degrees. Angles are made of a manufactured composition which is soft and pliable.

Continued from page 172

The Unit Cost System

We will not attempt to say much about the Unit Cost System at this time because so much has already been said about this system by others. We only wish to call to the reader's attention that it makes little difference whether we choose a Unit of Material (a common commercial unit), say 1,000 brick, and then group the quantities and costs of all the incidental items such as sand, lime, cement, labor, etc., around the cost of this one item, or whether we take 100 square feet of *finished wall* as a unit and list all the materials required in constructing this amount of wall. The one point that we should remember, however, is that in changing from one unit to another we will in most cases change the size of the unit, and we must expect slightly different results owing to the peculiar mathematics involved.

Because of the slightly varying answers that one sometimes obtains by using one or two different methods, we often hear the statement made that one method is not as accurate, when as a matter of fact one is just as accurate as the other. The question is whether either one is *exactly* right. These varying answers are caused, not by the method in particular, but generally by the *size of unit* employed. For example, if we make a small error when using a large number of small units, this error will be multiplied a rather large number of times. Of course this applies in the reverse manner to using a small number of rather large units, in which case any error we make will not appear so large. In fact, we must be more careful, perhaps, to see that unit costs are *high enough when larger units are used*. For example, in using 1,000 brick as a unit, if we should make an error of say five cents in figuring the unit cost of 1,000 brick, the ultimate error would be approximately twice as great as the same sort of error made if we were using 100 square feet of wall, in which case, of course, the unit is approximately twice as large, but there would only be slightly more than half as many units in a building.

If this peculiar mathematical condition is thoroughly understood, a great deal of the discussion in regard to the inaccuracy (?) of certain systems will be seen to be without point.

In general, however, we would like to call to the reader's attention the convenience of using a decimal unit as far as possible, that is, a unit which is some power of 10, such as 100, 1,000, etc., whether it applies to 1,000 numerical units such as brick, or 100 square feet of wall.

THE GEOMETRICAL SYSTEMS
The Square Foot Method

Although not so well known, the Square Foot Method (this is the proper use of the term) should be considered first. This method is based on the area covered by the building in square feet, measured over all. For example, a bungalow 24 feet by 55 feet (outside dimensions) would be figured as 1,320 square feet, and the cost per square foot would be equal to the total cost divided by 1,320. If the total building cost was $6,600.00, the square foot cost would be $5.00. This applies here to a "one-story-area." For two floors it is figured in the same manner, but the area is doubled and the cost is usually less.

The Cubic Foot Method

The cubic foot method is not so simple nor in general is it as accurate, but it can be applied to buildings having no definite regular story heights such as theaters, or to extremely high buildings, say over four or five stories. It is based on the *cubic contents* or *volume* of the building. The cubic foot cost is derived by dividing the total cost of a building by the figures representing the contents or volume in cubic feet. Compared with the Square Foot Method is requires *twice as much work, doubles the chances for error,* and is *not as accurate.* The real difficulties encountered with these systems are:

1. Getting proper data or original costs.
2. Making adjustments for variations from the typical building used as the basis for costs.
3. Applying some standard system of measuring.

In the hands of experienced estimators having the data available, wonderful results may be obtained in the shortest possible time, but in the hands of beginners these methods are deceiving and dangerous.

The Percentage System

(a) *Total Cost Equals 100%.* As will be noticed, there are two general ways in which we can apply the idea of percentage in estimating a building, and as these are really so different from each other, it will be almost necessary to consider them as separate systems. It is difficult to say which is the most common, but for the sake of simplicity we will take the one which is better known to the general reading public, that is, where the total cost of the building equals 100%, and the cost of each part of the building, whether it be foundation, brickwork, carpentry, or plumbing, is considered to be a percentage of the total cost. Thus we may say that the foundation, for example, is quite often about 10% of the total cost of the building.

This system is particularly useful for certain workers in the building profession where, as we may say, they are compelled to work backwards from a given cost. It is really not intended as a system of estimating, although attempts have been made by many to utilize it as such. For example, if a certain prospective builder goes to an architect to obtain drawings, he usually tells the architect how much money he wishes to spend and the architect can get a fairly clear idea of how much can be spent for each part of the building if he has in his records some data giving the percentage of the total cost of each of the various parts of a building and for different classes of work.

To have data for only one class or price of building is sometimes misleading and useless because quite often as the price of the building increases the relationship of different parts of the building to other parts changes greatly. This is because in the more expensive structures the same amount of money might be expended for the foundation, but the interior might be finished off in a manner that is three or four times as expensive as buildings which are more moderate in price.

(b) *The Cost of Material Equals 100%.* In this system of estimating we have something which is entirely different from the one we have just discussed, although the idea of percentage is applied here also. Here, however, the base of our system is considered to be the *total cost of the material,* and the cost of labor for placing this material is considered to be a certain percentage of the cost of material.

Continued on page 176

This study closes the explanations relative to the tools needed in drawing. Most all drawing made or read by the building apprentice are drawn in pencil. It might be of interest to the apprentice to learn how to use ink in the making of a drawing but this is not needed. A good reference on Mechanical Drawing should be consulted for ink work. The remaining studies in drawing will deal with work other than the mechanics of shape representation or the tools or medium through which these various systems of shape representation are expressed.

The following is a list of reference books having interesting information for the building apprentice.

ARCHITECTURAL DRAWING -- W. B. Field -- McGraw-Hill Co., New York.

ARCHITECTURAL DRAFTING -- Svenson & Shelton -- McGraw-Hill Co., New York.

ARCHITECTURAL DRAFTING -- C. W. Seaman -- The Manual Arts Press, Peoria, Ill.

ARCHITECTURAL DETAILS -- Frank Halstead -- Wiley & Sons, New York.

ORDERS OF ARCHITECTURE -- A. B. Greenberg -- Wiley & Sons, New York.

PROBLEMS IN ARCHITECTURAL DRAWING -- F. G. Elwood -- Manual Arts Press,
                              Peoria, Ill.

BUILDERS ARCHITECTURAL DRAWING -- F. T. Hodgson -- F. J. Drake Co., Chicago.

HOUSE FRAMING DETAILS -- American Forest Products Industries, Washington.

HOW TO JUDGE A HOUSE -- Government Printing Office, Washington.

HIGH COST OF CHEAP CONSTRUCTION -- Weyerhaeuser Sales Co., St. Paul, Minn.

<u>Mathematics.</u> Roofing for frame houses may be obtained in the following materials.

a. wood shingles
b. slate shingles
c. roofing tiles
d. sheet metal tiles
e. tin sheets
f. slag or gravel roofing
g. asphalt gravel roofing
h. galvanized iron
i. corrugated steel roofing
j. copper roofing

The sizes of the different pieces of the above materials are as follows:

Material	Size of typical piece.	Amount to Weather.	Lap.
a.	4" x 14" or 16" or 18"	4"-5"-6"	10"
b.	9" x 18"	15"	3"
c.	$5\frac{1}{2}$" x $9\frac{1}{2}$"	$4\frac{1}{2}$" x $8\frac{1}{2}$"	1"
d.	8-3/4" x 11-5/8"	$4\frac{1}{2}$" x $8\frac{1}{2}$"	1"
e.	14" x 20"	$12\frac{1}{2}$" x $18\frac{1}{2}$"	$1\frac{1}{2}$"
f.	36" rolls 30' long	10"	16"
g.	36" rolls 30' long	34"	2"
h.	36" x 8' # 16	32" x 7'8"	4"
i.	36" x 8' # 14	35" x 7'11"	1"
j.	2'6" x 5'	2'5" x 4'11"	1"

Continued from page 174

Now in the past few years the relationship between the cost of labor and the cost of material has perhaps run close enough for any locality, but it varies widely in different localities. That is, the cost of material may be the same in two different localities, but the labor costs are not the same. Also the reverse may be true. Therefore, the relationship between labor and material is not the same. Hence, this system, although very useful at times for certain lines of work, is only useful where the contractor himself has perhaps engaged in a certain line of work for years and does not do work out of a certain locality, nor does he change the quality of his material to any great extent.

Attempts have been made to analyze this system into a more systematic and accurate method, but we find that if we are to consider only two or three variations, that is,

high, medium and low cost material; high, medium and low cost of labor; and conditions requiring a great deal of labor, a moderate amount of labor, or little labor, the various combinations possible to arrange from these simple conditions are so numerous and complex that the system gets unwieldly and almost impossible to apply. Yet unless we make some distinction between the different grades of material, the different amounts of labor required, and the relative cost of that labor, the system is misleading and inaccurate except for certain cases as we have noted.

Conclusion of 'Kelly' article on estimating which began on page 172

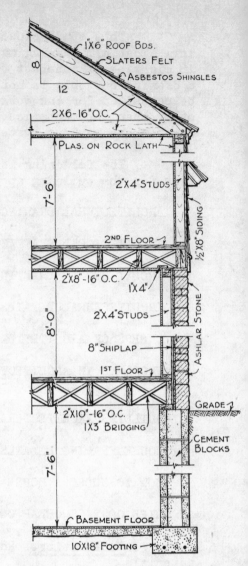

Complete wall section showing stone veneer

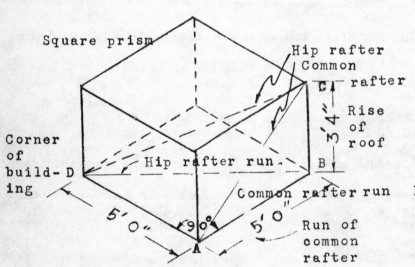

Using square prism to show comparative lengths of common and hip rafters. DA equals side of building, at plate. AB equals distance from plate to center of building. BC equals height of or rise of roof. Other lengths as indicated.

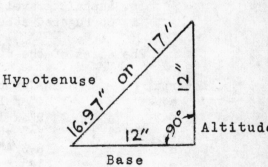

Showing why constant of 17" is used in figuring lengths of hip rafters instead of constant of 12" as used for common rafters. Refer to pg. 177, section 18.

Find the area of each piece or unit of roofing. Find the area of the amount of material exposed to the weather. Which type offers the greater or lesser area?

Cornice trim is estimated by the actual lineal feet of measure. It is sold by the 100 foot measure and sold by the pattern or stock number.

Roofing material is estimated by the square. A square is 10' x 10' or 100 square feet. Order kind of roofing by the square. Find the amount of sheathing required for the roof of the house in the accompanying set of plans. Find the amount of roofing material needed.

To find the length of a common rafter by geometrical methods one draws a horizontal line of indefinite length. On this line, which is called line XY, is laid off a line AB equal to the run of the rafter. This line becomes line BC, AB and BC form a right angle triangle ABC. Connect AC. This line AC is length of a common rafter.

To find length of a hip rafter. Proceed as above. Let EF equal to run of hip rafter. Let FG equal rise. EFG form a right angled triangle. EG is length of hip rafter. The following illustrations show the main points of above.

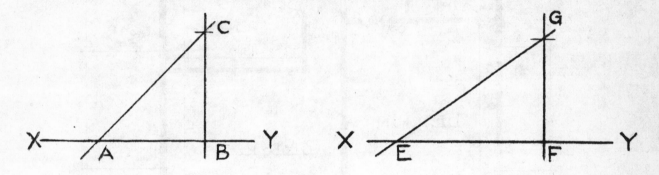

Science. The following discussion is Sections 18, 19 and 20 of the discussions under Science in the previous chapter.

<u>Section Eighteen.</u> <u>Location of hip and valley rafters.</u>

Refer to Section 11 of previous chapter and learn the appearance and location of hip and valley rafters.

Refer to section 15 of previous chapter and pages 153-157 of this text for discussion on common rafters. To find the length of a hip rafter one takes the constant 17" instead of 12" on the framing square. See drawing pg. 176.

Project.. Frame a pattern for a hip rafter. For a valley rafter.

<u>Section Nineteen.</u> <u>Side cuts on hip and valley rafters.</u>

In addition to the method of laying off and cutting a hip rafter as stated in Section 18 there is another cut known as the side or bevel cut to be made when a hip rafter frames itself into a ridge. Refer to the face of the steel square and

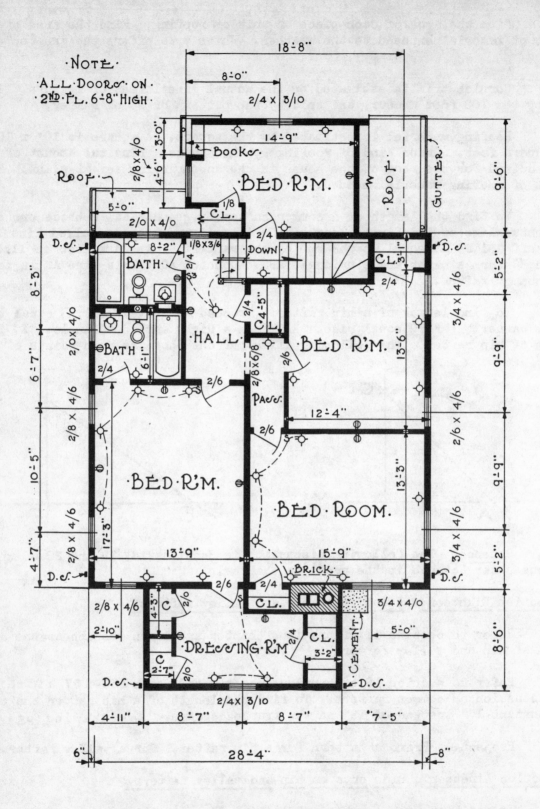

·SECOND·FLOOR·PLAN·
·SCALE·1/8"=1·0"

in line of rafter tables under inch mark (rise-per-foot-of-run) find a figure. Use this figure on body of square and 12" on tongue of square to lay off side cut.

Project.. Place side cut on hip rafter.

Section Twenty. Ridge deduction for hip or valley rafters.

The ridge reduction for a hip or valley rafter is the same as for a common rafter except that half the diagonal thickness of the ridge must be used instead of half the actual thickness.

Project.. Deduct for ridge piece on rafters (hip or valley) as layed off and framed in sections 19 and 18.

The following illustrations show important items in roof framing.

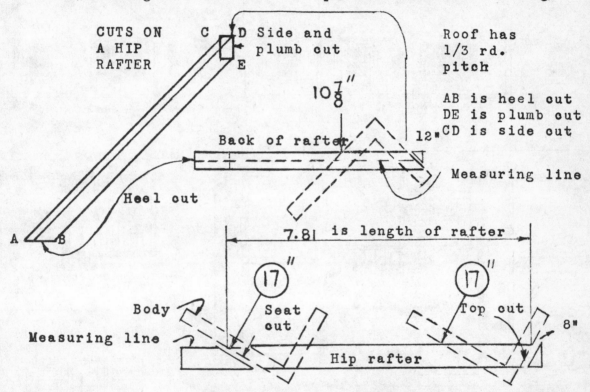

English. Word descriptions or lettering which is placed on house plans is very important. One should obtain a set of house plans and note the drawings or views on the sheets. Each view is different. Each view is named; for example one finds the names or titles to be: Plot plan, Foundation plan, etc. From the set of house plans list all the different titles of the different views. Find and list the following information which might be taken from the set of plans:

Who is the builder of the house?
Who is the owner of the house?
Where is the house to be built?
Has the building permit stamp been placed on the plans?
Who is the architect?
To what scale is each drawing made?

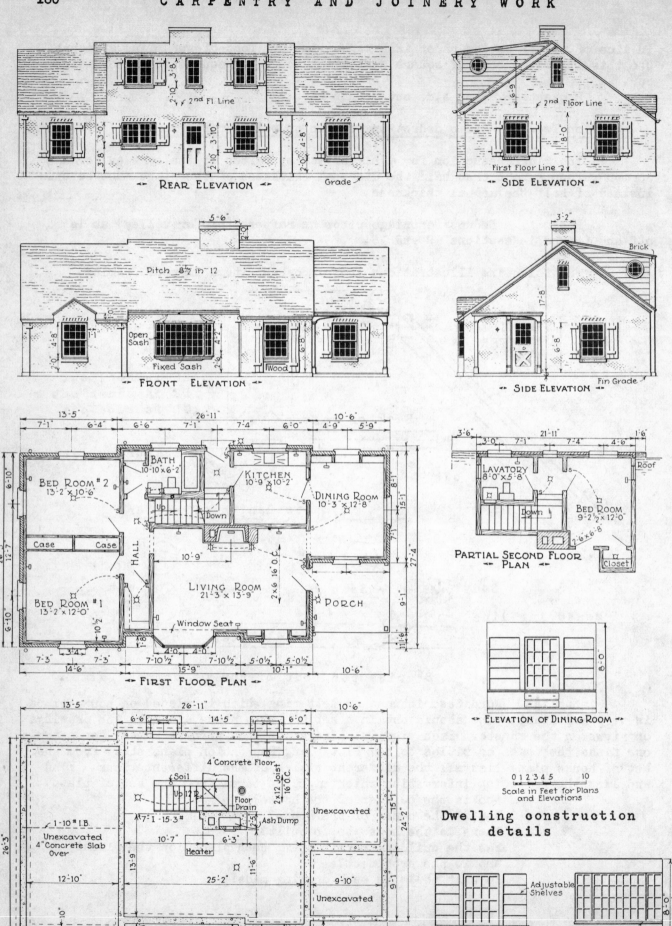

← REAR ELEVATION →

2nd Fl Line

Grade

← SIDE ELEVATION →

2nd Floor Line

First Floor Line

Pitch 8½ in 12

Open Sash

Fixed Sash

Wood

← FRONT ELEVATION →

Brick

← SIDE ELEVATION →

Fin Grade

BED ROOM #2
13'-2" x 10'-6"

BATH
10'-10" x 6'-2"

KITCHEN
10'-9" x 10'-2"

DINING ROOM
10'-3" x 12'-8"

Case   Case

HALL

Up   Down

2x6 16"O.C.

BED ROOM #1
13'-2" x 12'-0"

LIVING ROOM
21'-3" x 13'-9"

PORCH

Window Seat

← FIRST FLOOR PLAN →

LAVATORY
8'-0" x 5'-8"

Roof

Down

BED ROOM
9'-2½" x 12'-0"

Closet

PARTIAL SECOND FLOOR
← PLAN →

← ELEVATION OF DINING ROOM →

4" Concrete Floor

Soil

Up 12 12

Floor Drain

2x12 Joist 16" O.C.

Ash Dump

Unexcavated

Heater

Unexcavated 4" Concrete Slab Over

1-10 # I.B.

Unexcavated

← BASEMENT PLAN →

0 1 2 3 4 5   10
Scale in Feet for Plans
and Elevations

**Dwelling construction
details**

Adjustable Shelves

Window Seat

← ELEVATION OF LIVING ROOM →

What is mentioned about the pitch of the roof?
What kind of flooring is to be used?

The specifications or written instructions accompanying a set of house plans contain descriptions of the kind of material, the type of work to do and much other important information about the construction of the house. The apprentice must be able to read the set of specifications with some understanding.

Obtain the specifications available with the set of house plans and read them over carefully. Make a list of the topics that seem difficult to understand and have them explained. Give a detailed report on what is said about the kind and size of roof covering and roof material to use.

Study the spelling and meaning of the following trade terms:

face nail	face plate	fascia	fall	felt paper
fence	field stone	file	filler	filler coat
fillet strip	finial	fine work	finish	finish floor
finished	finish carpenter		finished roofing	
finish hardware		finishing nails		fire block
fire cut	fire plate	first course		fitting
flashing	fitting doors	fitting sash		flat ways
flight of stairs		floater	floor	flooring
floor plan	flue lining	flush	fold	foot
footing	forms	foundation	foundation wall	
frame	framed up	frame work	framed roof	framing
framing details		frame house	framing square	
framing timber	french doors	frog	front	front elevation
front porch	front view	frieze	furnace	furring

Civics.

Two other lessons in civics have been devoted to the health and first aid phases of dwelling construction. This lesson; is to be devoted to the safety precautions to be taken about construction work and the making of a list of NEVERS.

It is well to be told what NOT to do in construction work as well as what TO DO, particularly when such activities pertain to ones own safety. This list of precautions is to be added to as you go along in your experiences. Begin this list now, adding to the following suggestions as you can.

SAFETY FIRST

NEVER use a dull or partially broken tool.
NEVER assume that it is the other fellow's job to sharpen or clean tools.
NEVER 'strike' an edge tool toward the body.
NEVER work on stock that is not held or resting firmly.
NEVER push a hand saw at the first stroke.
NEVER strike a nail a hard blow for the first few strikes.
NEVER use scaffolding that is unsafe.
NEVER use an electrical tool that is not 100% safe.

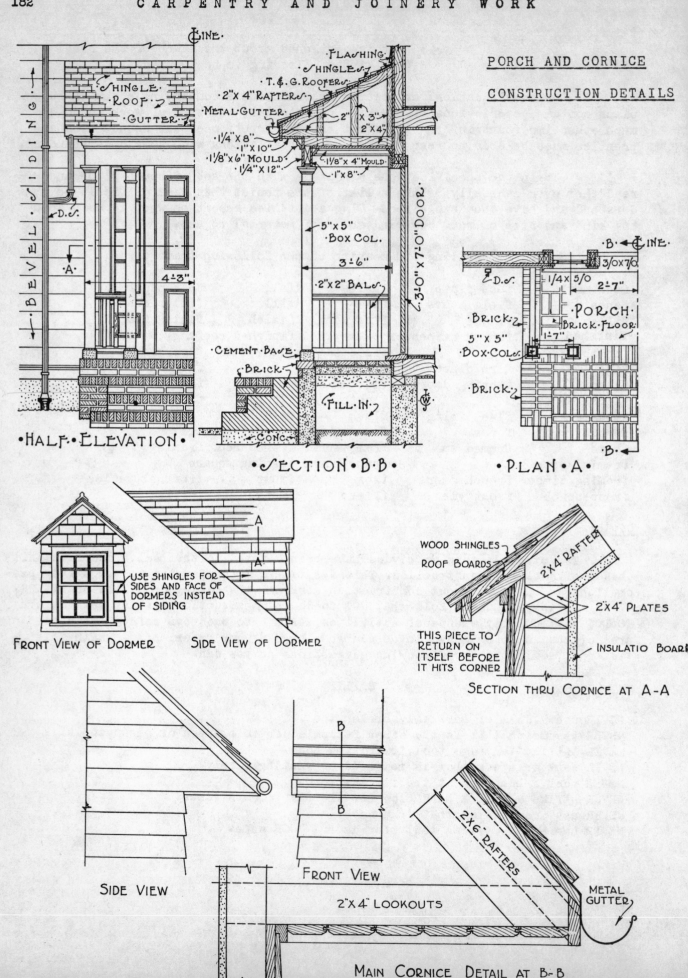

PORCH AND CORNICE
CONSTRUCTION DETAILS

·HALF·ELEVATION·

·SECTION·B·B·

·PLAN·A·

FRONT VIEW OF DORMER

SIDE VIEW OF DORMER

USE SHINGLES FOR SIDES AND FACE OF DORMERS INSTEAD OF SIDING

WOOD SHINGLES
ROOF BOARDS
2"X4" RAFTER
2"X4" PLATES
INSULATIO BOARD
THIS PIECE TO RETURN ON ITSELF BEFORE IT HITS CORNER

SECTION THRU CORNICE AT A-A

SIDE VIEW

FRONT VIEW

2"X6" RAFTERS
2"X4" LOOKOUTS
METAL GUTTER

MAIN CORNICE DETAIL AT B-B

Chapter XVIII

Cornices

The covering of the framed roof by sheathing is followed by the building up of the lower part of the rafters. The lower part of the rafters, often called the tails, is built up into a part called the cornice.

Refer to the set of plans and study the details or cross sections of the cornice construction.

The illustrations following this explanation show typical details. The details of cornice construction in the accompanying set of house plans should be studied with care.

There are two types of cornices, the open type and the built in type. If the open cornice is to be made nail the floating rafter, the crown moulding and the bed moulding in place as indicated on each detail.

If box or closed cornice is to be made lookouts and floating rafters should be nailed in place. The box gutter or cornice should be so built up as to allow for proper drainage. The gutter is lined with tin, the finish roofing applied before the soffit, facia, crown or bed moulding strips or any other finish lumber or trim is nailed in place.

Practical jobs. Build up an open cornice. Build up a closed or box cornice. Build up an open cornice. Build up a closed gable end.

Related Studies

Drawing. In the related drawing study of Chapter XV detailed steps and directions were given for the making of a drawing of a carpenter's saw horse. This work was to be done on a good grade of drawing paper. The apprentice should learn how to use drawing paper for sketching and some types of drawing but he should early become acquainted with another type of drawing paper commonly known as tracing paper. This tracing paper was originally used for copying drawings but it is now used in the making of original drawings from which copies can be made.

Refer to the drawing study of Chapter XV. Make a drawing of this saw horse, in exactly the same manner, but on tracing paper.

A word should be said about the case instruments, for they are the precision tools. The largest tool in the case is the large compass. It has a pencil foot and a pen foot. It is used to construct large circles and arcs. The next instrument in size is the large dividers. This tool is used to transfer distances only and consists of two legs having sharpened points. Three small bow instruments are the bow pen, the bow pencil and the bow dividers. The first is used in the making of small inked circles and arcs, the second in the making of small penciled circles and arcs and the third in the transferring of distances and some scribing, and this alone. The ruling pen is used in the ruling of straight lines in ink, not to do inked lettering work. The lengthening bar is an extension for the large compass enabling one to make very large cirles with

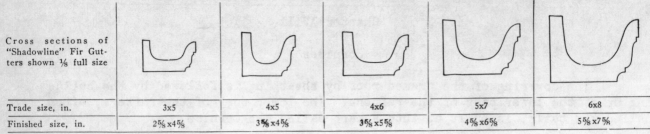

Cross sections of "Shadowline" Fir Gutters shown ⅛ full size					
Trade size, in.	3x5	4x5	4x6	5x7	6x8
Finished size, in.	2⅝ x 4⅝	3⅝ x 4⅝	3⅝ x 5⅝	4⅝ x 6⅝	5⅝ x 7⅝

Front of all gutters worked lower than back

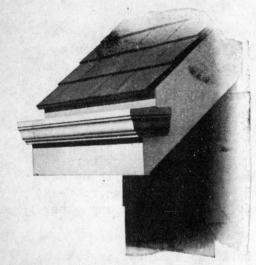

GUTTER AND CORNICE DETAILS

Formed Valley

Eaves Trough

O. G. Gutter

Beautiful exterior millwork and clear Cypress moldings—neat and lasting trim.

Gutter and downspouts of rust resisting galvanized steel.

Four stages in the erection of a group of "American Homes" at Cambridge, Mass.

an extension for the large compass enabling one to make very large circles with the pen or pencil foot. A screw driver and lead box complete the instruments in the drawing case.

Drafting Room Papers

In Engineering Offices drawings are frequently traced, requiring a paper through which the lines of the underlying drawing are clearly visible. This paper is correctly termed "Tracing Paper." In architectural work, little tracing is done, since the original drawings and sketches are made directly on paper sufficiently transparent to produce blueprints. This paper, however, is also known as "Tracing Paper." Consequently, while the term "Tracing Paper" is used for all transparent drawing papers, many of these papers are not used for tracing.

In the first case, where the paper is really used for tracing, the visibility of the lines of the original drawing through the tracing paper is of great importance. The special characteristics of a paper conforming to this requirement we shall call **"Tracing Transparency"**. In the second case, since the transparency of the paper is required only for making blueprints, we shall call it **"Blueprinting Transparency"**, which represents the amount of actinic light rays passing through the paper. While it generally goes hand in hand with Tracing Transparency, yet in some papers a considerable difference does exist between the Tracing Transparency and the Blueprinting Transparency. This is especially true with prepared (oiled) papers, in which the Tracing Transparency is greater than the Blueprinting Transparency. In other words, some prepared tracing papers may appear very transparent in tracing lines, but will not produce as good blueprints as their apparent transparency would seem to indicate. Natural tracing papers also vary considerably in this respect, due to the difference in surface and material.

In order to facilitate selection we have endeavored, as far as it is feasible, to classify "Tracing Transparency" and "Blueprinting Transparency" in the description of our tracing papers. For determining Tracing Transparency we employ the K & E Color Analyser, a highly scientific instrument for measuring light and color rays. Our classification of Blueprinting Transparency is based on comparative blueprints made with the same exposure, the paper producing the darkest print being classified as the most transparent. Hence the classification is only relative, since good blueprints can be obtained from papers with only "fair" blueprinting transparency, provided that they are exposed for a sufficient length of time.

In tracing papers we must differentiate between natural tracing papers, and prepared tracing papers.

Natural Tracing Paper: Much that has been stated about the qualities of good drawing paper also relates to good natural tracing papers. In order to obtain the necessary strength in a relatively thin paper and the highest transparency compatible with its weight, even greater care must be exercised in the selection of the raw material, which, for the best papers, must be of 100% clear, white rag stock. Natural tracing papers made of inferior material soon discolor and become brittle.

Prepared Tracing Papers; Most prepared tracing papers are those in which the transparency of the paper has been increased by the use of acids or oil. All prepared tracing papers are subject to some discoloration with age. Those that are made of improperly selected material are naturally subject to quick discoloration and to brittleness.

Continued on page 200

PHYSICAL CHARACTERISTICS OF WOOD

STRUCTURE OF WOOD

Wood, like all plant material, is made up of cells, or fibers, which when magnified have an appearance similar to though less regular than that of the common honeycomb. (Fig. 152.)

The walls of the honeycomb correspond to the walls of the fibers, and the cavities in the honeycomb correspond to the hollow or open spaces of the fibers.

SOFTWOODS AND HARDWOODS

All lumber is divided as a matter of convenience into two great groups, softwoods and hardwoods.

The softwoods in general are the coniferous or cone-bearing trees, such as the various pines, spruces, hemlocks, firs, and cedar.

The hardwoods are the noncone-bearing trees, such as the maple, oak, poplar, and the like.

These terms are used mainly as a matter of custom, for not all so-called softwoods are soft nor are all so-called hardwoods necessarily hard. As a matter of fact, such so-called softwoods as longleaf southern pine, and Douglas fir are much harder than poplar, basswood, etc., which are called hardwoods.

Other and perhaps more accurate terms often used for these two groups are the needle-bearing trees and the broad-leaved trees, respectively.

In general, the softwoods are more commonly used for structural purposes, such as for joists, studs, girders, posts, etc., while the hardwoods are more likely to be used for interior finish, flooring, and furniture. The softwoods are also used for interior finish and in many cases for floors, but are not often used for furniture.

MOISTURE CONTENT

While the tree is living, both the cells and cell walls are filled with water to a greater or lesser extent. As soon as the tree is cut, the water within the cells, or "free water," as it is called, begins to evaporate. This process continues until practically all of the "free water" has left the wood. When this stage is reached the wood is said to be at the fiber-saturation point: that is, what water is contained is mainly in the cell or fiber walls.

Except in a few species, there is no change in size during this preliminary drying process, and therefore no shrinkage during the

evaporation of the "free water." Shrinkage begins only when water begins to leave the cell walls themselves. What causes shrinkage and other changes in wood is not fully understood; but it is thought that as water leaves the cell walls they contract, becoming harder and denser, thereby causing a general reduction in size of the piece of wood. If the specimen is placed in an oven which is maintained at 212° F., the temperature of boiling water, the water will evaporate and the specimen will continue to lose weight for a time. Finally a

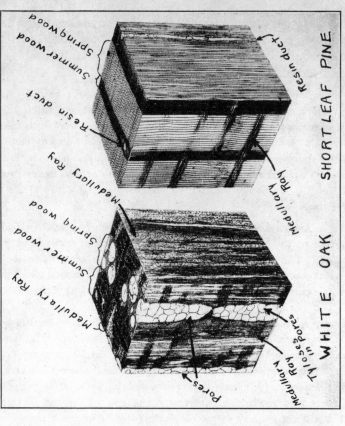

FIGURE 152.—Cubes of white oak and shortleaf pine magnified. The top of each cube represents the end or transverse surface. The left side shows the quartered or radial surface. The right side illustrates the bastard or tangential surface.

(Photographs of cubes by courtesy of the Forest Products Laboratory.)

point is reached at which the weight remains substantially constant. This is another way of saying that all of the water in the cells and cell walls has been driven off. The piece is then said to be "oven dry."

If it is now taken out of the oven and allowed to remain in the open air, it will gradually take on weight, due to the absorption of moisture from the air. As when placed in the oven, a point is reached at which

Continued on page 187

Mathematics. Any circle contains 360 degrees. In a fourth of a circle, a quadrant, there are 90 degrees. 4 x 90 equals 360. An angle at the center is measured by the number of degrees of arc intercepted between the sides of the angle. The number of degrees in the arc gives the number of degrees in the angle. For precision instruments degrees are divided into minutes and minutes are divided into seconds. There are 60 seconds in one minute and 60 minutes in one degree. Degrees, minutes and seconds have these symbols, (o) (') (") respectively. Thus 60 degrees, 5 minutes and 2-1/2 seconds are written 60°, 5', 2-1/2".

The area included between two radii and the arc is called a sector. A segment is that part of a circle which is included between an arc and its chord. This is explained graphically in the following diagrams.

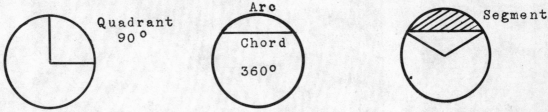

In estimating the trim for the cornice one must estimate it by the linear foot and by the pattern of the mouldings used. About 75 linear feet of cornice trim can be worked up in an eight hour day. G reat care should be taken in estimating work as there is so much variation.

Produce the above figures by the use of drawing instruments. Estimate the amount of trim necessary in a cornice construction.

Science. A trough or gutter is placed at the lowest part of each slope of a roof. Most gutters are made of metal and hung or built on to the roof. Some gutters are built up in the form of a box cornice with the trough lined in metal. Much can be said of metal gutters but a wooden gutter has points of superiority.

Refer to any issue of Sweet's Architectural Catalog and find the descriptions of wooden and metal gutters. Make a synopsis of each type. Sketch the several styles illustrated. The following illustrations will prove helpful. The following discussion, taken from the booklet, LIGHT FRAME HOUSE CONSTRUCTION, by permission of the Federal Board for Vocational Education, will help to clear up much misunderstanding about wood.

the weight of the wood in contact with the air remains more or less constant. Careful tests, however, show that it does not remain exactly constant, for it will take on and give off water as the moisture in the atmosphere increases or decreases. Thus, a piece of wood will contain more water during the humid, moist summer months than in the colder, drier winter months. When the piece is in this condition it is in "equilibrium with the air" and is said to be "air-dry."

A piece of lumber cut from a green tree and left in the atmosphere in such a way that the air may circulate freely about it will gradually arrive at this air-dry condition. This ordinarily takes from one to three months, and the process is termed "air seasoning." It can be greatly hastened by placing the wood in an artificially heated oven or "dry kiln" until the moisture content of the wood is that of air dryness.

Continued on page 188

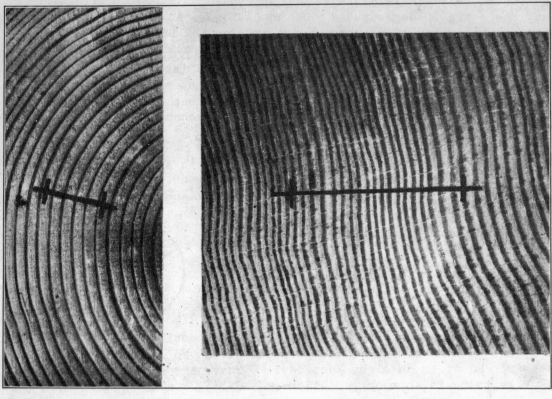

FIGURE 154.—The upper photo shows a 3 by 8 pine joist with five annual rings to the inch and 25 per cent summer wood. It is neither close grained nor dense. The lower photo is part of the end section of a 6 by 8 pine beam. It has six annual rings to the inch and 51 per cent summer wood. It is classified as dense

carried through the cells to the rapidly growing branches and leaves at the top of the tree. This water passes upward mainly in the outer layers of the tree. The result is that the cells next to the bark, which

Continued on page 190

The amount of water contained by wood in the green condition varies greatly, not only with the species but in the same species, and even in the same tree, according to the position in the tree. But as a general average, at the fiber-saturation point, most woods contain from 23 to 30 per cent of water as compared with the oven-dry weight of the wood. When air-dry most woods contain from 12 to 15 per cent of moisture.

SHRINKAGE

As the wood dries from the green state, which is that of the freshly cut tree, to the fiber-saturation point, there is no change other than that of weight. It has already been pointed out that as the moisture dries out of the cell walls, in addition to the decrease in weight, shrinkage results in a definite decrease in size. It has been found, however, that there is little or no decrease along the length of the grain, and that the decrease at right angles to the grain—that is, radially, or to and from the heart of the tree—is approximately half of the shrinkage parallel to the grain or around the tree.

This is an important consideration to be remembered when framing a building. For example, a stud in a wall will not shrink appreciably in length, whereas it will shrink somewhat in both the 2-inch and the 4-inch way. In like manner, a joist, if it is green when put in place, will change in depth as it seasons in the building.

These principles of shrinkage also explain why an edge-grain or quarter-sawed floor is less likely to open up than a flat-grain floor.

DENSITY

The tree undergoes a considerable impetus early every spring and grows very rapidly for a short time. Large amounts of water are

DIRECTION OF LEAST SHRINKAGE

DIRECTION OF GREATEST SHRINKAGE

LOG

FIGURE 153.—The shrinkage of wood from end to end is negligible, but in cross section it shrinks approximately one-half as much at right angles to the annual rings as it does parallel to them. This fact is important to remember in selecting flooring. Edge or vertical grain flooring, if not properly seasoned when installed, will shrink approximately only one-half the amount of similar unseasoned flat-grain flooring. The above illustration shows in an exaggerated manner the results of seasoning in different parts of a log

Air dry and dry in a kiln pieces of wood. Weigh each piece before drying. Weigh after drying. Try to find examples of annular growth. Try to perform certain strength tests on lumber. Try to find various examples of wood characteristics as mentioned.

English. In using a dictionary one should know something about the make up of a modern 'word book' in order to get the full value from it. Obtain a volume of any standard type of dictionary. Turn to the word STUD, a definition something like this will be found:

> STUD (stud), n. A small timber or piece to support the joists of a building; an ornamental nail, a short projecting rod in machinery.

The meaning of the above is as follows:
a. The word is set forth in bold type.
b. The aid in pronunciation is enclosed in brackets.
c. The part of speech is designated, n for noun, v for verb, etc.
d. A definition is given. The definition is one fitting all uses of the word.

Refer to a dictionary and find the meaning of the following words; sheath, sheathe, stock, stick, earth joint, plans, flush, level, girder, nail and plane.

Study the spelling and meaning of the following trade terms.

gable	gable ends	gable rafter	gable roof	galvanized
gambrel	gauge	garage	gas line	gas log
gate	girder	girt	glass	glazier
glazing	glazing points	glue	golden rule	goose neck
grade	grade line	grading	grain	grass
grate	gravel	green	grinding	grounds
gutter				

Civics. Newspapers and magazines have sections devoted to house plans and architectural information of common interest. Much of this information is very interesting and helpful.

Obtain the building sections of one newspaper and one magazine. Study the information given. Start a scrap book, particularly of newspaper plans of houses.

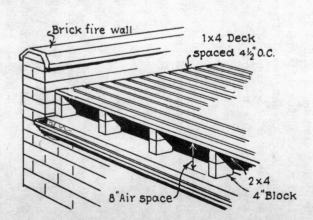

Method of placing cooling deck on roof.

Continued from page 188

are formed during the period of rapid growth, have thin walls and large passages.

Later on, during the summer, the rate of growth slows up and the demand for water is less. The cells which are formed during the summer have much thicker walls and much smaller pores. Thus it is that each year's growth is of two types, the spring wood as it is called, being characterized by softness and openness of grain and the summer wood by hardness and closeness, or density, of grain. The spring wood and summer wood growth for one year is called an "annual ring."

There is one ring for each year of growth. This development of spring wood and summer wood is a marked characteristic of practically all woods and is clearly evident in such trees as the yellow pines and firs, and less so in the white pines, maple, and the like. Careful examination will reveal this annual ring, however, in practically all species.

It follows, therefore, that a tree, in which the dense summer wood predominates, is stronger than one in which the soft spring wood predominates. (Fig. 154.) This is a point which should be borne in mind in selecting material for important members such as girders and posts carrying heavy loads. The strength of wood of the same species varies markedly with the density. For example, Douglas fir or southern pine, carefully selected for density, is one-sixth stronger than lumber of the same species and knot limitations in which the spring wood predominates. Trees having approximately one-third or more of cross-sectional area in summer wood fulfill one ot the requirements for structural timbers.

ESTIMATING DENSITY

It must be remembered that the small cells or fibers which make up the wood structure are hollow. Wood substance itself has a specific gravity of about 1.5, and therefore will sink in water. On good authority, it is stated that wood substance of all species is practically of the same density. Strength of wood depends upon its density and varies with its density. The actual dry weight of lumber is a good criterion of its strength, although weight can not always be relied upon as a basis for determining strength, as other important factors frequently must be considered in a specific piece of wood.

The hardness of wood is also another factor which assists in estimating the strength of wood. A test sometimes used is cutting across the grain. This test can not be utilized in the commercial grading of lumber because a moisture content will affect the hardness and because hardness thus measured can not be adequately defined.

The annual rings found in practically all species are an important consideration in estimating density, although the annual rings indicate different conditions in different species. In ring-porous hardwoods and in the conifers, where the contrast between spring wood and summer wood is definite, the proportion of hard summer wood is an indication of the strength of the individual piece of wood. The amount of summer wood, however, can not always be relied upon as an indication of strength, because summer wood itself varies in density. When cut across the grain with a knife the density of the summer wood may be estimated on the basis of hardness, color, and luster.

In conifers annual rings of average width (see fig. 154) indicate denser material or a larger proportion of summer wood than in wood with either wide or narrow rings. In some old conifers of virgin growth in which the more recent annual rings are narrow the wood is less dense than where there has been normal growth. On the other hand, in young trees where growth has not been impeded by other trees, the rings are wider and in consequence the wood less dense. These facts may account for the beliefs that all second-growth timber and all sapwood are weak. In accepting wood for density, the contrast between summer wood and spring wood should be pronounced.

Oak, ash, hickory, and other ring-porous hardwoods in general rank high in strength when the annual rings are wide. In this respect they contrast with conifers. These species have more summer wood than spring wood as the rings become wider. For this reason, oak, hickory, ash, and elm of second growth are considered superior because of fast growth and increase in proportion of summer wood. These conditions do not always exist, however, for exceptions occur, especially in ash and oak, where, although the summer wood is about normal, it may not be dense or strong. Very narrow rings in ring-porous hardwoods are likely to indicate weak and brashy material composed largely of spring wood with big pores. Maple, birch, beech, and other diffuse-porous hardwoods in general show no definite relationship between the width of rings and density, except that usually narrow rings indicate brash wood.

STRENGTH

Wood, when used in ordinary structures, is called upon to have three types of strength—tension, compression, and shear.

Tension.

Tension is the technical term for a pulling stress. For example, if two men are having a tug of war with a rope, the rope is in tension. The tensile strength of wood, especially of the structural grades, is very high.

Compression.

If, however, the men at opposite ends of a 2 by 4 inch are trying to push each other over, the timber is in compression. Tension and compression represent, therefore, exactly opposite forces.

Continued on page 192

Chapter XIX

Roofing

The roof boards may be covered with wood shingles, asbestos shingles or roll roofing paper. Slate shingles, tile shingles and rolled tin are also used as roofing. Study the house plans and specifications for the type of shingles to use or the type of roofing to use on the house.

If a manufactured shingle is specified be certain to obtain the directions given with each roll or bundle of roofing material and lay the roofing according to these directions.

In applying shingles made of wood one should open the bundles and throw water on each shingle in order to allow some moisture to enter before the shingles are nailed down. If the shingles are very dry when applied they will absorb moisture, swell and pull away from the nails.

In placing the shingles on the roofing boards, begin placing the shingles in a row at the eave and nail down at the middle with 3 d. galvanized or copper nails. Do not use iron or steel nails as these will rust away long before the shingles begin to rot. Place the first row of shingles down so that the water fall will have no chance to run anywhere but into the gutter. Extend shingle from facia molding over one half width of gutter. Place shingles down edge to edge along this row. Line up the shingles with a chalk line strung from end to end of this row. The first course of shingles must be double.

Place second row of shingles over the first row taking care to cover all joints and nail heads in the first row. Line up this second row by use of chalk line with the first row. Place third row of shingles down in like manner but about five or six inches from the neds of the first and second rows of shingles. This allows a certain amount of each row of shingles to be exposed to the weather. Use toe cleats where needed to facilitate the work.

Work all rows along like the third row taking care not to place a joint or joining place above nails or a joining place below. The last row at the ridge should be made up of the butt end or the lower part of the shingle and should be matched carefully with the row on the other side of the ridge.

The following illustrations will help to make clear many of the foregoing statements. Page 198.

<u>Practical jobs</u>.. Cover roofing boards with wooden shingles or other specified material.

Contined from page 190

Shear is harder to explain. If two or three planks are placed one upon the other between two blocks, and one were to stand in the middle, the planks would bend and assume a position similar to that shown in Figure 155. It will be noted that at the outer ends the boards tend to slip past each other.

If the planks were securely spiked through from top to bottom, the slipping would be in a great measure prevented and the boards would act more as one piece of wood. In every solid timber there is the same tendency for the various parts of the piece to slip past each other. This tendency is called "horizontal shear." A defect, such as a check, which runs horizontally through a piece of a timber and tends to separate the upper from the lower part, is a weakness in shear.

It is well to analyze this matter a little further. Suppose that the planks were spiked through at the center of span only, i. e., halfway between the blocks. Such spikes would not increase the stiffness of the planks. It is clear, therefore that there is no horizontal shear near the center of span (fig. 156), and that the shear increases as one approaches either end of the beam. This will explain why, as most carpenters have doubtless observed, steel stirrups are used in concrete beams (weak in shear), why there is usually none near the center, and why they are put closer together near the ends of the beams.

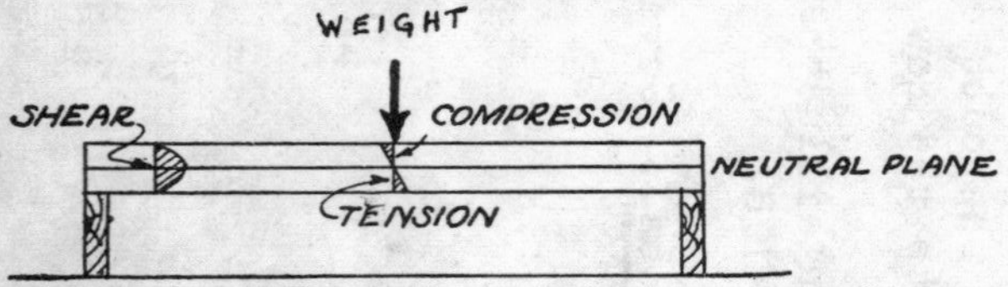

For all practical purposes the compressive strength of wood may be considered to equal its tensile strength. It has been extremely difficult to make any direct measurements of the tensile strength of wood. In an experiment designed to ascertain the tensile strength of a specimen of wood, a 4 by 4 inch piece was selected. A portion about a foot in length near the center was carefully cut down on all four sides until it was exactly ¾ inch square. The test specimen was placed in

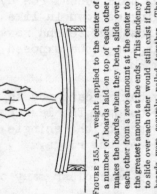

FIGURE 155.—A weight applied to the center of a number of boards laid on top of each other makes the boards, when they bend, slide over each other from a zero amount at the center to the greatest amount at the ends. This tendency to slide over each other would still exist if the boards were securely nailed together. The need for nailing increases toward the ends

FIGURE 156.—This illustrates the differing proportions of tension, compression, and shearing when weight is applied to a beam. It will be noted that compression and tension are zero at the neutral plane, whereas shear is greatest at the neutral place

a machine which gripped the 4 by 4 inch ends securely and a pull was exerted. The specimen did not pull apart. The ¾-inch square section held and actually pulled out of one end of the 4 by 4 inch, leaving a ¾-inch square hole. This is an excellent illustration of how a piece may fail from shear rather than tension, the shear in this case being insufficient to prevent the ¾-inch square piece from pulling out.

SOME UNFOUNDED BELIEFS

Deadwood.

Because in some instances persons are prejudiced against the use of timber cut from dead trees, it is customary for individuals to specify that only timber cut from live trees will be accepted. It is true, however, that when sound trees which are dead are sawed into lumber and the weathered or charred outside is cut away, the resulting lumber can not be distinguished from that coming from live trees except in so far as the lumber from dead trees may be somewhat seasoned at the time it is sawed. It must be remembered that the heartwood of a living tree is fully matured and that in the sapwood only a small portion of the cells are in a living condition. As a consequence most of the wood cut from trees is already dead even when the tree itself is considered alive.

For structural purposes, it may be said that lumber cut from fire or insect killed trees is just as good as any other lumber unless the wood has been subjected to further decay or insect attack.

Dry-Rot.

Loosely used, the term "dry-rot" is applied to any type of dry crumbly rot and includes under these circumstances all types of brown decay in wood. The pathologist uses the term "dry-rot" in the limited sense as it applies to the work of certain decay fungi which are frequently found growing in timber where they appear to have access to no moisture. Decay fungi will not grow in perfectly dry wood and no material decay need be expected in wood used under shelter and maintained in a normal air-dry condition. With moist wood the fungi are able to penetrate amazingly long distances because they extend their water-supply system by means of slender, minute, porous strands. Fungi of other kinds produce a rot not unlike dry-rot, but brown or yellow in color. The wood in an advanced state is shrunken, and in some places the cracks are filled with a white soggy mass, the wood itself being brittle, friable, and easily crushed into powder.

Virgin and Second Growth.

Occasionally an order calls for lumber of either virgin growth or second growth. The terms, however, are without significance, as an individual can not tell one type from the other when they are

Related Studies

Drawing. A drawing made on tracing paper is used as a means to obtain a duplicate of the drawing. Three different processes are in general use for copying drawings from tracing paper and tracing cloth by means of light:

Blue print process: producing a negative print (if prints are made
                     from the original tracing), with white lines on
                     blue background.
Maduro process;   producing a negative print (if prints are made
                     from the original tracing), with white lines on
                     a brown-black background.
Black Print process: producing positive prints from the original trac-
                     ing; that is, black lines on a white background.

The information on a following page, taken from the K & E catalog, gives much interesting information relative to printing papers.

After reading this information, print the tracing which was made as suggested in the previous chapter. Have the print made at a commercial establishment or a school print machine. Seek one who is able to advise you how to make a print before attempting to make it.

Mathematics. See page 196.

Science. Roofing material has two purposes to serve, one is appearance, or beauty, the other protection from heat, rain, wind and snow. This material is made from the following raw products; wood, slate, tile (clay), tile (metal), tin sheet, slag or gravel, asphalt, steel and copper.

Wooden shingles are made of cypress, cedar or redwood lumber. They are durable, warp very little, are easily applied, but are not very fire resisting.

Slate shingles should be hard, tough and free of soft ribbons. They should have a metallic appearance and a metallic ring when struck. They are inexpensive and are available in a variety of color schemes.

Tile shingles are not so serviceable but more attractive. They are available in a variety of patterns and colors. They are heavy and hard to handle.

Metal tile shingles are cheaper than clay tile shingles. They offer a cheap first cost but must be painted to be kept up.

Tin sheet roofing is inexpensive. It is easily laid and light in weight. It requires painting. It is very flexible.

Slag or gravel roofing is seldom used on frame house or any type of residence. It is hard to apply but very durable. It is acid and fume resisting. Often guaranteed upward to twenty years.

Asphalt roofing has asphalt in it to take the place of tar. It does not last as long as tar roofs, but is quite attractive.

Steel and galvanized iron roofing is easy to apply. It is very heavy and requires paint.

Copper roofing is very durable and easy to apply. The first cost is

Continued from page 192

The virgin growth, which is also called old growth or first growth, refers to timber which grows in the forest along with many other trees, and therefore has suffered the consequence of the fight for sunlight and moisture.

The second growth is considered as that timber which grows up with less of the competition for sunlight and moisture which characterizes first-growth timber.

Because of environment, the virgin growth is usually thought of as wood of slow-growing type, whereas the second growth is considered as of relatively rapid growth, evidenced by wider annual rings. In such hardwoods as ash, hickory, elm, and oak these wider annual rings are supposed to indicate stronger and tougher wood, whereas in the conifers such as pine and fir, this condition is supposed to result in a weaker and brashier wood. For this reason, where strength and toughness are desired, the second growth is preferred among hardwoods, and virgin growth is desired in conifers. Because of the variety of conditions under which both virgin and second growth timbers grow, because virgin growth may have the characteristics of second growth, and because second growth may have the characteristics of virgin timber, it is advisable in judging the strength of a wood to rely upon its density and rate of growth rather than upon its being either virgin growth or second growth.

Time of Cutting Timber.

The time when timber is cut has very little to do with its durability or other desirable properties, if, after it is cut, it is cared for properly. Timber cut in the late spring, however, or early summer is more likely to be attacked by insects and fungi. In addition, seasoning will proceed much more rapidly during the summer months; and, therefore, will result in checking, unless the lumber is shaded from the intense sunlight. It is stated that there is practically no difference in the moisture content in green lumber, either during the summer or winter.

Air-Dried and Kiln-Dried Wood.

There is a prevailing misapprehension that air-dried lumber is stronger or better than kiln-dried lumber. Exhaustive tests have conclusively shown that good kiln-drying and good air-drying have exactly the same results upon the strength of wood. Wood increases in strength with the elimination of moisture content. This may account for the claim that kiln-dried lumber is stronger than air-dried lumber. This has little significance, because in use wood will come to practically the same moisture content whether it has been kiln-dried or air-dried.

The same kiln-drying process can not be applied to all species of wood. Consequently it must be remembered that lack of certain

strength properties in wood may be due to improper kiln-drying. Similar damage also may result from air seasoning under unsuitable conditions.

Sapwood Versus Heartwood.

The belief is common that in some species the heartwood is stronger than the sapwood and that the reverse is the case in such species as hickory and ash. Tests have shown conclusively that neither is the case, and that sapwood is not necessarily stronger than heartwood or heartwood stronger than sapwood, but that density rather than other factors makes the difference in strength. In trees that are mature the sapwood is frequently weaker, whereas in young trees the sapwood may be stronger. Density, proportion of spring and summer wood, then must be the basis of consideration of strength rather than whether the wood be sapwood or heartwood.

Under unfavorable conditions the sapwood of most species is more subject to decay than the heartwood.

Blue Stain.

In the sapwood of many species of both softwoods and hardwoods there often develops a bluish-black discoloration known as blue stain. It does not indicate an early stage of decay, nor does it have any practicable effect on the strength of the wood.

Blue stain is caused by a fungus growth in unseasoned lumber. Although objectionable, where appearance is of importance, as in unpainted sash or trim, blue stain need cause no concern for framing lumber. Precaution should be taken, however, to make sure that no decay fungus is present with the blue stain.

Cure for Leaky Gutters

JOINTS in wood gutters have a tendency to leak if some method is not used other than filling the joint with paint or white lead.

My solution of the problem is to cut a piece of sheet lead just a little larger than the size of the gutter and insert in the joint. After the gutter has been securely nailed to the building, upset the lead sheet by means of a nail set and hammer, thus wedging the metal into the joint very tightly and firmly so that it will not come out as white lead often does.

Roy H. Berrs, Seattle, Washington.

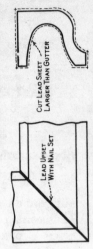

CUT LEAD SHEET LARGER THAN GUTTER

LEAD UPSET WITH NAIL SET

Sheet Lead Is Used to Prevent Gutter Leaks.

the greatest cost.

Obtain several samples of roofing. Find advertisements in Sweet's giving features of various types of roofing. Find the costs. Perform several tests on roofing. Paint some, soak all in water over a period of time. Weather certain kinds in the sun. Observe results carefully.

English. A standard dictionary gives the meaning of words but not a complete technical discussion. Trade texts must be consulted for particular scientific information.

Refer to a set of house plans and find the symbol for the chimney. Refer to a technical book or bricklayer's manual for additional information. Refer to any trade magazine available. Write a good description of a chimney. List the technical words found. Write the meaning of these words from their particular use as found in the text.

Study the meaning and spelling of the following technical terms:

half hatchet	half newels	halved	hammer	handsaw
hang	hangers	hanging sash	hard pine	hardware
hardwood	hardwood flooring		hatchet	haul
head casing	headed	header	head room	hearth
heavy construction		heavy paper	height	high
hip	hip jack rafter		hip rafter	hinge
hollowed out	hook	horizontal	horse	house
housed out	housing	hung	hypotenuse	

inch	incombustible	material	information	inside door
inside edge	insulation	interior	interior finish	interior trim
intermediate girder		intersect	iron lintel	

Civics. Insurance rates offered by fire insurance companies on houses having various types of roofs is valuable information. According to a publication of the Ohio Inspection Bureau, 'Dwelling Circular of September 1, 1932' cities and towns are divided into ten classes according to the type of fire protection offered. Buildings are classified into five classes; they are, brick buildings- frame building- approved roof- unapproved roof and mixed construction. These fice classes are defined in an exact manner in this circular, too. Refer to this schedule or any other fire insurance schedule. Ascertain rates for different types of roofing.

This Helps in Nailing Ceiling

I AM offering a little idea which is, like most of these helpful ideas, so simple that I cannot understand why I did not think of it before. When working alone I have always found it very difficult to put up ceiling. I had a terrible time trying to hold a long piece while I nailed it. It finally occurred to me to tack a piece of 2 by 4 along the wall at each end of the room, just far enough down from the ceiling to let the material slip in on top of it. This held the end of the material up while I nailed the other end and I have had no more difficulty with such work since.

H. A. FARRELL, 813 S. Sheridan Ave., Tacomah, Wash.

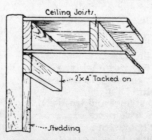

A 2 by 4 Tacked to the Studs Just Below the Ceiling Simplifies Nailing the Ceiling.

__Mathematics__. Continued from pg. 193.

A Bill of Material or Stock Bill for a frame dwelling.

Item No.	Purpose	Materials Required	Board Feet
1.	Girder	6x8 or triple 2x8	144
	(or)	6x10 or triple 2x10	180
2.	Ledger Strip	2x4	48
3.	Girder Post	3 Pcs. 6x6—8	72
4.	Box Sills	2x6 and 2x10	320
	(or)	2x8 and 2x10	360
5.	Joist 16″ oc	31 Pcs. each 2x10—10′ & 14′	1,240
6.	Cross Bridging	54 sets 1x3	60
	(or)	1x4 or 2x2	80
7.	Subfloor *(10%)	Boards	950
	(or)	10″ Ship	1,050
	(or)	8″ Ship	1,070
	(or)	6″ Ship	1,110
8.	Sole and Plates, Walls	360 lin′ 2x4	240
9.	Wall Studs 16″ oc	120 Pcs. 2x4—8	640
10.	Let-in Corner Braces	8 Pcs. 1x4—12	32
11.	Gable Studs 16″ oc	18 Pcs. 2x4—8	96
12.	Fire Stops, Walls	120 lin′ 2x4	80
13.	Wall Shtg(Opgs. & 5%)	Boards	1,400
	(or)	10″ Ship	1,540
	(or)	8″ Ship	1,570
	(or)	6″ Ship	1,630
14.	Paper, Walls	1,500 sq. ft. per ply	
15.	Corner Boards	40 lin′ 1¼x4 & 1¼x5	38
16.	Siding (10%)	4″ Bvl	1,610
	(or)	6″ Bvl	1,460
	(or)	4″ Rustic	1,430
	(or)	6″ Rustic	1,320
17.	Ceiling Joist 16″ oc	31 Pcs. each 2x6—12′ & 14′	806
18.	Part'n Sole and Plates	354 lin′ 2x4	236
19.	Part'n Studs 16″ oc	118 Pcs. 2x4—8	629
20.	Part'n Bridging	2x4	80
21.	Insulation, Walls	(Add flange and 450 lath if between studs)	1,020
22.	Insulation, Ceiling	(Add lap or flange)	864
23.	Plaster, Ceiling	83 yds.	
24.	Plaster, OS Walls	106 yds.	
25.	Plaster, Part'ns	215 yds.	
26.	Metal Corner Beads	360 lin′ for ceiling angles and 352 lin′ for wall angles	
27	Grounds	300 lin′ for base and 600 lin′ for opgs.	
28.	Rafters	16″ oc 56 Pcs. 2x6—18	1,008
	(or)	24″ oc 38 Pcs. 2x6—18	684
29.	Collar Beams 48″ oc	8 Pcs. 2x6—6	48
30.	Ridge Board	1x6	18
31.	Roof Shtg. (5%)	Boards, solid	1,430
	(or)	50% open	715
	(or)	8″ Ship	1,610
	(or)	6″ Ship	1,670
32.	Roof	13½ sqs. plus 80 lineal feet starting course	
33.	Fire Stop at Eaves	1x10	100
34.	Ridge Roll	40 lin′ and 2 finials	
35.	Cornice Plancher(10%)	4″ Clg	400
	(or)	6″ Clg	380
36.	Cornice Frieze (10%)	144 lin′ 1x8	97
37.	Cornice Facia (10%)	160 lin′ 1x4	53
38.	Crown Mldg. (10%)	160 lin′ crown mldg.	
	(or)	82 lin′ gutter & 76 lin′ cr.mldg.	
39.	Bed Mldg. (10%)	144 lin′	
40.	Basement Stairs	2x10 strings and treads	130
	(or)	same with risers	150
41.	Closet Shelving	Inc. book strips	50
42.	Paper for floor	1,000 sq.′	
43.	†Finish Flooring	3/8x1½ and 13/16x2¼	1,000
	(or)	13/16x1½	1,125
	(or)	1x3 (5%)	1,050
	(or)	1x4 (5%)	990
44.	Chimney Brick (5%)	8x8 flue 750 brick	
	(or)	8x12 flue 875 brick	
	(or)	12x12 flue 1,000 brick	
45.	Mortar	1 bbl. lime and 2/3 yd. sand	
46.	Flue Lining	26′ per above size	
47.	Flashing, etc.	8 lin′ and Cleanout door	
48.	Labor, Chimney	8x8—12 hrs. each mason & tender	
	(or)	12x12-15 hrs. each mason & tender	
49.	Base Boards	300 lin′ each member	
50.	Picture Mldg.	200 lin′ in 4 rooms	
51.	Front Door	1 door with lock, butts, bell and house numbers	
52.	Rear Door	1 door with lock and butts	
53.	OS Door Frames	2 frames	
54.	Threshold	2 pieces	
55.	Storm Doors	2 with hardware	
56.	Screen Doors	2 with hardware	
57.	Interior Doors	10 (inc. cased openings)	
58.	Locks and Butts	10 sets for above	
59.	Door Jambs	10 with stops	
60.	Door Trim	22 sides	
61.	Windows	12 Dbl. hung or casmt. sn.	
62.	Window Frames	12 single frames	
63.	Window Trim	12 sides	
64.	Sash Cord	2 hanks	
65.	Sash Weights	For 26x26—2 lt. wds. 288 lbs.	
	(or)	For 24x24—2 lt. wds. 264 lbs.	
66.	Window Hardware	12 sets sash locks and lifts	
67.	Storm Sash	12 for above windows	
68.	Window Screens	12 screens	
69.	Screen and Sash Hdw.	12 sets	
70.	Weather Strips	2 Doors and 12 Windows	
71.	Flashing	Top and bottom all frames, 112 lin	
72.	Outside Paint	190 yds. or 17 sqs. with 14 opgs.	
73.	Floor Finish	83 yds. or 7½ sqs.	
74.	Int. Trim Varnish	280′ or 6 rooms base and 22 sides doors and 12 sides wds.	
75.	Window Shades	12 sets shades and curtain rods	
76.	Nails	450 lbs.	
77.	Carpenter Labor	See footnote (‡)	
78.	Overhead	Arch't. fee, insurance, bond, permits, etc.	
79.	Profit	Contractor's profit	

(*) *The percentage that WAS ADDED for waste (exclusive of due allowance for matching) is indicated thus: (5%), (10%), etc. For item 13, the openings were not deducted and 5% was added for waste besides proper allowance for matching.*

(†) *Item 43 is based on net floor surface. If sub-floor is omitted, increase quantities 15%. Change materials or omit items to conform to local construction and customs.*

(‡) *Carpenter and common labor averages 648 hours, without storm sash and screens, and 670 hours if these items are included. This usually is 10% to 20% liberal for good work with wall sheathing and 6″ siding, bridged joist, diagonal sub-floor and 2¼″ hardwood flooring hand sanded, walls and ceiling insulated, pine interior trim including shingling but not lathing. Include lath and plaster labor with items 23, 24 and 25. If labor is included it is best to consult local contractors or carpenters and use their labor records or have them figure on all labor.*

Chapter XX

Porch and Bay Framing

Generally speaking, a porch is virtually another structure when compared with the main structure. A porch has a foundation, sill, joists, flooring, posts or columns, casing plate, ceiling joists, roof rafters, roof sheathing and roofing.

Check over placement of porch foundation or piers. Refer to the set
of house plans. See that the porch foundation or piers, if of masonry, are in
the correct position. Obtain length and width of porch and select 2" x 8" or
2"x 10" stock for sill. The sill is usually the 2" x 8" stock placed on edge
flush with the outside face of the foundation or pier. This forms a header or
carrying member for the porch floor joists. Give this sill structure a slight
fall, 1/4" to the 1', away from the house, to provide proper water fall for the
flooring.

The porch floor joists are spaced 16" cc with the length running parallel to the house. The end of each joist is butted into the sill member and
the top edges are nailed flush. This allows the porch flooring to be placed at
right angles to the wall and gives a drainage fall to the porch floor away from
the house. Build up floor frame work and then begin on roof frame work.

The framing of a porch roof is not unlike the framing of one-half of a
gable roof or a hip roof. The plate member of a porch is made up of 2" stock,
usually 2" x 6" or 2" x 8", which is cased up in wooden trim. The plate rests
on the porch posts or columns and carries the ceiling joists and rafters.
Frame up the porch ceiling joists in the same manner as the second floor joists.
The ceiling joists will rest on the plate of the main structure and the casing
plate. Allow enough overhang of the joists to form a box gutter if specified.

Frame up the porch roof rafters in much the same manner as the roof
rafters are framed for the main structure.. Refer to previous chapters for descriptions of methods used in framing a gable or common rafter.

Refer to the details in the set of plans for information on roof rafter
framing. Sheathe porch roof as one would sheathe a gable roof. Refer to previous chapters for descriptions of methods relative to placing of roofing on
sheathing.

If a box gutter is required build it up in the same manner as given in
a previous chapter. Place ceiling on porch and erect columns in place. If a
railing is to be attached build it up as specified. Build up steps and lattice
work as specified.

To frame up a bay window refer to details on page 79-84. Bay framing is
practically the same as other types of framing already explained in this book.

Porch construction for a steel framed house is built up by carpenters
in much the same manner as a wooden porch. Details should be studied carefully.
Since many porch framing requirements are the same as the framing requirements
for the main frame the descriptive method for the main frame is applicable to

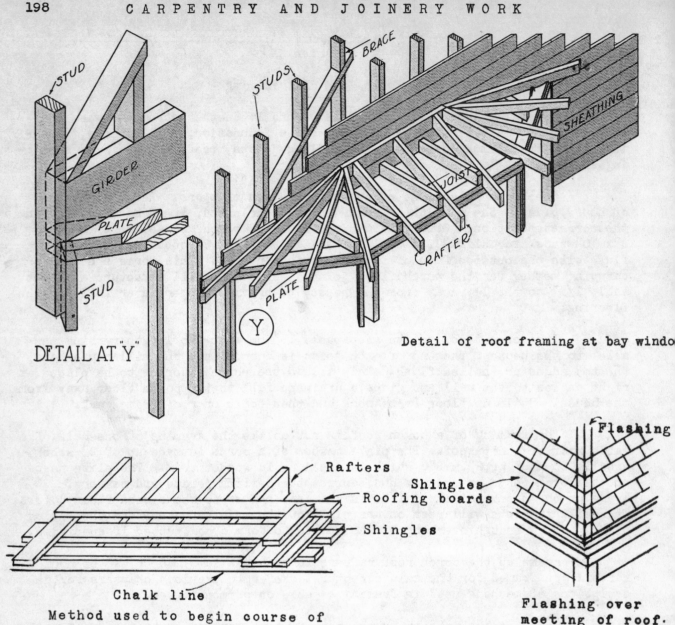

DETAIL AT "Y"

Detail of roof framing at bay window

Method used to begin course of shingles.

Flashing over meeting of roofing boards and under shingles

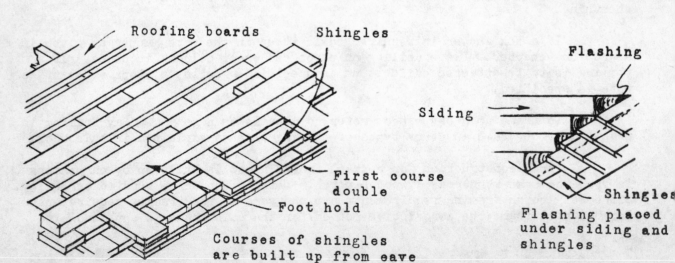

Courses of shingles are built up from eave

Flashing placed under siding and shingles

to the descriptive method for the porch frame.

Practical jobs.. Frame a porch floor, columns and plate. Frame a porch roof. Roof a porch. Frame a bay window floor and studding. Frame a bay window roof. Roof a bay window. Build up porch steps. Build up trim around a porch. These jobs should be done in wood or steel. The details on this and the following pages will illustrate some popular methods of framing for porch construction.

Related Studies

Drawing. Most of the remaining studies in related drawing will consist of drawing or sketching assignments of construction details of pertinent illustrations. Sketch or draw, by mechanical means, the details of porch construction. Obtain additional details from other sources. Draw these details on tracing paper and have them printed, if possible.

Mathematics. Bays or recesses are placed in living rooms or dining rooms. Good design demands a certain part, within rather strict limits, be used as bay window or recess space. A bay window floor area would not be 3/4ths of the living room area. It might, however, be 1/4th of the living room area. If a living room measured 10' x 15' (150 square feet of area) and a bay measured 3' x 5' (15 square feet of area) the bay would occupy 15/150th, or 1/10th of the floor area proper.

150 square feet plus 15 square feet equals 165 square feet in all floor area. The bay floor area is 1/11th of the entire floor area of the living room. 165 divided by 15 equals 11. To express this fraction in a decimal fraction divide the numerator by the denominator. 1 divided by 11 equals 9.0909 plus. This is read 'nine hundredths percent' and often expressed as 9.09%.

Refer to a set of house plans having a bay window or recess. Find the percentage of floor space devoted to the bay. Again, total the entire floor area and find the percentage each room occupies.

Porch costs are estimated by the piece. About 25 lineal feet of porch trim, such as lintel, railing can be built in an eight hour day. Porch framing costs are the same as regular framing costs. Bay framing costs are the same as regular framing costs. Bay trim costs will be the same as outside trim costs to be studied in a later chapter.

Science. Strict building code requirements regulate the size, location and height of bay windows. Certain types or styles of framing require certain styles of bays.

Find, in a city building code, all requirements relative to bay windows. Find a certain type or style of framing and frame a small bay in model form. Make sketches before beginning work. What is the purpose of a bay window?

English. A public library is an institution patronized by people from all walks of life. A visit to a library will reveal many interesting activities. In a library will be found trained workers who have at their command the following equipment: a. A card catalog of every book in the library; b. A number of technical, popular, scientific and social magazines; c. A number of newspapers from the daily press; d. Dictionaries and encyclopedias, and e. Illustrations and maps.

A portion of the study of Drafting Room Papers begun on pg. 185.

BLUE PRINT PAPERS.

K & E Blue Print Papers have been developed over a period of 40 years to the high standard of quality which they have now attained. The raw papers are made to strict specifications; and each shipment is tested in our humidity and temperature controlled paper testing laboratory. Comparative paper tests can be made only under standardized conditions of this kind. The solutions with which these papers are coated have been developed in our research laboratory; and the quality of the solution is controlled by the chemical laboratory. The coating is performed on special machines designed and made by us. In these elaborate machines the temperature of the drying boxes is controlled automatically; and use is made of many other devices to insure a uniformly good product. The coated paper is re-rolled and carefully inspected. This policy of controlling quality of raw material, coating solution, and finished product is responsible for the steadily increasing demand for K & E Blue Print Papers.

PRINTING SPEED. Each paper is available in a number of printing speeds. These speeds are kept constant; so that once our customers have determined upon a certain speed, they can always feel assured of getting the same speed on a re-order. The speeds are known as Speed 4 (Electric), Speed 3 (Quick) and Speed 2 (Slow).

Speed 4 is used when an electric blue printing machine of ordinary speed is available for printing.

Speed 3 is the most popular speed, and gives excellent results on the modern continuous printing machines with high powered arc lamps.

Speed 2 is used for sun printing in frames. Some of the electric printing machines with very high powered arc lamps can also produce excellent blue prints with Speed 2.

Roughly, Speed 4 prints twice as fast as Speed 2, and Speed 3 takes its place midway between them. It is always advisable to use as slow a printing speed as possible. A slow paper gives a richer blue and has a greater printing range. That is, a fast paper must be exposed exactly the right length of time, whereas a slow paper has a greater range of exposure over which a good blue print may be produced. Thus it is advantageous to use a high powered arc lamp with a relatively slow paper, rather than a poor lamp with fast printing paper. The first combination will give a good print no matter what type of negative is used, whether a typewritten paper or an ink drawing on fine tracing cloth.

K & E coated papers exhibit to a remarkable degree what is known as "Keeping Quality." It is not necessary to buy K & E Blue Print Papers from day to day, since they will keep in good condition for months. This exceptional Keeping Quality has been attained without sacrificing the other properties which a good Blue Print Paper should have, such as a brilliant blue and a clear white.

MADURO PAPERS.

Maduro prints (made from line tracings) are negative; that is, they show white lines on an opaque brown-black background. In order to obtain a positive print, that is, dark lines on a white background, the first print from the original tracing, should be made on thin Maduro Paper (229T or 229TL) which is sufficiently transparent to permit of making positive prints. When many reproductions of a tracing are desired, it is economical to first make a number of negatives on thin paper and then use these negative Maduro Prints to make positive prints. This saves the tracing and produces pleasing and legible blue or brown line prints. Usually the medium weight Maduro paper is used for positive prints, since it results in beautiful prints with nearly black lines on a clear white background.

When corrections or alterations on tracings are necessary, a negative of the tracing may be made on thin Maduro Paper, and from this a positive print made on thin Maduro Paper, with the portion to be altered or corrected blanked out by inserting opaque paper between the negative and the positive print which is being made. The correction can then be drawn in with ink and the amended positive print used in the same manner as a tracing. This saves the expense of altering the original tracing or of making a new one.

Maduro solution has been developed to give clear whites on a perfectly opaque deep brown-black background. The Speed of this solution is about equivalent to our Speed 3 blue print solution; for which reason Maduro Prints can readily be made on modern continuous printing machines. Maduro Prints are developed in water and fixed in a bath containing fixing salt. A box of Fixing Salt, 229S, with directions for use, is furnished with each roll.

All brownprint papers must be stored in a cool place in order to prevent deterioration in strength.

BLACK PRINT PAPERS.

UMBRA Black Print Paper is a positive paper giving an exact facsimile of the original drawing in clear black lines on a white background. UMBRA paper requires no chemical bath, but is developed in a water-bath, like blueprint paper. While UMBRA Paper produces a handsome black line positive print, it requires a very long exposure, approximately twice as long as our Speed No. 2, or 4 to 5 minutes clear sunlight. When sufficiently exposed the background will be perfectly white and the black lines will not fade. Owing to the nature of the chemicals required for making black print paper, the strength of the paper will deteriorate quickly if it is not stored in a cool place. Furthermore, the raw paper itself must be made of finely beaten stock, and consequently cannot be made as strong as a high grade Blue or Brown Print Paper. Even at its best, a black print paper will not bear rough handling.

Courtesy KEUFFEL & ESSER CO. New York.

Visit a public library and get a list of two or three books, from the card catalog, dealing with frame house construction. Obtain the title of the book, the author of the book, the library call number and the name of the publisher. Obtain this book through the proper loan channels and study it carefully. Get some sketches or drawings relative to porch and bay framing.

| jack rafter | jack cheek bevel | jack plane | jack rafters | jamb |
| join | joint | joist | joist hangers | |

keeper	kerf	key	knurl	keyed
keyhole	keys	kink	knife	knob
knocked down	knocked out	knot	knot holes	

land	landing	lap	lap joint	lapped
latched	lath	lather	lathing	laying
lay out	leaf	lath nails	lean to	length
length ways	level out	ledger board	legs	level
leveling	leveling board	level up	light construction	
lime	line	lined up	line of house	lintels
lip	live load	load	lock	
lumber crayon	lookouts	lock keeper	loose pin butts	

Civics. Windows are just as essential to a room as the walls. Most code requirements state 'windows shall be in every room and shall aggregate at least 10% of the superficial floor area of a room but in no case shall the area of a window be less than eight square feet'.

Ventilation, light and window area are very essential to a house.

Search a building code for definite requirements regarding window and door sizes. From a set of plans establish definite information as to the area and percentage of walls area given to window area.

Showing the use of shingles on   roof and side walls.

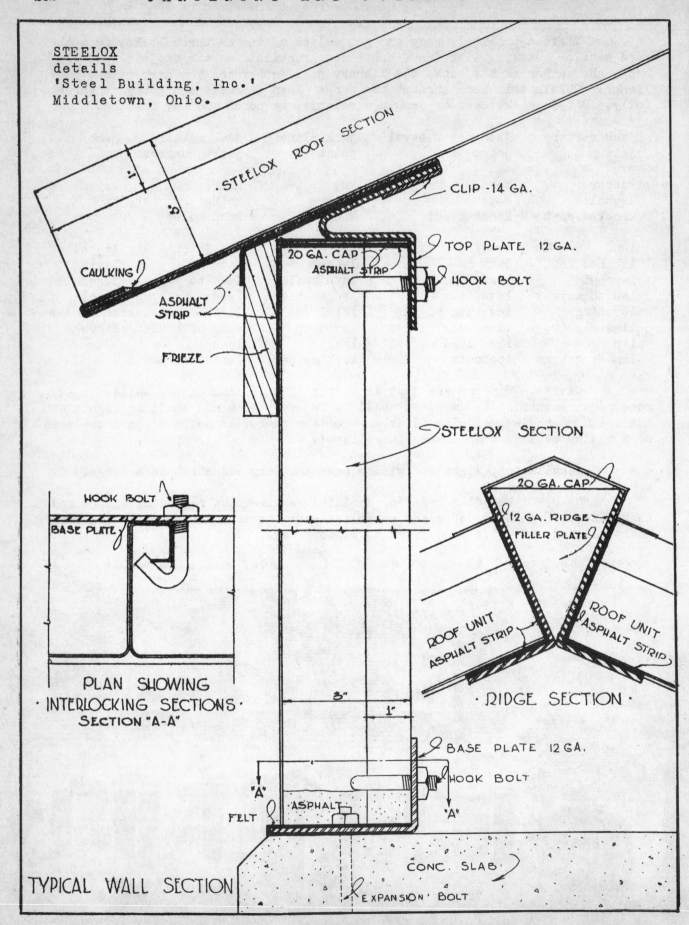

STEELOX
details
'Steel Building, Inc.'
Middletown, Ohio.

STEELOX ROOF SECTION

CLIP -14 GA.

TOP PLATE 12 GA.

20 GA. CAP
ASPHALT STRIP

HOOK BOLT

CAULKING

ASPHALT
STRIP

FRIEZE

STEELOX SECTION

20 GA. CAP

12 GA. RIDGE
FILLER PLATE

HOOK BOLT

BASE PLATE

ROOF UNIT
ASPHALT STRIP

ROOF UNIT
ASPHALT STRIP

PLAN SHOWING
· INTERLOCKING SECTIONS ·
SECTION "A-A"

· RIDGE SECTION ·

3"

1"

BASE PLATE 12 GA.

HOOK BOLT

"A"

"A"

FELT

ASPHALT

CONC. SLAB

TYPICAL WALL SECTION

EXPANSION BOLT

Chapter XXl

Exterior Wall Covering

The exterior trim of a house varies and one must consult the specifications and house plans and obtain the definite requirements. The exterior trim, however, is the 'finish' woodwork or metal work attached to the sheathing. This woodwork, in general, consists of beveled siding or shiplap siding, corner boards, window and door frames, drip cap, water table, ribbands, cornice finish or in the case of some metal framing, steel plates may be used.

Refer to Chapter XVIII. Build up the cornice finish in the manner described. This will bring the work of finishing down to the side walls.

Before applying the building paper and siding, the door and window frames must be set in place and plumbed. The door sill is set in all outside door openings in the following manner. Obtain the door sill stock and mark distance on rough floor equal to the amount of distance the sill will project back into the floor. The sill will have a 3/4" or 1" over-hang beyond the water table on the outside of the building. Allow for this over-hang and mark on the floor and remove this portion of the floor so that the sill and finish floor will be level. The length of the sill will be given in the details. The sill will have a slight fall to the outside. Place the door jamb side pieces in place, allow for slight fall of the sill in fitting the jamb at the sill and plumb the jamb. Before the jamb is nailed in solidly, building paper should be placed under the jamb and extended sheathing a short distance in order to be connected up with the building paper to be placed under the siding. Square up head piece of the jamb and nail in place. Place on the side casing or trim, the back band or moulding and head trim. Insert wedges where needed.

The window frames are placed in position and wedged plumb and square and nailed in place. The outside casing is put on but the inside casing, the stool, the apron, the stop bead and the blind and parting strip need not be placed until the plastering is done.

Any other trim with which the siding is in contact is placed in position. Work up all porch trim and nail in place. The following illustrations show many items of trim placed in their respective places.

The sheathed side walls are usually covered with a heavy building paper before the beveled siding or ship lap siding is applied. This building paper acts as an insulator and must be placed with care. Hold the paper on the sheathed walls with small scrap strips of stock until the siding is placed over the paper. Do not cover the walls with building paper too far in advance of the siding application.

Siding is nailed in place over the building paper and sheathed side walls. Start siding at bottom just above drip cap on water table and work up the frieze board at the eave. Work siding in using dividers or mathematically determining lap for even spacing. Face nail each piece in two places at each stud and work up all pieces perfectly level. Join each piece of siding at the door or window frames and at the corner boards.

Floor plans and elevations.

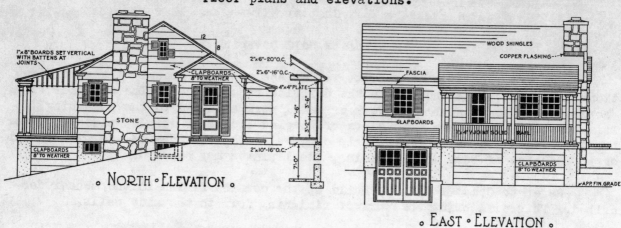

. NORTH . ELEVATION .

. EAST . ELEVATION .

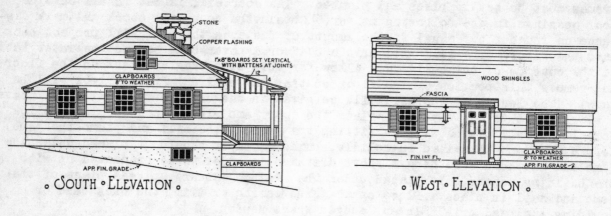

. SOUTH . ELEVATION .

. WEST . ELEVATION .

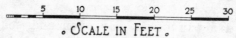

. SCALE IN FEET .

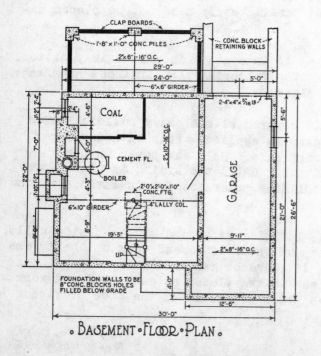

. BASEMENT . FLOOR . PLAN .

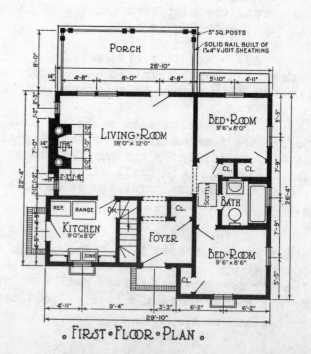

. FIRST . FLOOR . PLAN .

Practical Jobs. Place siding on exterior walls. Place any other type of exterior wall covering on for finished portion.

Related Studies

Drawing.

The following is a list of details which will show types and phases of construction in house construction. The list will serve as a catalog of possible assignments in sketching or a ready reference guide.

single line room arrangement	single line plot plan
single line elevation of house front	batter boards
single line elevation of house sides	excavation layout
single line elevation of house rear	pier footing form
pier form	foundation wall in solid earth
foundation wall above grade	foundation wall key
foundation wall in soft earth	foundation wall openings
flat sill	T sill
box sill	solid sill
pier footing	pier
girder post	bridging
joist-balloon frame	joist-braced frame
joist-box sill	anchors for sill
anchors for piers	anchors for girders
braced frame sill	balloon frame sill
box frame sill	western frame sill
lapped joist on top of girder	girder ledger strip with joists
girder-balloon frame	girder-braced frame
girder-western frame	girder-hung joists
girder sized down	corner posts
studs	stud ribbon
stud plate	stud sole-shoe
stud girt	stud bracing
stud with diagonal brace let in	stud with knee brace let in
rough flooring	second floor joists
second floor flooring	ceiling joists
partition framing	partition corner construction
common rafter	hip rafter
ridge	cripple rafter
balloon frame corner construction	braced frame corner construction
western frame corner construction	western framing girt
braced framing girt	partition parallel with joists
partition at right angles with joists	stripping in floors
terrace and porch footings	porch foundation wall-forms
porch girders	porch joists
porch end girders	porch flush girder
porch sunken girder	tile floor
framing for openings in walls	joists at bay window
rafters at bay window	studs at bay window
scuttle framing	dormer framing
dormer over stairs	gambrel roof construction

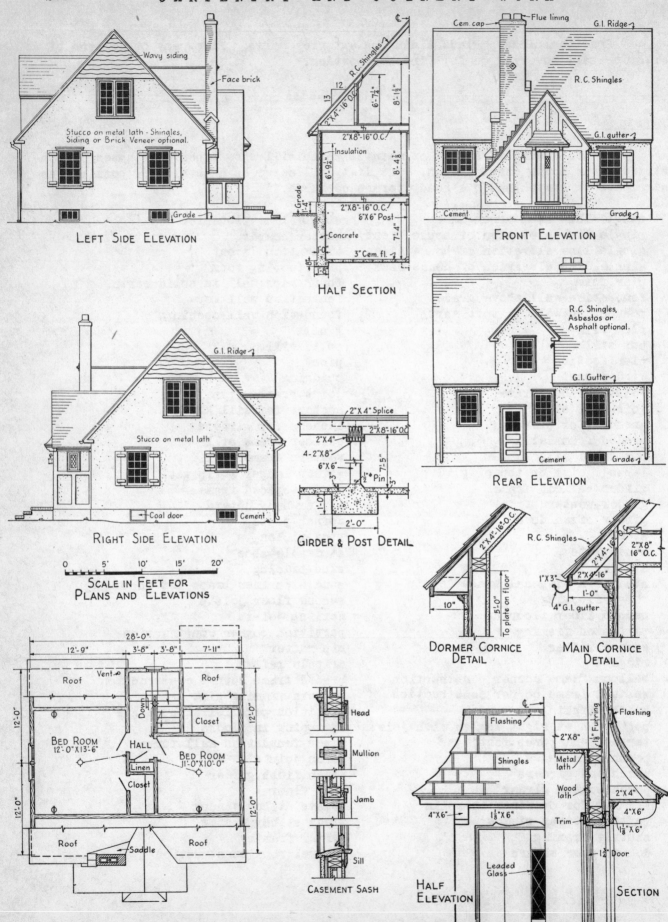

LEFT SIDE ELEVATION

HALF SECTION

FRONT ELEVATION

RIGHT SIDE ELEVATION

GIRDER & POST DETAIL

REAR ELEVATION

SCALE IN FEET FOR PLANS AND ELEVATIONS

DORMER CORNICE DETAIL

MAIN CORNICE DETAIL

SECOND FLOOR PLAN

CASEMENT SASH

HALF ELEVATION

SECTION

DETAILS

DETAIL OF ENTRANCE AND HOOD

gable roof construction	stair string
stair well	wall string
stair tread	stair plan
stair elevation	chimney framing at roof
chimney framing above fireplace	draft stopping at ribbon
draft stopping at partitions-sill	fire stopping at cornice
fire stopping at partitions-chimney	exterior door sill
exterior door jamb	exterior door casing
exterior door drip cap	window sill
window bead stop	window side casing
window head casing	window drip cap
window parting strip	porch column
porch crown mould	porch column base
porch fascia	porch lintel
porch steps	porch bed mould
cornice bed mould	cornice frieze
cornice lookout	cornice plancher
lap siding	beveled siding
shiplap siding	corner boards
bed mould	door casing
door base block	window casing
window stool	corner boards
base mould	base mould shoe
finish flooring	built in equipment

Mathematics.

Some exterior work on a house consists of the following items. The methods of estimating and time taken in applying are as follows:

Item	Method	Time
porch flooring	by square feet-add 20%	35 hrs. per 1000 sq.ft.
porch column	by actual count	1 hour each
porch water table	by lineal feet	200 lineal ft. per hr.
porch lintel	by lineal feet	200 lineal ft. per hr.
porch moulding	by lineal feet	100 lineal ft. per hr.
porch ceiling	by square feet-add 20%	100 sq. ft. per hr.
siding	by square feet-deduct openings and add 1/3	4 8 hr. days per M.
porch balustrade	by lineal feet	200 lineal ft. per hr.
cornice trim	by lineal feet	100 lineal ft. per hr.
roof trim	by lineal feet	100 lineal ft. per hr.
exterior trim	by lineal feet	200 lineal ft. per hr.

Estimate the amount of trim needed on the house in the set of plans. The use of porcelain enamel sheets for the exterior of a house should be estimated by the piece. The time taken to build on this trim will be about one hour for each square, 10' x 10'.

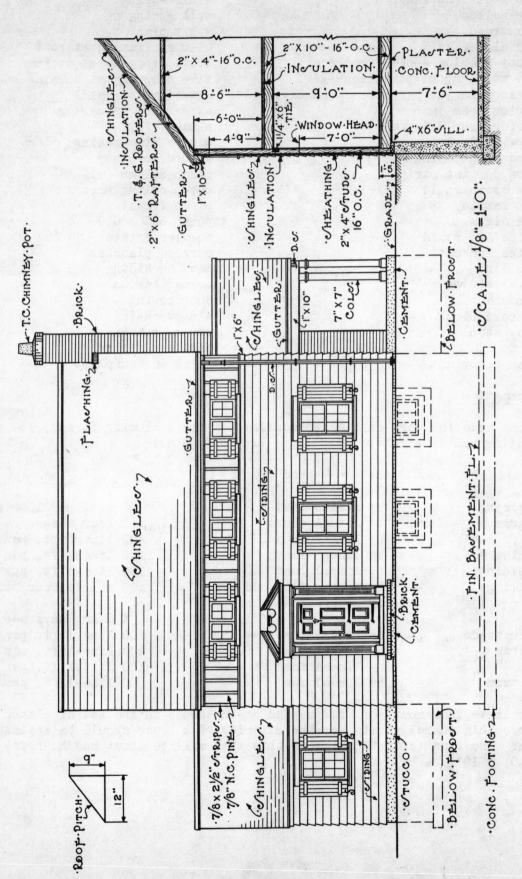

SECTION.

2"X 4"-16"O.C.
2"X 10"-16"-O.C.
PLASTER.
INSULATION.
CONC. FLOOR.
8'-6"   9'-0"   7'-6"
SHINGLES.
INSULATION.
T. & G. ROOFERS.
2"X 6" RAFTERS.
GUTTER.
1"X 10".
SHINGLES.
INSULATION.
6'-0"
1 1/4"X 6" TILE.
WINDOW HEAD.
7'-0"
4"X 6" SILL.
4'-9"
SHEATHING.
2"X 4" STUDS.
16"O.C.
GRADE.
1'-5"
D.C.

T.C. CHIMNEY POT.
BRICK.
SHINGLES.
GUTTER.
1"X 6".
1"X 10".
7"X 7" COL'S.
CEMENT.
BELOW FROST.
SCALE 1/8"=1'-0".
FLASHING.
SHINGLES.
GUTTER.
SIDING.
D.C.
BRICK.
CEMENT.
FIN. BASEMENT FL.

FRONT ELEVATION.

ROOF PITCH.
9"
12"
7/8 X 2 1/2" STRIPS.
7/8" N.C. PINE.
SHINGLES.
SIDING.
STUCCO.
BELOW FROST.
CONC. FOOTING.

Science.

House trim, the curved and special shaped mill pieces other than straight framing stock, has curved lines of Greek and Roman origin. A study of these historic curves and the method of generation is of extreme interest.

A common curve used in trim is the cove or scotia curve. It is generated as follows:

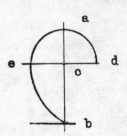

Divide line ab into 3 equal parts. Use c as center, with radius ca, draw circle dae.
Use d as center, de as radius, draw curve eb.
aeb is scotia curve.
Often ab is divided into 7 equal parts and 3 parts used as radius in curve ae and 4 parts in curve eb.

Another curve is the ovolo or echuins curve. It is generated as follows:

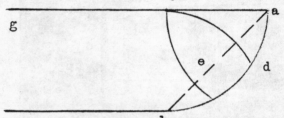

Divide line ab into 7 equal parts.
Use b as center cut line ag
Use a as center cut line ab at e
Use b as center cut line ab at d
Use c as center-produce with radius ca or cb the curve ab.

Another moulding curve is the cavetto. It is generated as follows:

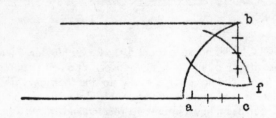

Divide line bc into 5 equal parts.
Make ac equal to 4 of these parts.
Join ba. With a and b as centers, respectively, and distance greater than half of ab draw arcs meeting at f.
With f as center and fa as radius draw arc ab.

Another moulding curve is the cyma recta. It is generated as follows:

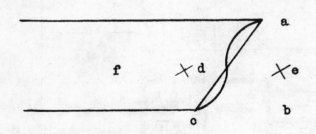

Lines at a and b are the top and bottom of moulding. bc is amount of projection.
Divide line ac into 12 equal parts.
Point a center of ac is d. With d as center and radius ad and d as center and radius cd produce point e. Likewise produce point f. With f as center and radius fc produce arc cd. Likewise with e as center and radius ea produce arc da.

Following the above directions, produce the curves. Find actual examples of such in building construction.

Leads to Outdoors

THIS COLONIAL house designed by R. C. Hunter, New York Architect, opens out attractively upon the porch and terrace, leading people easily to the outside. The floor plan is an unusual variation of Colonial planning but has many features to recommend it.

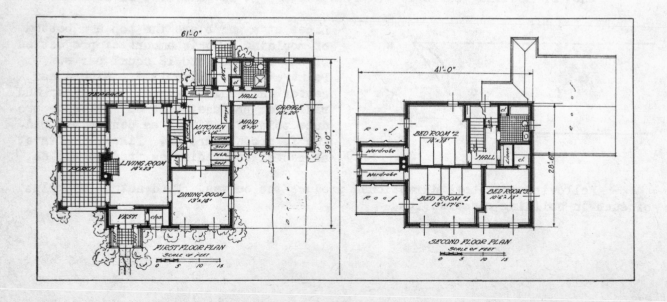

English.

A newspaper has many interesting sections or divisions. It is well to learn of these sections by searching and studying an edition of a popular daily.

Obtain a copy of a recent issue of any daily newspaper and locate the follow-- ing classes of items. Cut clippings of a sample of each. Advertisements, classi- fied and display - editorials - continued stories - stock reports - market reports - cartoons - news items - automobile news and building news.

Study the meaning and spelling of the following trade terms:

mansard roof	material	manufactured shingle	mark off
mark out	matched	match	materials
measure	measurement	meeting rails	member
metal dowel	muntin	metallic reinforcement	mullion
mouse	moulds	moulding	mortising
mortiser	mortise and tenon		mortar
mixture	mitering	miter box	miter
mill work	milled	mill construction	mill

nail	nail apron	nailing	nailing down
nailing strip	nailing surface	nailing up	nail set
neck	necking	newel	nog
nosing	nosing strip	notch	

octagon	oil stone	octagonal dome	on center
openings	operation	open stringer	open joint
oregon fir	outside base	outside door	outside edge
outside lines	outside wall	overhang	

paint	painter	painting	paper
parallel	parting strip	partition cap	partition
pattern	pencil	pencil clasp	penny weight
perpendicular	picture mould	pier	pilaster
pine	pitch	plan	plan view
plancher	plane	plane iron	planish
planking	plaster	plasterer	plate
plinth	plinth block	plaster ground	platform
plot plan	ploughed	plumb	plumb bob
plumb cut	plumb down	plumb rule	plumbed
plumb up	plumbing	ply wood	pocket piece
pocket knife	point	point up	porch framing
posts	pour	principle	procedure
profile	project	projecting	prop
property	property line	protractor	pulley stile
putty	pwt.		

quartered oak	quarter round	quarter sawed

rabbet	rafter	rafter plate	rail
railings	rake	red prints	ribbon
ridge	right angle	rip	ripping bar
rip saw	rise	rise-per-foot-of-run	riser
rod	roof	roofing	roofing boards

Small Brick Cottage With Enclosed Porch

THIS COMPACT LITTLE HOUSE has a charming exterior and practical plan, including 2 bedrooms upstairs and a small maid's room and kitchen downstairs.

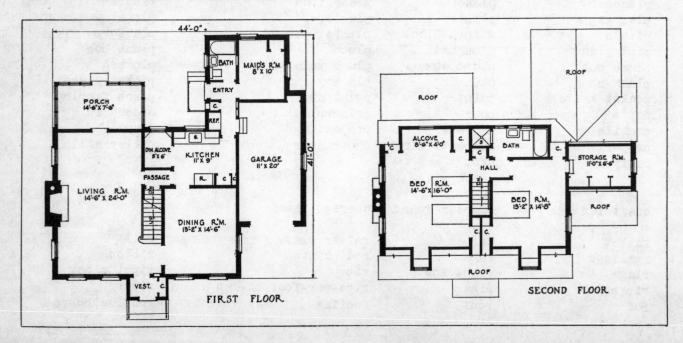

FIRST FLOOR.

SECOND FLOOR.

roofing material	roof plate	roof tree	rough board
rough carpenter	roughed cut	rough flooring	rough opening
rough work	rounded off	rounded out	rows
rule	rule of three	rule of thumb	run
running joint	rust	runs	

Civics.

The treatise on FIRST AID is a courtesy of the Metropolitan Life Insurance Company, New York. Study each and every paragraph of this work carefully.

WHAT TO DO FIRST

1. TAKE CHARGE—A life may be lost for want of some one to take charge and give first aid when an accident has happened.

2. FIND OUT HOW BADLY THE PATIENT IS HURT—Look the injured person over carefully to see how badly he is hurt. Treat the more serious injuries first. Look for bleeding, wounds, broken bones, burns, signs of shock. If necessary, rip or cut the clothing from the injured part. Move the victim only if necessary and then with the greatest care; it is easy to make a bad matter worse by pushing a broken bone through the skin or by injuring the spinal cord in a broken back.

3. ACT PROMPTLY BUT NOT HASTILY—Decide what needs to be done and do it promptly. If there is bleeding, stop the flow of blood. Treat various injuries as suggested in this booklet. Keep calm and quiet. Cheer the patient, and do whatever is necessary to make him comfortable and no more.

4. SEND FOR A DOCTOR OR AMBULANCE—Call a doctor at once. Tell him what has happened and what you have done.

SAVING LIFE

Bleeding

Severe bleeding must be checked as quickly as possible to prevent death. The blood may flow in quick spurts or in a steady stream. Spurts of blood mean that an artery has been cut; a steady flow means that a vein has been cut. Bleeding from an artery can usually be stopped by pressing with thumb at the spot where the artery crosses a bone. The main spots upon which to make pressure are shown in the figure on page 3 (figure 2). When an artery is bleeding, the pressure spot is *between* the bleeding point and the heart. When the bleeding is from a vein (steady flow), pressure must be made on the side away from the heart. If the flow of blood is not violent, a compress placed over the wound may be sufficient. Only when these methods fail to check the hemorrhage should the use of a tourniquet be considered, and then

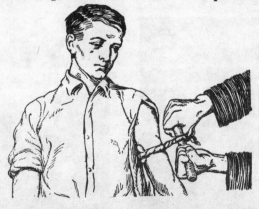

only by one familiar with its application. So many serious results, including the necessity of amputating a limb, have followed the use of the tourniquet, that the tendency is to dispense with tourniquets altogether in first aid work A

FIGURE 1—*How to apply tourniquet to arm*   Continued on pg. 218.

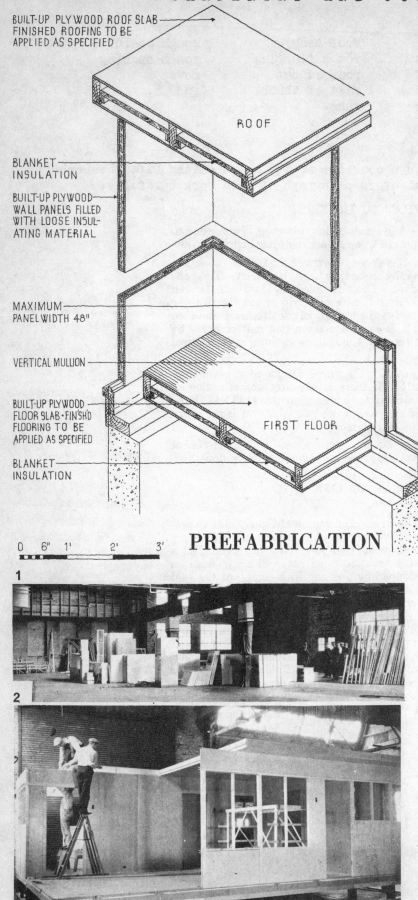

BUILT-UP PLYWOOD ROOF SLAB—
FINISHED ROOFING TO BE
APPLIED AS SPECIFIED

ROOF

BLANKET
INSULATION

BUILT-UP PLYWOOD
WALL PANELS FILLED
WITH LOOSE INSUL-
ATING MATERIAL

MAXIMUM
PANEL WIDTH 48"

VERTICAL MULLION

BUILT-UP PLYWOOD
FLOOR SLAB·FIN'SH'D
FLOORING TO BE
APPLIED AS SPECIFIED

BLANKET
INSULATION

FIRST FLOOR

0   6" 1'   2'   3'

PREFABRICATION

FOREST PRODUCTS LABORATORY
Madison, Wisconsin

This house is experimental. In general the wall and floor panels are built up of a wood frame with plywood glued on both sides. The plywood acts as a flange for the members of the wood frame and the whole virtually forms a box girder.

Wall panels consist of $\frac{1}{4}''$ 3-ply wood, 4'x8', glued to $\frac{3}{4}''$x1$\frac{3}{8}''$ strips. All outside strips are set in $\frac{3}{4}''$ from the edge of the plywood to form a connection joint. Air spaces between strips are filled with insulation.

Floor and roof panels are 4' wide and 8' to 14' long. The top surface is $\frac{5}{8}''$ plywood, 5 plies, and bottom surface is $\frac{3}{8}''$, 3 plies, glued to 2"x6" joist. Blanket insulation is attached within the panels. Such panels are stronger than regular construction with 2"x10" joists.

Built-up vertical mullions connect the wall panels. Joints are buttered with mastic before panel is shoved in place.

The sill is rabbetted so that edges of wall panel fit over the rabbet. Similarly the top edges fit over a $\frac{3}{4}''$x1$\frac{3}{8}''$ member glued to the bottom of the roof panels at exterior wall and partition lines.

Roof and wall sections are grooved and splined where they come together.

Window and door frames built into panels. Sash larger than opening and has spring bronze strip to seal against weather with projecting drip cap over.

Electrical conduit and fittings built into panels. Heating and plumbing are standard; with quantity production they could be partially prefabricated.

1. Prefabricated units before assembly.
2. Six hours later.
3. Floors are laid in 4-foot units to correspond with wall panels.

Chapter XXII

Interior Wall Covering

Covering for interior walls may be of plaster or manufactured boards. Regardless of the type of covering used the carpenter has some work to do.

Clear the inside of the building of any obstructions that would hamper the free movement of the lather or plasterer.

Plaster grounds are nailing backgrounds for some members of the interior trim. The plaster ground stock is generally 3/4" x 2" in size. This stock should be straight or pulled straight by nailing. Nail grounds at inside edge of all openings. One must be able to visualize the work of the lather and plasterer and see the need of the grounds at the various places. These pieces form a margin and straight edge to which the plaster is worked and all wall space should be encased at the extreme borders.

Lathing is done by the lather but the work should be understood by the carpenter. Lathing consists of placing narrow strips of wood about 3/8" apart on the studs to act as a support and background for the plaster. Wire lath is often used instead of wooden lath and is applied by the lather. Plastering is done by the plasterer and consists of placing a rough or ground cover of plaster on the lathed walls and then following this coat, when dry, with a finish coat of plaster.

Interior wall may be covered with plaster board, masonite, celotex or any manufactured wall covering instead of plaster. In this case plaster grounds are not needed. The wall covering is applied direct to the studded walls by the carpenter. Refer to illustrations on page 128 of this text showing the use of manufactured wall covering.

Practical jobs. Place plaster grounds around all wall spaces to be plastered with lath and plaster finish. Cover walls with a manufactured covering.

Related Studies.

Drawing.

Two important items in frame house construction are framing and mechanical work. Framing and mechanical work must be in accord with the building code requirements and accepted trade practices. There is another very important item in dwelling work that comes even before any construction activities are begun. This is room arrangement. A house is made of several rooms in which people live and pass from room to room. If a house has poor and unhandy room arrangements many inconveniences are suffered.

One of the best methods to use in arranging rooms is the three point analysis of functions. An analysis might be based on: (1) activities of occupants; (2) furniture sizes; (3) furniture placement. Item one, the analysis of the activities of occupants, is made by listing the number of people living in a house and listing their activities. Examples are shown on the following pages:

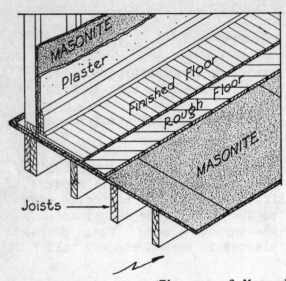

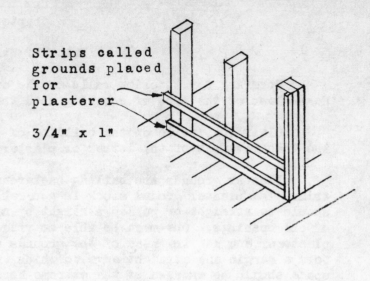

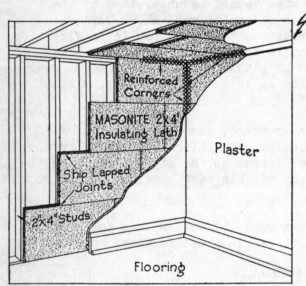

The use of Masonite boards for insulation.

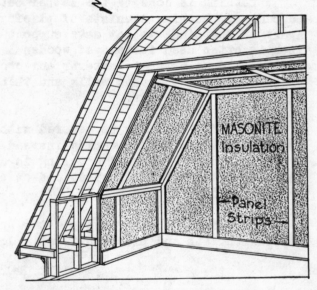

OCCUPANT	ACTIVITIES
Father	a. bathing
	b. eating
	c. sleeping
	d. lounging
	f. hobbies, etc.

Item two, the analysis of the furniture and furniture sizes needed to carry on these activities, is made by listings as follows:

ACTIVITIES OF FATHER	FURNITURE REQUIRED
b. eating	aa. kitchen table (size)
	bb. kitchen chair "
	cc. dining table "
	dd. dining chair "
	ee. stove "
	ff. kitchen cabinet "
	gg. kitchen sink "
	hh. refrigerator "
e. hobbies	ii. bookcase "
	jj. table "
	kk. chair "

Item three, the analysis of the placement of furniture is made by taking the items of furniture required in (2), listing each, eliminating duplicates, choosing appropriate sizes, cutting small rectangles of paper to scale, placing on paper and grouping according to functional activities. A single line sketch of the floor plan can be made so that the small rectangles can be spaced around. A floor plan is not to be made first but the rectangles spaced in such a way that the rooms of the floor plan can be drawn around the rectangles.

Several typical sizes of furniture are as follows:

davenport	32" x 80"	range	28" x 36"	bookcase	16" x 42"
buffet	36" x 60"	dresser	24" x 42"	dresser	24" x 42"
rocker	26" x 26"	straight chair	18" x 18"		
double bed	54" x 80"	morris chair	26" x 26"		
single bed	36" x 78"	dining table	48" x 48"		
kitchen table	24" x 36"	library table	30" x 48"		
refrigerator	26" x 36"	upright piano	38" x 78"		
kitchen cabinet	26" x 48"	etc.			

Consider a family of five - parents, two boys and a girl. Analyze the room arrangements by taking the steps just described. Place data on paper, locate furniture rectangles advantageously and build up floor plan around furniture rectangles.

Mathematics.

Refer to a building code and find the requirements on lighting and ventilation of residence rooms. Find the requirements on room sizes. Find the requirements on room heights. Find the requirements on alcoves and alcove rooms. Find the requirements on access to rooms.

Continued from page 213

description of their use is given here for the information of those in isolated communities where a doctor cannot readily be reached and in case of a serious injury with severe bleeding which cannot be checked by the pressure methods described. On the arrival of the doctor, his attention should be called at once to the tourniquet. Any belt, strap, necktie, handkerchief or similar article, which can be tied around an arm or leg over a pad, will serve as a tourniquet. Any hard pad the size of an egg or a little larger will do. The strap is tightened by twisting with a small stick or pencil until the bleeding stops. The tourniquet is applied on the near side to the heart for arterial bleeding and on the far side for bleeding from a vein.

The points at which the arteries cross bones (shown in figure 2), known as pressure points, should be memorized.

Do not twist too hard—just enough to stop bleeding.

Loosen tourniquet every twenty minutes and let a little blood escape.

Serious damage may be caused by blocking off the blood supply too long. If the bleeding has stopped when the tourniquet is loosened, do not again tighten, but have it in place in case the bleeding returns

FIGURE 2—*Where to apply pressure to stop bleeding from arteries*

If there is severe bleeding in a place where a tourniquet cannot be used, *especially from the neck, groins and armpits, press the fingers directly over the wound.* Replace the fingers, as soon as possible, with clean gauze, a freshly laundered handkerchief, or other sterilized material.

Internal Bleeding

Internal bleeding, as into the brain, stomach, intestines, cannot be seen. It causes weakness, pallor, faintness, feeble and irregular breathing, and, later, loss of consciousness. While waiting for a doctor, treat as surgical shock (see following):

Shock

Most serious accidents and many slight ones may cause shock. *Shock is dangerous.* Treatment should begin immediately after any bleeding has been controlled.

SIGNS—Patient seems stupid and loses interest in what is happening, or he may be partly or totally unconscious. The skin is pale and covered with a cold clammy sweat; the lips and nails may be blue. The pulse is rapid and hard to find; breathing is feeble.

TREATMENT—Send for a doctor. Lay patient flat on back with head low, unless there is bleeding about the head, in which case the head should be raised slightly. Remove from his mouth removable false teeth, gum or tobacco. Keep warm with coats, blankets, and with hot-water bottles, hot bricks or stones which have been covered with cloth or newspapers to prevent burning the patient. It is best to test the heat on your own forearm. Aromatic spirits of ammonia—a teaspoonful in a half glass of water—hot coffee, hot tea, or hot water, may be used to stimulate. But do not give any stimulants to an unconscious patient, or to a conscious patient who may have internal bleeding

Electric Shock

Marked by sudden loss of consciousness, stopping of breathing and severe burns where the wire has touched the flesh.

RESCUE—*Do not touch the victim's bare skin, while he is still in contact with the wire or rail.* It is as dangerous for you to touch his flesh as to touch the wire itself. Turn off the current, if you are near the switch or power-house. If this cannot be done stand on a

Continued on page 220

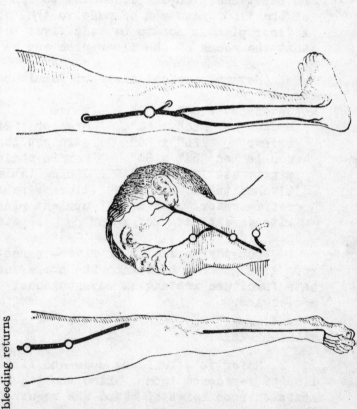

Obtain a set of house plans and apply the above code rules to the respective features. Estimate the cost of lathing and plastering the house. The cost of plaster will be determined by the amount of wood lath needed, the amount of plaster and the amount of sand required. Refer to a good handbook on building estimating, KIDDER'S for example, to learn of the several amounts to apply to plaster board, metal lath, brick or wooden lath.

Science.

Plaster is applied to lath and lath is applied to the studded members of walls. Lath should be made of spruce, hemlock or white pine which has been well seasoned, sap free, dead knot and bark free. Pine containing too much pitch is not good. Metal lath is available as well as wood lath.

Plaster is applied in three coats - the scratch, brown and finish coats. The scratch coat consists of one part lime paste, two parts sand and two parts hair. The brown coat consists of 2-1/2 bushels of lime, seven barrels of screened sand and one bushel of hair. The finish coat consists of one part lime and one part white sand. Like plaster is a product of lime powder and water. Lime is sold as quicklime, hydrated lime and alca lime.

In the making of masonite structural insulation and presdwood boards the sawmill edgings, slabs and short lengths are reduced to chips about the size of a dime. These chips are then exploded under terrific steam pressure into a mosslike mass of ling fibres. The fibres, without any artificial binder, are then thoroughly felted together into thick, heavy blankets, which steam heated hydraulic presses form into boards 7/16" thick, honeycombed with millions of dead air cells, the most effective type of insulation. By means of additional pressure, a product known as presdwood is produced. It is 1/8", 3/16", 1/4" and 5/16" thick, extremely dense, strong and moisture resistant.

Obtain samples of plaster, sand, hair and mix into a compound. Find samples of masonite insulation boards, subject these to tests of moisture, nailing, pulling, weather, etc.

Refer to an encyclopedia for additional facts on plaster and wall coverings. Tabulate all this information.

English.

The following typical personal letter is presented in order to acquaint the apprentice with the proper conventional methods of letter writing.

                                        337 Concord Street,
                                        Hamilton, Ohio.

                                        Jan. 23, 1935.

Dear Friend:

You will be interested to know that I am getting along satisfactorily in my trade training work.

This week, Mr. Huber, our trade teacher, gave me the task of placing

ARTIFICIAL RESPIRATION
*(The Schaefer Method)

Lay the patient on his belly, one arm extended directly over-head, the other arm bent at the elbow and the face turned outward and resting on hand or forearm, so that the nose and mouth are free for breathing. (See figure 3.)

Kneel straddling the patient's thighs, with your knees placed at such a distance from the hip-bones as will allow you to place the palms of the hands on the small of the back with fingers resting on the ribs, the little finger just touching the lowest rib, with the thumb and fingers in a natural position and the tips of the fingers just out of sight. (See figure 3.)

FIGURE 3

With arms held straight, swing forward slowly, so that the weight of your body is gradually brought to bear upon the patient. The shoulder should be directly over the heel of the hand at the end of the forward swing. (See figure 4.) Do not bend your elbows. This operation should take about two seconds.

Continued from page 218

folded dry coat, or on newspapers or dry board while with one hand—and the hand should be protected with several thicknesses of dry cloth or newspaper—grasp a dry part of the victim's coat and drag him away from the wire, if possible, or remove the wire from the victim, using a dry wooden stick. Another method of removing the victim found lying on the wire is to pull him off by looping over his foot or hand a piece of dry rope, belt or handkerchief.

TREATMENT—Start artificial respiration at once (see page). Apply dressings to burn (see page)

Sunstroke (Heatstroke)—Follows long exposure to hot sun or to intense heat indoors.

SIGNS—Always unconscious. Patient's skin is dry and hot, his face is flushed, the pupils of his eyes are enlarged.

TREATMENT—Remove to a shady place and take off as much of the victim's clothing as possible. Send for a doctor. Cool his body by cold sponges, using ice water, if possible. Keep this up until patient becomes conscious. Then give him all the cool water he will drink. *Give no stimulants.*

Heat Exhaustion—Cooks, bakers, firemen, miners and others who work in very hot places often have heat exhaustion.

SIGNS—The patient's skin is covered with a cold sweat. He is usually conscious. His breathing is shallow and rapid. He is generally pale and anxious looking. His pulse is feeble and rapid.

TREATMENT—Same as for shock (see "Treatment for Shock," page)

Unconsciousness

Some of the more common causes of unconsciousness are the following:

Fainting—Usually results from some mental excitement, such as fear, sight of blood, or emotional shock, but may accompany slight injuries or exposure to overheated rooms.

SIGNS—Patient becomes dizzy and weak and turns pale. He either sinks into a chair or falls unconscious.

TREATMENT—If you notice a person is going to faint, you can sometimes revive him by bending his head down between his knees. If he does not improve, lay him flat on his back and lower his head by raising his hips. Loosen all clothing around neck and waist. See that he gets plenty of fresh cool air. Sprinkle cold water on his face and neck or hold a handkerchief containing a few drops of aromatic spirits of ammonia to his nose every minute or two. When consciousness returns, the patient should continue to lie quiet for a while before getting up.

sheathing on a roof. It seemed to be a hard job at first but after I fully understood what to do it was easy.

You know, I get a thrill from working on top of a house that I have helped to build.

Try to come over to see us some day. We are working on Jefferson Avenue, near James Street.

Sincerely,

Elmer Kull.

Study the foregoing letter. Write a letter to a friend of yours. Note the points of sentence structure, of punctuation, of address, of closing, etc.

The following forms will show the conventional way to address an envelope.

| Front of envelope | Mr. Carl Meir, 832 Smith St., Xenia, Ohio | Back of envelope | 337 Concord St. Hamilton, Ohio. |

Study the meaning and spelling of the following trade terms:

s. 1 s.	s. 2 s.	s. 4 s.	s. 2 x. 1 e.	sand paper
sash	sash cords	sash lifts	sash weights	saw
saw horse	scaffold	scale	score	screw driver
screw	scribers	scrub plane	scuttle	seasoned
seat cut	secret nail	section	select	set
set of drawings		setting	setting frames	shelf
sheathing	shed roof	shelving	setting jambs	sheathe up
shim up	shingled	ship lap	setting nails	sheathing
shingle tins		shoe	shoe mould	shoe rail
shovel	shrink	shrinkage	side cut	side view
sidewalk line		sight	side light sash	siding
sight along sill		size	skirting	sketch
slate	slide doors	slope	socket chisel	soffit
soffit boards		soffit mould	soft wood	sole plate
solid bridging		sound	spaced	spacing
spade	span	special	spike	spirit level
split	specifications		spirit bulb	spruce
spreader	square	squared up	stagger	stair builder
stair details		stairs	stair horse	stairway
stakes	steel	steel framing square		steel jack plane
steel square		stile	stirrup	stock
stone	stool	stop bead	story	straight
straight edge		street line	stretch a line	stretcher
straight nailing		strength	stringer	strings
strip	structure	strut	stucco	studded up

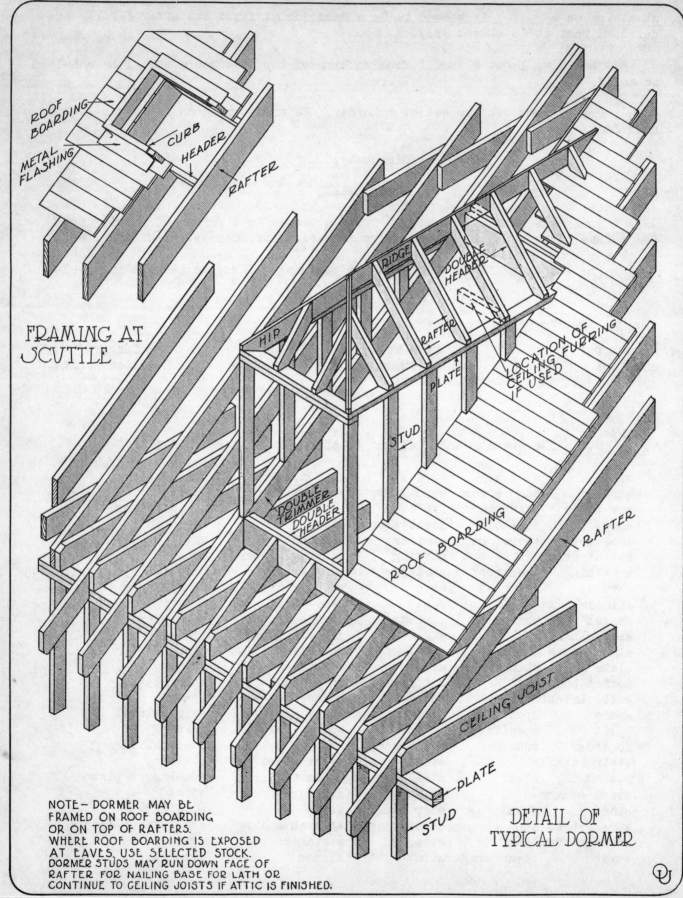

ROOF BOARDING

METAL FLASHING

CURB HEADER

RAFTER

FRAMING AT SCUTTLE

HIP

RIDGE

DOUBLE HEADER

RAFTER

PLATE

LOCATION OF CEILING FURRING IF USED

STUD

DOUBLE TRIMMER

DOUBLE HEADER

ROOF BOARDING

RAFTER

CEILING JOIST

PLATE

STUD

DETAIL OF TYPICAL DORMER

NOTE— DORMER MAY BE FRAMED ON ROOF BOARDING OR ON TOP OF RAFTERS. WHERE ROOF BOARDING IS EXPOSED AT EAVES, USE SELECTED STOCK. DORMER STUDS MAY RUN DOWN FACE OF RAFTER FOR NAILING BASE FOR LATH OR CONTINUE TO CEILING JOISTS IF ATTIC IS FINISHED.

stud	studding	stud wall	sub flooring	sub sills
support	surface one side	strop	supporting posts	
surface two sides		surface two sides one end		

Civics.

Write letters to the Department of Labor, the United States Department of Interior and the American Federation of Labor, Department of Building Trades, all of Washington, D. C., and ask for a listing of the several trades of the construction industries. Compare these trades and groupings, such will be quite interesting.

Continued from page 220

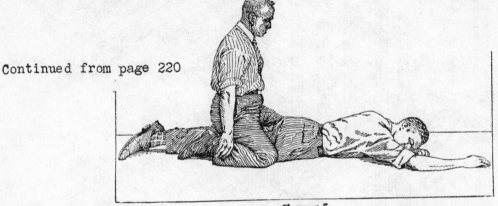

FIGURE 5

Now, immediately swing backward, so as to remove the pressure completely. (See figure 5.) After two seconds, swing forward again. Repeat twelve to fifteen times a minute, the double movement of pressing and letting go, making a complete respiration—drawing in and letting out of the breath—in four or five seconds.

Continue without interruption until patient breathes naturally; if necessary, four hours or longer, or until a physician declares the patient is dead.

As soon as this artificial respiration has been started and while it is being continued, an assistant should loosen any tight clothing about the patient's neck, chest, or waist. *Keep the patient warm.* Do not give any liquids whatever by mouth until the patient is fully conscious.

To avoid strain on the heart when the patient revives, he should be kept lying down and not allowed to stand or sit up. If the doctor has not arrived by the time the patient has revived, he should be given some stimulant, such as one teaspoonful of aromatic spirits of ammonia in a small glass of water or a hot drink of coffee or tea. He should be kept warm.

Resuscitation should be carried on at the *nearest possible point* to where the patient received his injuries. He should not be moved from this place until he is breathing regularly and then moved only in a reclining position. Should it be necessary, due to extreme weather, etc., to move the patient before he is breathing normally, artificial respiration should be kept up during the time that he is being moved.

A brief return of natural breathing is not a certain indication for stopping the resuscitation. Often the patient, after a temporary recovery, stops breathing again. The patient must be watched; if natural breathing stops, artificial respiration should be begun again at once.

If it is necessary to change the operator, this change must be made without losing the rhythm of respiration. In this way, no confusion results at the time of change, and a regular rhythm is kept up.

Continued on page 228

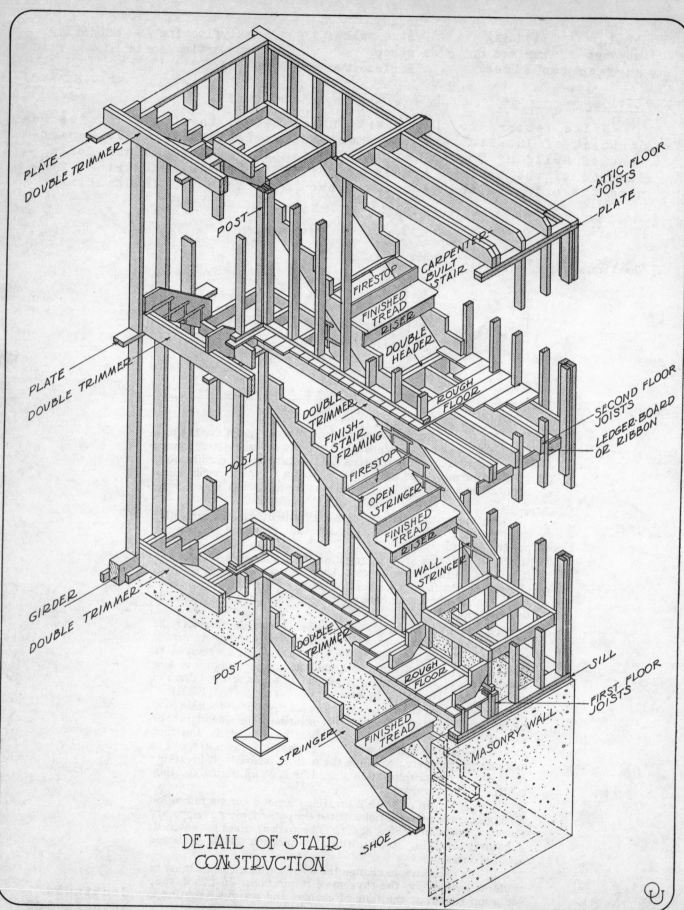

DETAIL OF STAIR
CONSTRUCTION

Chapter XXIII

Stairs

All framing must be done with due regard for stair construction. When proper openings are allowed in the framed work for stair construction observe the following steps in stair work.

Study the stair details in the set of plans. Study the stair details in this chapter. If the specifications and details call for stairs to be made at a mill and constructed by a stair builder there is not much that can be done by the carpenter. Only the rough stringers, in this case, are put up by the carpenter. The stair builder does his work after the walls have been lathed and plastered.

To construct a straight stairs as illustrated in this chapter one may proceed as follows:

Obtain a piece of straight stock and place on it the distance from floor below to floor above. This is the room height plus the thickness of the ceiling joists, plaster and flooring of the second floor, or floor above.

Set a dividers at 7" and step off this distance on the stock which has on it the total rise or height of the stairs. If 7" will not divide into this distance evenly, increase the dividers span slightly and try again. Continue to step off this distance on the pole until the total rise is divided evenly with a distance as close to 7" as possible. The 7" distance represents the rise of one stair or the height of one tread.

Count the number of spaces stepped off by the dividers; this will be the number of risers in the stairs. Obtain the total run of the stairs from the details and divide this total run by the total number of risers, less one, this giving the width of the run of each tread or the width of the tread less the nosing overhang. Check head room allowed in second floor joist framing and make certain this run can be used.

Use these numbers, the height of each riser and the run of each tread, on the steel square and lay off the string of the stairs. Lay off the required number of risers and treads and reduce the bottom riser by the thickness of one tread. This will allow the entire stair string or stringer to drop down so that the first and last riser will equal other risers and the top riser will receive the top tread and be even with the top of the second floor.

Erect the stringers as shown in the following illustrations. Finish tread and riser stock usually comes from the mill ready to be placed in position and nailed. A great deal of care should be taken in framing the stairs as this is a source of much trouble if the work is improperly done.

Illustrations in previous chapters, especially IX, X and XI, show a good many details of stair construction. Both wood and metal members are used and illustrated in these drawings and photographs.

Practical jobs. Lay off a stair horse. Construct a stair horse. Construct a straight stairs. Construct a stairs with a platform, with winders.

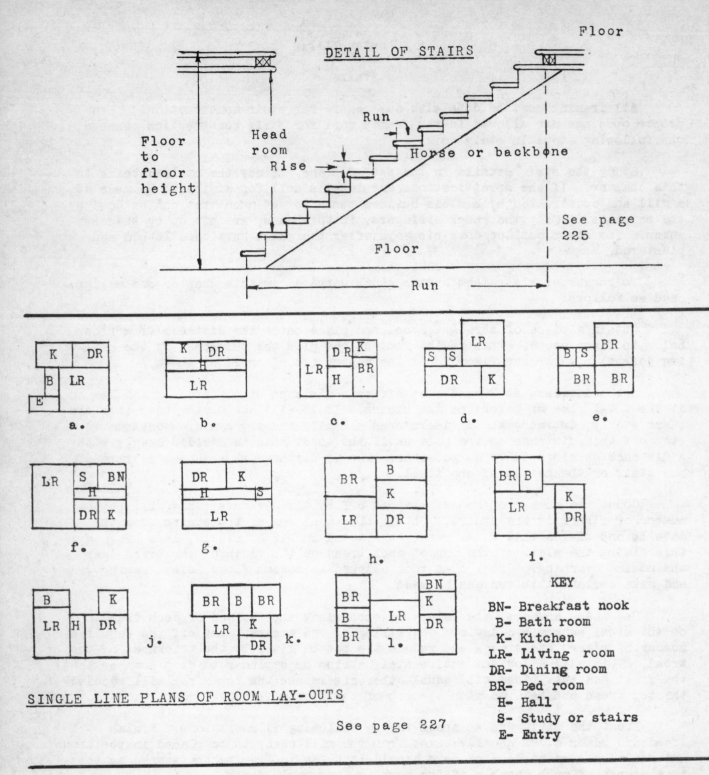

DETAIL OF STAIRS

Floor

Floor to floor height

Head room

Rise

Run

Horse or backbone

See page 225

Floor

Floor

Run

SINGLE LINE PLANS OF ROOM LAY-OUTS

a. b. c. d. e.

f. g. h. i.

j. k. l.

KEY

BN- Breakfast nook
B- Bath room
K- Kitchen
LR- Living room
DR- Dining room
BR- Bed room
H- Hall
S- Study or stairs
E- Entry

See page 227

TWO SINGLE-STROKE FREE-HAND ALPHABETS

Slant and Vertical

ABCDEFGHIJKLMNOPQRSTUVWXYZ

See page 227

abcdefghijklmnopqrstuvwxyz: 123456789

ABCDEFGHIJKLMNOPQRSTUVWXYZ

abcdefghijklmnopqrstuvwxyz.   123456789

Related Studies

Drawing.

The previous study dealt with the arrangements and services of the several rooms. This study leads into a consideration of room layout or floor plan layout. Floor plans may be classified as, a. no hall type, b. central hall type, c. one floor plan type, d. two or more floor plan type, e. side stairway type, f. central stairway type. Then again, perhaps another way to classify floor plans would be, g. square or rectangular type, h. 'L' shaped type, i, 'U' shaped type, j. 'T' shaped type and k. 'H' shaped type.

The following sketches illustrate the above named types. Copy these several sketches and label each.

In labeling or placing a title or lettered description on a drawing or sketch one must use great care. A common mistake is to use the term printing to mean the fine art of lettering. Lettering is a term applicable in particular to the freehand process of drawing titles, descriptive strips, etc., by the use of letter characters, such as A, B, C, etc., on drawings.

The building apprentice is concerned with a free style of letter. This style is not made by the aid of a straight edge but is entirely free hand or unaided by mechanical means. The groups of letters and figures on the opposite page are known as the single-stroke free-hand letter characters. The characters or letters should be studied with great care and thought. It is common mistake of the beginner to think that he knows all about the shape and method of letters or that he cannot letter at all. Hence he feels it is useless to try.
Practice these characters diligently until perfection is reached.

Mathematics.

Staircases are of many types, some of very complicated design, such as the winding stair. Only two general types, however, will be treated here; the closed type and the open type. The closed type is built between two walls. The open type is built free of walls or one side free of a wall.

The combined total of a tread and riser should generally, equal 17" with the tread 10" wide and the riser 7" high. The head room should be not less than 7' in height.

The following drawing will illustrate these points. Copy these several views in this drawing. Note the distance between the floors, change this distance slightly, not over 12", and calculate the head room, tread and riser sizes. Use freehand or scaled sketches to illustrate the changes made.

Science:

The word STAIR is a noun meaning - any one of a set of steps connecting different levels - and is usually used in the plural as STAIRS which implies the entire group or flight of steps. The word STAIR-CASE is a noun meaning - a flight of steps with handrail, balusterse, etc. This term implies the whole unit of stair work as done by a stair-case builder. The term STAIR-WAY is a noun which carries the same general meaning as the terms STAIR or STAIRS.

Continued from page 223
TREATMENT OF WOUNDS

A wound is any injury to the skin or tissue, either within the body or on its surface. First-aid treatment of wounds consists of stopping bleeding and preventing germs from getting into the wound. Germs may be present on the skin, fingers, clothing and unclean dressings.

Dressings

Nothing should touch the wound except clean cloth or gauze which has been prepared for the purpose. Cloth or gauze so prepared is called a sterilized dressing. A supply of these dressings (for sale at any drug store) should be kept in a covered container in every home. If none are at hand, take a piece of clean, unstarched cloth, and iron it flat, or boil it in water for ten minutes. Old pieces of linen so treated make good dressings.

In putting on a dressing, care should be taken not to touch with the fingers, or any other object not sterilized, that part of the dressing next to the wound, and to make sure that the dressing is large enough to cover the wound completely. Hold the dressing in place by a bandage or adhesive tape.

All serious wounds, and particularly wounds caused by rusty nails and gunpowder, on account of the possibility of tetanus (lockjaw), should be shown to a doctor.

Antiseptics

The cleaning and disinfecting of all serious wounds should be left to the doctor. First-aid treatment stops with the checking of bleeding and application of a sterile dressing.

Small injuries, such as cuts and scratches, which probably will not be seen by a doctor, may be treated with an antiseptic, such as mercurochrome or tincture of iodine (3½% solution). When dry, apply a sterile dressing as described above.

FRACTURES (Broken Bones) AND DISLOCATIONS

A fracture, or broken bone, when there is no break in the skin, is called a simple fracture. When there is a wound as well, it is called a compound fracture. Careless first-aid handling of a simple fracture may cause the splintered ends of the broken bone to cut through the tissues and skin, thus making the injury a compound fracture.

Fractures of the Arms and Legs

SIGNS—The patient complains of pain at the place where the bone is broken, and the pain is more severe on pressure or movement. He may not be able to move the limb. The broken ends of bone may be overlapping noticeably or the injured limb may be shorter or bent when compared with the uninjured side. Swelling is usually marked and appears quickly.

TREATMENT—When in doubt, treat as a fracture. Send for a doctor. If there is shock or a wound, treat as described under these headings. If it is necessary to move the patient, a splint must be applied to keep immovable the broken parts of the bone.

Splints

Any rigid material—a light board, umbrella, cane, broom handle—that is long enough to reach beyond the joints above and below the break will serve as a splint. Pad the splint thickly with cloths, excelsior, hay, newspapers, pillows or leaves, and cover with cloth. Bandage to the broken limb firmly, but gently, along its length, but not over the frac-

Continued on page 230

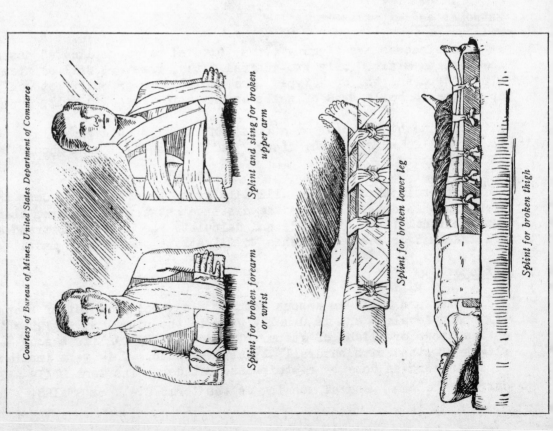

Courtesy of Bureau of Mines, United States Department of Commerce

Splint for broken forearm or wrist

Splint and sling for broken upper arm

Splint for broken lower leg

Splint for broken thigh

The purpose of a stairs is to afford a means, by a series of convenient heights, of climbing from one floor height to another.   A stairs likewise affords a means of descending from one floor height to another. Elevators, ramps and escalators are likewise used to get from floor to floor.

The rise of a stair step is taken from the top of one tread or step to the top of the next. The total rise of the stairs or steps is the height from floor to floor.

The sum of the rise and run of each step should equal 17" or 17-1/2".

No stairway or series of steps should have more than 15 steps or risers in a flight.

Stairs are of certain types, the straight, straight with platform, straight with winders and spiral types.

Stair work is generally milled at a wood mill and assembled on the job. Stair work is generally done by an expert mechanic, either a finish carpenter or expert cabinetmaker who has had much experience and has acquired a high degree of technique.

By use of the foregoing information, construct a stairs of about 1/4th or 18th actual size. Make the construction of wood or paper. Tackle a straight stair job at first with the floor to floor height of about and not less than 8'6".

English.

In general, there are two ways of applying for a job or position. One way is to apply in person and ask for work. Another way is to make application in writing either in answer to an advertisement or by formal request.

Read and study the following letter.

327 Wells Street,
Cleveland, Ohio,
June 15, 1935.

The Williamson Construction Co.,
25 E. Vine Street,
Cleveland, Ohio.

Gentlemen:

Please consider this application for a junior apprenticeship with your concern.

I am a young man, seventeen years of age, a graduate of the Building High School, in good health and have missed but one day in school attendance.

During my time spent at the trade school I have had twelve months shop experience and twelve months of training in drafting,math-

Signs—Extreme pain in back and legs with numbness or tingling. Patient may not be able to move feet and legs. Deformity may be present at the point of fracture.

Treatment—Send for a doctor at once. Place patient in a comfortable position. Do not try to straighten him, if his back is bent. If moving is necessary, keep him in the same position. Use a board or improvised stretcher for moving, so that patient may remain reclining. Two or three people will be needed to lift or slide him onto the stretcher, so as not to disturb his position. Place pillows around his back, so that he can lie comfortably without moving his back muscles.

Fractured Skull

Signs—If the patient received a blow on his head or a severe fall and seems stunned or is unconscious, there may be a fracture of the skull and the patient should be treated accordingly.

Treatment—Send for a doctor. Check severe bleeding, if present, by placing a gauze compress over the wound. There may be a fracture, however, when there is no wound. Lay the patient flat on his back, with head slightly elevated. Keep him warm. Give him nothing by the mouth.

Dislocations (Bone Out of Place at the Joint)

Signs—The joint looks out of shape when compared with a similar joint, and its motion is limited.

Treatment—Send for a doctor. Do not try to replace the joint; merely place it in a comfortable position. For pain, apply to the joint, cloths frequently wrung out in very cold water.

Treatment of Dislocation of Finger and Lower Jaw

(The only dislocations you may attempt to replace in emergency.)

For Dislocated Finger—Face injured person and pull the end of the finger toward you. With thumb and forefinger of other hand, gently press on dislocated joint until it slips into place.

For Dislocated Jaw—Wrap own thumbs in several thicknesses of cloth to protect from patient's teeth. Then put your covered thumbs into the injured person's mouth, resting them on his lower teeth well back on each side, while your fingers grasp the jaw under the chin. Press first downward and then backward. As the jaw closes, slip the thumbs off the teeth to the inside of the cheeks, so they will not be caught between the teeth when the jaw springs into place.

SPRAINS, STRAINS AND BRUISES

Sprains

The ligaments supporting the joints or attaching the muscles to bones are torn and a sprain is the result. There is pain, swelling, and usually discoloration. What seems like a bad sprain may be a fracture. Therefore, a doctor should be called for a sprain, unless it is slight.

Treatment—Raise the injured joint, so that it will get less blood. Apply first hot then cold cloths for several hours. Bandage snugly to prevent motion, but loosen bandage frequently if swelling

Continued from page 228

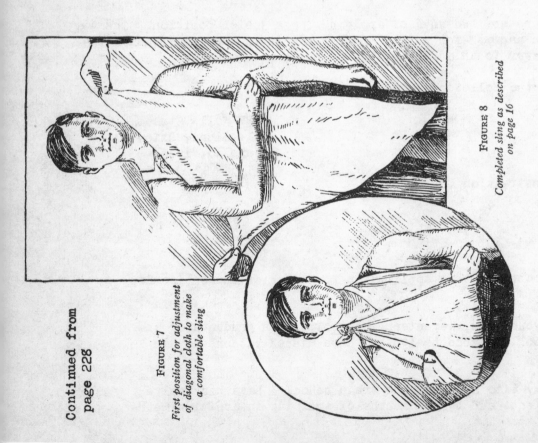

Figure 7
First position for adjustment of diagonal cloth to make a comfortable sling

Figure 8
Completed sling as described on page 16

Fractured Collar-Bone

Signs—As the patient stands or sits straight, the shoulder on the injured side hangs much lower than the other shoulder.

Treatment—Place a large pad under the armpit. Make a triangular sling bandage from a piece of cloth about 2½ feet square. (See figures 7 and 8.) Support the arm on the injured side by the sling. Tie the ends of the bandage behind the neck and pin the middle end across the front piece. Let the doctor complete the treatment.

Fractured Spine

These injuries are serious. The patient should not be moved unless it is absolutely necessary and then *extreme* care should be used. Otherwise, the broken ends of the spine may pinch the spinal ematics, English, science and civics.

By permission I refer you to Mr. G. W. Hook of the Building High School.

Very truly,

Carl Meier.

Write a letter applying for some position you would like to have. Search the classified advertisements in the daily press for a possible opening. This work is very important as one is often in need of just this sort of training.

Civics.

All youths should make an attempt to acquaint themselves with the possible vocations, jobs and callings within their community or their possible interests. There are a few books describing the vocations of life as found in the United States. The purpose of the study will be to acquaint one with the many callings of life and to create an interest in a few.

Obtain the book, Vocational Guidance, by Wm. Proctor and the book Choosing a Career, by Smith. List the occupations that seem of interest. List the occupations you would not like to pursue. Study the entire works carefully.

Stair Platform

YOU will find here enclosed a sketch showing the conception I have of a better way of erecting platforms and laying out the stair sections.

As a stair builder, I have learned about small details that are not understood by many a good carpenter who comes across a stair job.

There are many things to be said about stairs, and the part they often play in the house should bring them oftener in the AMERICAN BUILDER.

Houses of good taste have a stairway well in view, so its design as well as its construction should be in line with the best in the home.   RENE LECHEVALIER, New York City.

Veneering Old Steps

HERE is a simple method of veneering old steps which is a successful way of putting a new surface on worn-out stairs.

Fig. 1 shows a section of the first step of a stair which is to be covered with veneering. The veneering in this case is 2¼-inch flooring. The dotted line shows where the nosing is cut off. It will be noticed here that a new floor has been laid; this usually is necessary about the time the stairs need renewing. The floor is laid up to the first riser which is covered with the same flooring. The last board of the riser is ripped off in such a manner that the nosing piece will rest tightly onto it as shown in Fig. 2.
—H. H. SIEGELE, Emporia, Kans.

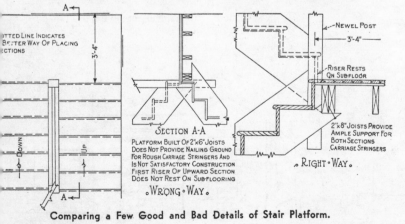

Comparing a Few Good and Bad Details of Stair Platform.

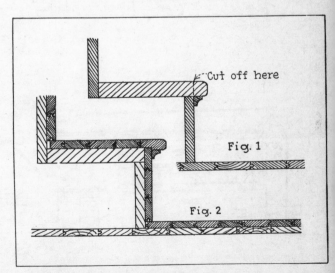

METHOD of veneering stairs when new floor is being laid.

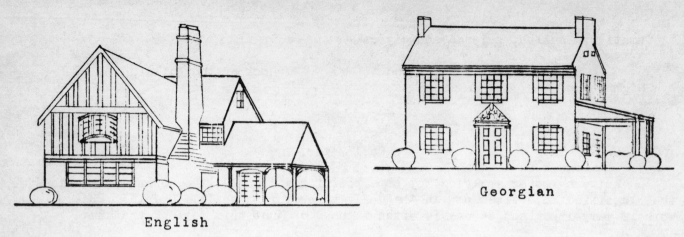

English

Georgian

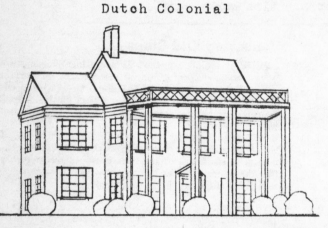

Dutch Colonial

Modern

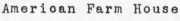

Southern Colonial

American Farm House

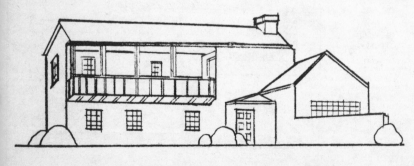

Spanish

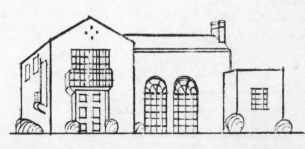

Italian

TYPICAL STYLES OF ARCHITECTURE DEVELOPED IN AMERICAN DWELLINGS

Refer to page 233

Chapter XXIV

Interior Trim

Study the details of the set of house plans and note the kind and sizes of trim or finished stock designated for use in the building. All interior trim as well as the exterior trim comes from the mill in a ready cut shape and needs but be fitted in position. Little sawing need be done, some planing but a great deal of squaring and plumbing is required.

Study the many illustrations of trim given in Sweet's Architectural Catalogs. Trim placed around windows and doors varies greatly according to the type of window or door used. Metal sash, doors or hollow metal trim worked up by the carpenter has its special application in each individual case.

Trim placed in stran-steel or frame-less steel houses may be of wood or of metal. The plan details should be studied in each case. The specifications will clear up any omissions or misunderstandings as to the type of trim to use if such omissions should be made in the plans.

In working up the trim around a door opening in a frame house one should place the base block on first, allowing for the thickness of the finish floor, then nail the block in place. Place the side casing in position, mark length, square and cut, plumb and nail in place about 3/8" from face of jamb. Place the head casing in position, allowing slight overhang at end of casing, 1/4" to 1/2", and nail in securely. Set nails so that painter may putty holes before applying varnish, paint or stain finish. Never use miter joints in casing work unless specified.

The trim around the window frame is worked up in much the same manner as the door trim except side and top casings are nailed flush with inside of stiles. Determine length of stool cut and notch to fit against sash. Cut and nail apron to hold stool level. Cut side and top casings and nail in place. Cut stop bead and nail in place. Allow sash to move easily but not loosely.

Other items of trim such as base board, picture mouldings, cased opening trim and any special moulding ot trim is applied by special fitting.

All membering joints on inside corners are coped. All joints on outside corners are mitered. A coped joint is a meeting of one member at a special point, the shape of the joint taking the shape of the member.

Practical jobs. Place trim around window openings. Place trim around door openings. Place trim around cased openings. Place trim around mantle. Place trim around built in book case. Place base trim on. Place picture moulding trim, plate rack, etc.

Related Studies

Drawing.

Having considered the arrangements of rooms and the types of floor plans it is well, before any mechanical drawing is done, to consider the exterior shape

French   Provincial   Refer to pages 232 and 233

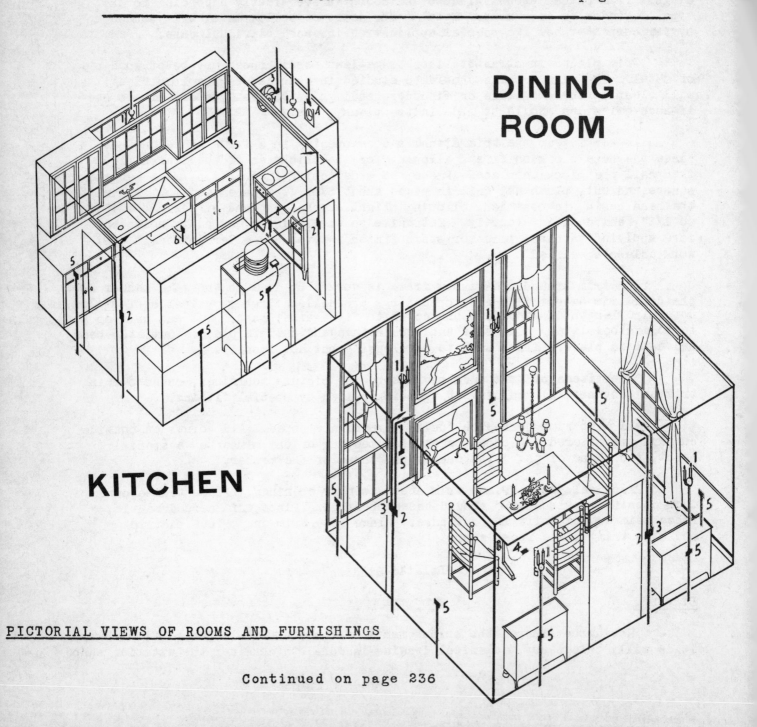

DINING ROOM

KITCHEN

PICTORIAL VIEWS OF ROOMS AND FURNISHINGS

Continued on page 236

of a building. This exterior shape is known as architectural style. There are nine popular styles of architecture in residence or dwelling design. These styles are illustrated in the preceding sketches. Sketch these styles. Find illustrations of each from a trade journal.

Mathematics.

Interior trim is ordered by dealers' catalog number and is sold in 100' lots. Doors and frames, sash and frames, all sorts of mouldings are milled in a planing mill. Doors and frames as well as sash and frames are sold in sets. Mouldings of all sorts are sold by the 100 linear feet according to pattern and number. Door and window trim are ordered by the set and dealers' catalog.

Estimate the amount of doors, windows (sets), trim and mouldings are required for the house in the accompanying set of plans. Place these estimates with other estimates for the same structure.

In Chapter XXV will be found a list of typical interior trim items, together with the time, on the average, taken to build this trim in place by a journeyman carpenter.

Science.

Domestic sanitation includes such phases of house construction as water heating, water draining and sewage disposal. A plumber installs such items of sanitation according to strict rules laid down by building laws and architectural specifications.

The several items used in a house and installed by a plumber are the sink, shower bath, bath tub, water closet, wash stand, wash tubs or laundry tubs, water heater and gas appliances.

From a building code obtain the requirements for the conveniences in the drwelling as given in the accompanying set of house plans.

Study the following illustrations. Each sketch shows a room fitted with furniture and conveniences. Sketch each room. List each item of furniture and convenience.

English.

About four-fifths of all books read are books of fiction. Story reading is now a favorite recreation for all ages of people. It is the purpose of this study to introduce one to a group of worth-while fiction literature.

Obtain the following books from the library and examine the lists of books suggested.

'Starbuck' - 'A Guide to Books for Character' - McMillan & Co.
'Washburne and Vogel' - 'What Children Like to Read' - Rand-McNally.

The following list is suggested as good fiction reading.

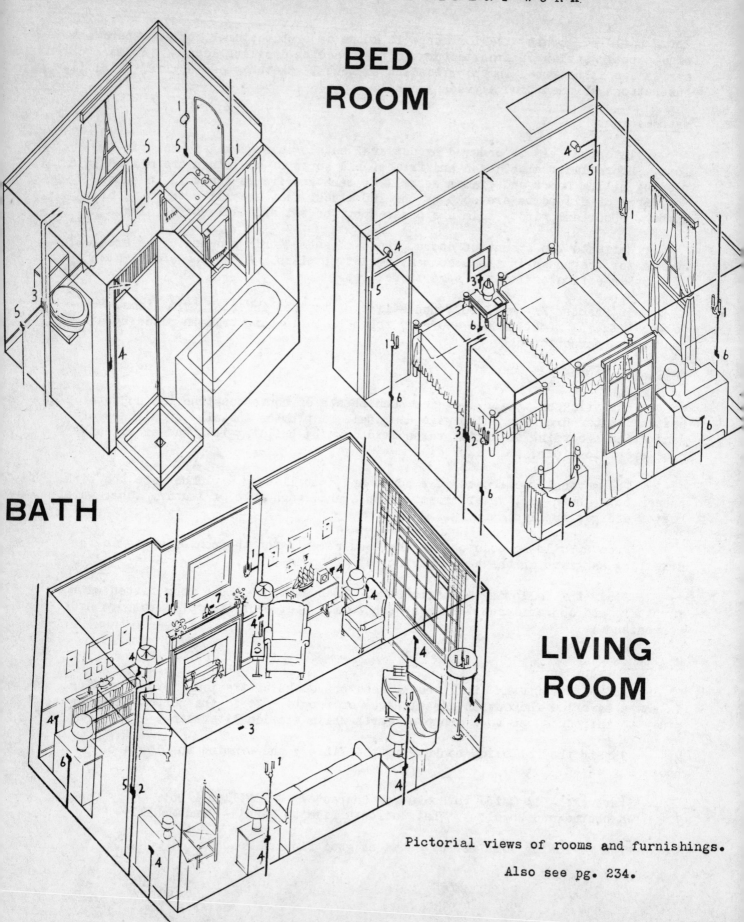

BED ROOM

BATH

LIVING ROOM

Pictorial views of rooms and furnishings.

Also see pg. 234.

Title	Author
Jim Davis	John Mansfield
Adventures of Sherlock Holmes	A. C. Doyle
Two Years Before the Mast	R. H. Dana
Bob, Son of Battle	Alfred Ollivant
Mysterious Island	Jules Verne
Tale of Two Cities	Charles Dickens
Ben-Hur	Lew Wallace
Connecticut Yankee in King Arthur's Court	Mark Twain
Captain Blood	Rafael Sabatino
Silas Marner	George Eliot
Boy's Life of Theodore Roosevelt	Herman Hagerdon
Black Wolf Pack	Daniel Beard
Bar Sinister	R. H. Davis
Lives of the Hunted	E. T. Seton
Westward Ho!	Charles Kingsley
Gold Seekers of '49	E. L. Sabin
Blue Magic	Edith Ballinger
White Fire	Mary C. Dubois
That Year at Lincoln High	Joseph Gollomb
Virginian	Owen Wister
Buff, A Collie	Alfred P. Terhune
Sefenteen	Booth Tarkington
Three Musketeers	Alexandre Dumas
Adventures of Huckleberry Finn	Mark Twain
David Copperfield	Charles Dickens
Erie Brighteyes	Henry R. Haggard
Barnaby Lee	John Bennett
A Man for the Ages	Irving A. Bacheller
In the Days of Poor Richard	Irving A. Bacheller
Heart of the Hills	John Fox
The Little Shepherd of Kingdom Come	John Fox
Moby Dick	Herman Melville
The Circuit Rider	Edward Eggleston

Civics.

There is, generally speaking, more trim used on the outside walls of a dwelling than on the inside walls. Different styles of houses demand different interior and exterior trim harmony. A small, inexpensive house should not have a room completely trimmed in wood. A large frame house should have more wooden trim used than a smaller house could demand.

Obtain mill catalogs and select several illustrations of interior trim. Refer to Sweet's Architectural Catalogs. Start a clipping file of trim illustrations. List the names of interior and exterior trim members. List the combinations of trim that will suit. List some poor or inartistic combinations.

Showing interior trim. Courtesy A. M. Lewin Lumber Co., Cincinnati, Ohio.

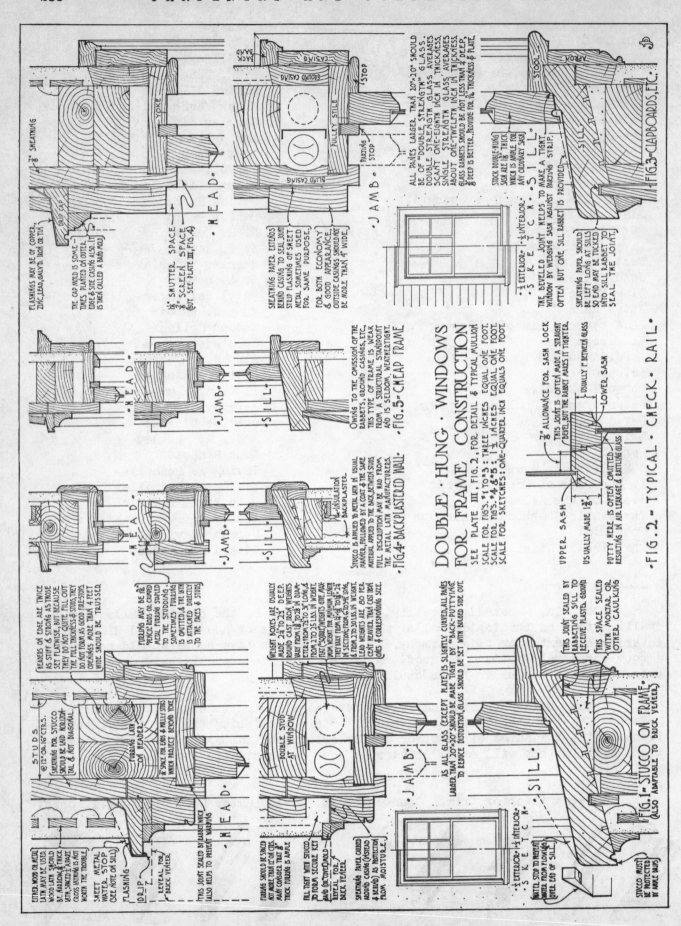

Chapter XXV

Windows

The sash, like the interior trim, is fitted after the plastering has been done.   Select the proper sash for the several openings and carry to their respective places.

The sash should be glazed and have a filler coat of paint before being hung in place.

Try the sash in the window frame and find out how much must be trimmed off. Measure the opening and trim sash to approximate size.   Plane off like amounts from both sides and try sash in opening again.   The sash should slide easily into the opening.   Round off the corners slightly.   Place upper sash in position and scribe lines across sash about 1/2" from top using parting strip as guide.   Trim top of sash, replace in frame and hold in place by nailing small block at bottom. Fit lower sash in place the same as the upper sash is fitted.

Both sash are now in place but the meeting rails are not level.   To bring the meeting rails together the distance or extension of the lower sash meeting rail above the meeting rail of the upper sash is measured.   This distance, taken on the dividers and marked along the inside of the lower rail of the lower sash. Plane off this distance and fit sash to fit slant or pitch of sill member.

The meeting rails must come together to allow the window latch to operate properly.   The rails should have a slight bevel to prevent the edges from catching and marring.   The bottom rail should have a slight bevel to fit the drop of the window sill.

Remove each sash from the frame and weigh each one.   Divide this weight of each sash by two to obtain weight of sash weight to use for balance.

Tie sash cord on the weight, bring sash cord through the sash weight pocket by using the 'mouse' and cut sash cord to proper length.   The length can be obtained by drawing the sash weight in the pocket and placing the sash in place and bring the sash cord down to the place of attaching in the side rail.   Allow enough length for a knot.   Tie the knot, slip it in the pocket in the side rail on the side of the sash and do the same for other side of sash.   The lower sash is hung in the same way.   Measure cord for lower sash the same as the length for the upper sash.   Close up the pocket in the frame, put in parting stop, blind stop and stop bead and the work is completed.   Casement type of sash are fitted similar to the fitting of a door.

In Chapter XI will be found many illustrations of sash frames for sash or windows as placed in steel framed dwellings.   These frames are placed in position in the same way as the window frames for wooden sash.

There are quite a number of steel sash on the market.   A study of a group of illustrations in the current number of Sweet's catalogs will show a total of more than 700 pages devoted to steel sash or metal windows.   Standard makes under the trade names of Ariston, Browne, Ceco, Cotswold, Easy Clean,

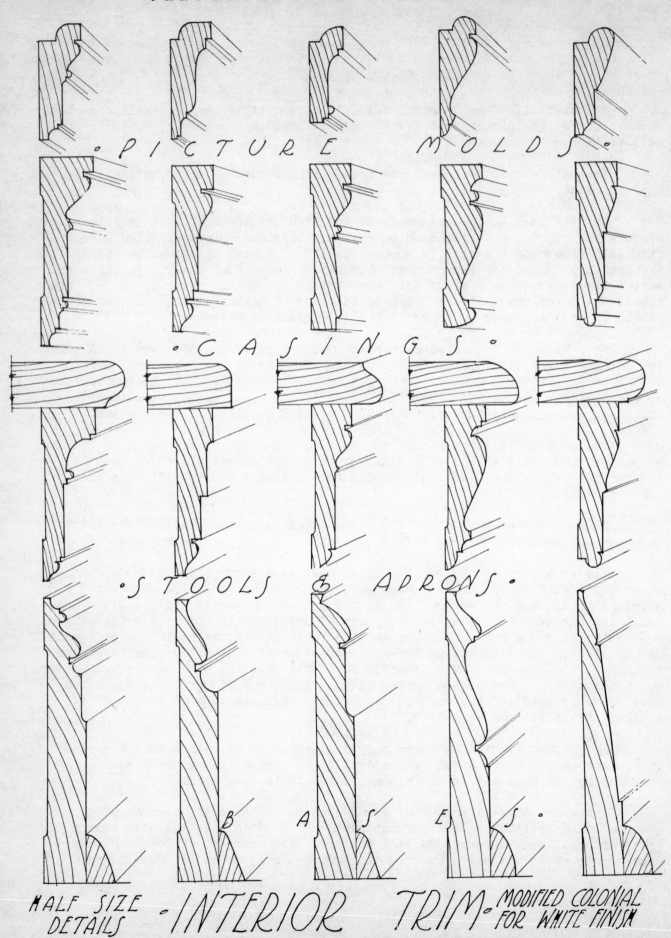

·PICTURE MOLDS·

·CASINGS·

·STOOLS & APRONS·

·BASES·

HALF SIZE DETAILS ·INTERIOR TRIM· MODIFIED COLONIAL FOR WHITE FINISH

Fencraft, Fenestra, Fenmark, Fenwrought, Hopkins, Lemco, Master and others are illustrated in Sweet's. These illustrations and details should be studied regardless of the specifications in any particular house as steel sash and steel windows are coming into use in dwellings, especially the higher priced dwellings.

Practical jobs. Fit an upper sash. Fit a lower sash. Fit a transom. Fit a casement sash. Fit a hinged sash. Fit a steel sash. Fit a sash or window in a steel framed house.

RELATED STUDIES

Drawing.

Previous studies in drawing have dealt with the topics of room arrangements, of floor plans and of elevations. So much for the freehand sketching of plans and elevations. It is well to turn attention to the work of drawing floor plans in a mechanical way or by the use of instruments.

Using the detailed steps given on pg. 243 draw a first floor plan. Draw this floor plan after due consideration of all the factors mentioned in Chapters XXII, XXIII and XXIV.

Mathematics.

A number is often multiplied by itself one or more times. The product is called the power of the number. Thus 3 x 3 equals 9; nine is the power of three. When three is multiplied by itself it is said to be squared. When three is multiplied by itself three times it is said to be cubed. The fourth or fifth power is called the fourth or fifth times, respectively.

Examples:

10^2	equals	10 x 10 or 100 which is called square.
10^3	equals	10 x 10 x 10 or 1000 cubed.
10^4	equals	10 x 10 x 10 x 10 or 10,000 which is called ten raised to the fourth power.
10^5	equals	10 x 10 x 10 x 10 x 10 or 100,000 which is termed ten raised to the fifth power.

When fractions are raised in power the numerator and denominator are raised equally.

Example: $\left(\dfrac{3}{5}\right)^2$ equals $\dfrac{3 \times 3}{5 \times 5}$ equals $\dfrac{9}{25}$

$\left(\dfrac{3}{5}\right)^5$ equals $\dfrac{3 \times 3 \times 3 \times 3 \times 3}{5 \times 5 \times 5 \times 5 \times 5}$ equals $\dfrac{243}{3125}$

To reverse the process of raising numbers to powers a process of factoring is employed called finding the root of a number. To find the number which, when multiplied by itself creates the square is called finding the square root of a number. To find the cube root is a process other than finding the square root. To find the square root of a number refer to page 245.

Unusual treatment of the panelled walls and beamed ceiling give this Colonial room a distinctive but pleasant air.

Pine in narrow panels, natural finish, gives this room charm.

Boy's bedroom with beamed ceiling.

Panelled walls and ceilings in three interiors

The following groups of steps represent the successive steps in the drawing of a typical floor plan.

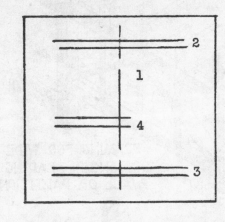

a. Find the center of working space and draw center line #1.

b. Choose the scale, locate front and rear walls as shown in lines of indefinite length, #2 and #3.

c. Locate any partitions parallel to front or rear walls, #4.

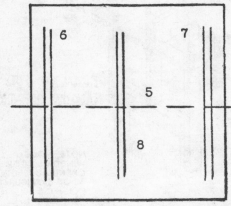

d. Find center of working space, draw center line #5.
e. Locate left and right outside walls, #6 and #7.
f. Locate end partitions parallel to front or rear walls, #8.
g. Connect up corners of wall lines.
h. Locate inside doors measuring from wall, #9.
i. Locate outside window measuring from outside wall corners to center of opening, #10.
j. Locate chimneys, #11, measuring from center and measuring overall dimensions of chimney.
k. Locate stair-way, #12.

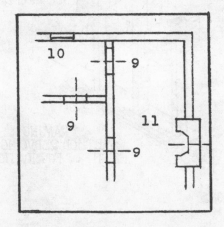

l. Place in all door, #13, and window symbols, #14.
m. Finish plans by placing in all additional features. Refer to the first floor plan in the accompanying set of house plans. The following items are intended to serve as a check for typical floor plan features.

Items #12, 13 and 14 are illustrated at the bottom of page

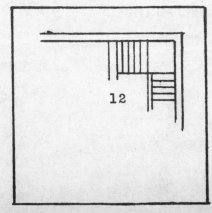

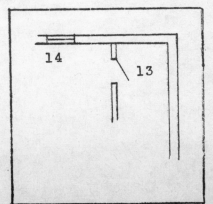

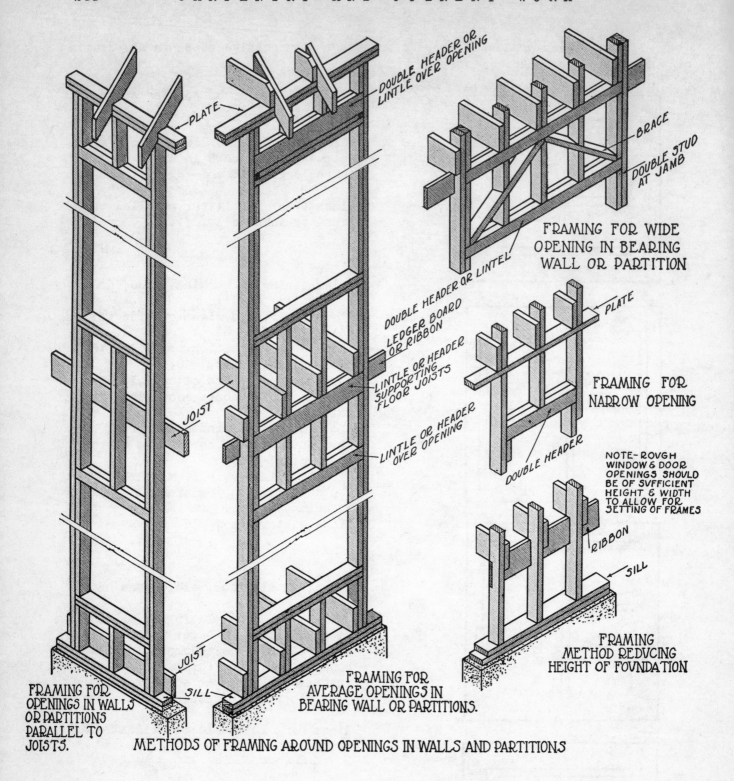

PLATE

DOUBLE HEADER OR LINTLE OVER OPENING

BRACE

DOUBLE STUD AT JAMB

FRAMING FOR WIDE OPENING IN BEARING WALL OR PARTITION

DOUBLE HEADER OR LINTEL

JOIST

LEDGER BOARD OR RIBBON

LINTLE OR HEADER SUPPORTING FLOOR JOISTS

LINTLE OR HEADER OVER OPENING

JOIST

SILL

PLATE

FRAMING FOR NARROW OPENING

DOUBLE HEADER

NOTE—ROUGH WINDOW & DOOR OPENINGS SHOULD BE OF SUFFICIENT HEIGHT & WIDTH TO ALLOW FOR SETTING OF FRAMES

RIBBON

SILL

FRAMING METHOD REDUCING HEIGHT OF FOUNDATION

FRAMING FOR OPENINGS IN WALLS OR PARTITIONS PARALLEL TO JOISTS.

FRAMING FOR AVERAGE OPENINGS IN BEARING WALL OR PARTITIONS.

METHODS OF FRAMING AROUND OPENINGS IN WALLS AND PARTITIONS

To find the square root of a number follow these steps.

a. Find the square root of 119025, which is the product of two factors.
b. Place marks 11'90'25 above every second figure beginning at the extreme right.
c. Find the largest perfect square contained in the first set of figures. Three is contained into 11, 3 times, since 3 x 3 equals 9.
d.
```
        √ 11'90'25      |345
            9
      64    2 90
            2 56
     685     34 25
             34 25
```
e. Bring down next set if figures, 90.
f. Multiply first root of figure 3 by 2 and write product 6 opposite next dividend.
g. Divide first two figures of next dividend, 290, which are 29, by 6 and write product 4 after 3 in product place, place 4 after 6 and multiply 64 by 4 which is 256. Subtract 256 from 290 and obtain a difference of 34.
h. Repeat twice 34 which is 68.
i. Plate opposite 34.
j. Bring down 25.
k. Find out by trial how many times 68 goes into 342, this is 5.
m. Multiply 685 by 5, this is 3425.
n. Therefore 345 is the perfect root of 119,025.
o. If a perfect root is not obtained in any problem add three decimal places and carry out same process.

Example
```
        √ 11'90'26.00'00'00      |345.104 plus
            9
      64    2 90
            2 56
     685     34 26
             34 25
    6901       1 00 00
                 69 01
   69024      30 99 00
              27 60 96
               3 38 04
```

Produce the square roots of 7, 14, 21, 33 and 47.
Produce the cube roots of 8, 11, 31 and 3.
Find the quare roots of 9096 and 8231. Prove that 6 plus 8 equals 10 .
Prove this by a right angle having sides 6 by 8 by 10 squared. The usual 6-8-10 method.

In estimating the quantity of trim to be used in house construction one must estimate by the piece or item. In estimating the time taken in placing this trim one must be extra careful as much time might be lost or gained according to the trim specified. The following table is an average of time taken to place the several items of trim in position by the carpenter. This table will be found on following page

Showing floor plan and framing plan.

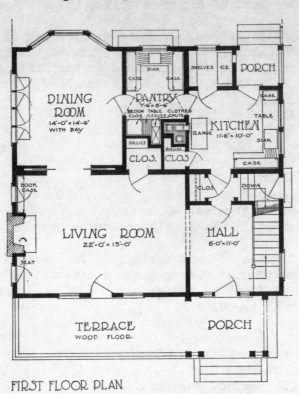

FIRST FLOOR PLAN

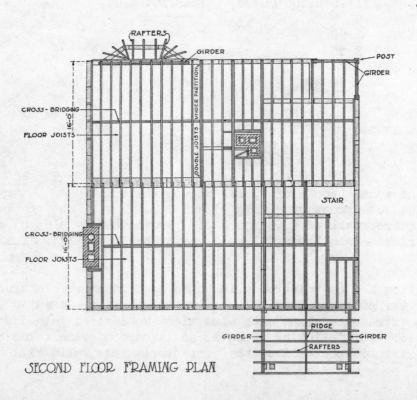

SECOND FLOOR FRAMING PLAN

Also see pg. 64.

Items		Linear feet.	8 hr. day.
Belt course		195	"
Corner boards	3 pcs.	100	"
Inside base	3 "	110	"
Cornice	5 "	50	"
Outside base	2 "	110	"
Picture moulding	1 "	225	"
Plate rail	2 "	50	"
Verge boards	1 "	110	"

Science.

Dwellings of former days had few conveniences compared with dwellings of today. One might list the items used in a dwelling in order to become aware of the many newer products of the building industry. Some items are: cluster lights, radios, air conditioners, furnaces, fireplace logs, incinerators, heaters, mixers, clocks, urinals, ironers, floor lights, showers, bath tubs, water closets, hand basins, sinks, stoves, health lamps, refrigerators, water heaters, clothes dryers, etc.

Many trade journals run annual producers' products numbers in which are featured the newer products in the building industry. Refer to the June, 1935 issue of ARCHITECTURAL FORUM or to any later issue of a trade journal in which newer products are featured. List these newer items or innovations. This is a feature, too, of AMERICAN BUILDER.

Equip the house in the accompanying set of plans with all items listed above or refer to other lists of newer equipment. Find the costs of each listing. This is a study in the newer household conveniences produced constantly by manufacturers.

English.

Many technical words, phrases and terms have been listed in previous chapters. Not all such words related to dwelling construction have been listed by any means. A study of these words, phrases and terms have been made and an alphabetical classification organized. The following words, as well as those given in previous chapters, are typical technical terms. The ones below have the initial letters of t, u and v, respectively.

T bevel	T sills	tack down	tack up	tack
tail cut	tails	tail piece	taper	tear
tear down	temper	tempered	templet	tenon
thickness	threshold	tie	tie piece	tile floor
tile shingle	timber	tin gutters	tinned	toe holds
toe nailing	tongue and groove		tongue	tool box
tool	top	top plates	top view	trade
trammel	transit	transom	tread	tree
trench	trestle	triangle	trim	trimmed
trimmers	trimming	try square	truncate	truss
tube hole	two by fours	two fold	two foot four fold	
two fours				

Showing floor plan and framing plan.

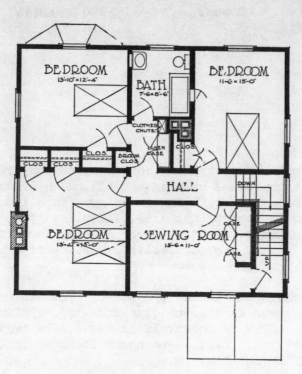

SECOND FLOOR PLAN

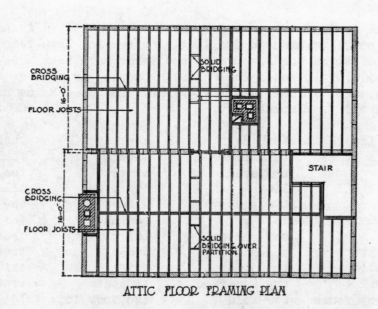

ATTIC FLOOR FRAMING PLAN

Also see pgs. 64 and 246.

unit	uprights			
valley	valley rafter		varnish	veneer
verge board	vertical	vise		

W. P.	wall	wall board	wall bolt	walks
wall stringer	warp out	washers	wax	wedge
water table	water proofing	weatherboarded	weatherboard	whet
weight space	well hole	western framing		white oak
white pine	width	wind	winders	window
winding stairs	wire edge	window apron	window frame	window latches
wood	window opening	window sills	window scotia	wooden
wooden bricks	wood shingles	wood working	worked	

Y. P.	yellow pine	yellow poplar	yoke	Y level

Civics.

Through the courtesy of the Metropolitan Life Insurance Company, New York, N. Y., the following studies in health under the caption, HEALTH THROUGH THE AGES, is offered. These studies which are beginning here, will continue in the following chapters.

ABOUT THE YEAR 1870, a wealthy German merchant named Heinrich Schliemann began to dig into a hill in Asia Minor. Tradition said that, under this hill, the ancient city of Troy lay buried.

Down, down through the earth dug the spades and the pickaxes. A city was unearthed, but it was not the Troy of which Homer sang, but a settlement of much later date. A little lower went the spades and the remains of another city, built by Alexander the Great, were found. Below this, a small unfortified settlement appeared. Then came Troy at last, the Troy of song and legend. But lower still went the spades and three more little settlements were found, one below the other. Under these came the ruins of a much larger city, with massive walls and a palace of sun-dried brick. Last of all, at the very bottom, on the virgin soil of the little hill and forming its core, the spades unearthed a rude village of the Stone Age. In the space of about 8,000 years, nine successive settlements had flourished and had passed away on that one site.

The men who excavated the hill of Troy started at the top and dug down through various stages of civilization until they reached the bottom. In order to learn what progress man has made in his search for health, we, too, shall examine various periods in the story of mankind, but we shall begin as near the bottom as we can. Starting from the Stone Age, we shall travel upward by successive stages until we reach the last stage of all, the period in which we are now living.

Cont'd on pg. 257.

FRED J. BURMEISTER, ARCHITECT

Chapter XXVI

Doors

The doors, like the interior trim, are fitted after the plastering has been done. Select the proper door for the opening and carry to the designated place.

Mark on the floor the sweep of the door. Sight along the door to see if it is true. If there is wind in the door the bow must be placed toward the swing of the door. Cut off stile extensions and dress sides until door will fit in the frame. Saw or plane off top of door until it fits squarely against the head of the frame. The door must swing free, about 1/2" above the finished floor or 1/16" above the threshold strip. Be certain to allow this in trimming the door to size.

Place the door in position. The door should fit tight against the hinge side but should have 1/16" clearance at top and on lock side. The lock side of the door should be beveled slightly.

With door in position mark off the position of the hinges on jamb and face of door. The hinge should be placed just below the top rail and just above bottom rail. Mark the position of the hinges with a sharp knife. Remove the door and lay out size of mortise by scribing around leaf of hinge. Mark position of hinge on jamb and chisel out sufficient wood to receive one leaf of the hinge and have it sink slightly below the surface of the door and jamb, respectively.

When proper mortises have been made for the hinges they should be held in position by screws. Loose pin butt hinges are used, allowing the hinges to be put in place and the door hung or removed at will.

Measure three feet from the floor to side of door and mark. Hold door lock against the side of door stile, face plate flush with the edge of the door. Mark with a sharp point the center of the knob and key hole of the lock. Hold in same position and mark height of top and bottom of body of lock on edge of door. Bore hole in edge of door and chisel out sufficiently to receive lock.

Set face plate of the lock against the edge of the door and scribe for mortise to take the selvage. Bore holes for knob shaft and key and insert lock. Hold the lock in proper place with screws. Insert knob bolts and knobs of the door. Close the door and mark on the door jamb the position of the latch. Measure distance from flat surface of latch to outside of door. Scribe distance on face of jamb between side marks for latch. Place latch plate in place and scribe mortise for it. Chisel out mortise and place latch plate in place.

Close the door and cut and nail door stops in place from inside of room. (Hinges might also be placed equi-distance from top and bottom). Reference should be made to Sweet's Architectural Catalogs for illustrations and details of wooden and metal doors. There are quite a number of metal doors on the market. Generally speaking, a concern marketing windows will market doors too. The accompanying illustrations will show how details and specifications are

STANDARD DOORS

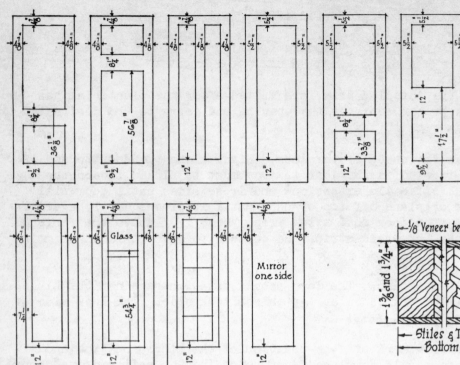

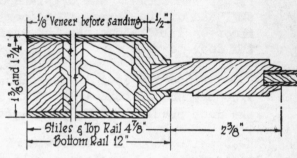

1/8" Veneer before sanding

Stiles & Top Rail 4⅞"
Bottom Rail 12"

2⅜"

In hanging doors there are three measurements to be marked—the location of the butt on the casing, the location of the butt on the door, and the thickness of butt on both casing and door. BUTT GAUGES have three separate cutters arranged with the necessary clearances so that no change of setting is necessary when hanging a number of doors. They are also Rabbet Gauges, Marking Gauges, and Mortise Gauges and have a scope sufficient for all door trim including lock plates, strike plates, etc.

The illustrations below show the method of using   Butt Gauges on doors having rabbeted jambs or nailed on strikes.

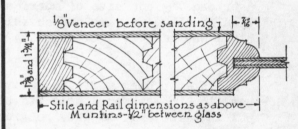

1/8" Veneer before sanding

Stile and Rail dimensions as above
Muntins-½" between glass

For Gauging Casings with Rabbeted Jambs

Set Cutter A to gauge from back of rabbeted jamb (Fig. 1); Cutter B is then in correct position for gauging from edge of door (Fig. 2) which engages in closing. These Cutters are made so as to allow sufficient clearance to enable the door to close properly, without catching or binding. (See dotted line Fig. 1.)

For Gauging Jambs to Which Strike is Nailed after Door is Hung

Reverse Bar to which Cutter B is attached, place Flange against edge of casing, and mark with Cutter B (Fig. 3). Use same setting of Cutter B for marking door, placing Flange against the outer edge (Fig. 4).

To Gauge for Thickness of Butt

Set Cutter C to depth required; gauge from depth of jamb (Fig. 5) and from edge of door (Fig. 6).

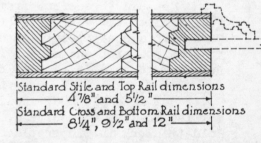

Standard Stile and Top Rail dimensions
4⅞" and 5½"
Standard Cross and Bottom Rail dimensions
8¼", 9½" and 12"

Standard panel designs as above or Special designs as desired with Special panel moldings Panel Splines may be added if desired at slight added cost These doors are economical

To Square for Mortise

On Rabbeted jamb place end of gauge against the rabbet or strike, and mark along edge of bottom (Fig. 8). On nailed-on jamb or strike or edges of door, place either one of the two Flanges against the edge and mark along bottom (Fig. 7).

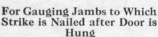

To Gauge for Mortise for Lock or Lock Strike

Set Cutter B to mark distance from edge of door or casing to mortise. Set Cutter C for width of mortise (Fig. 9). The bar to which Cutter C is attached can be turned to give a wider gauging face if desired. The bevel of the Cutters allow for working either front or back.

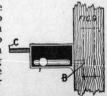

Left - HINTS ON DOOR HANGING

are handled for particular makes of doors and windows.

Practical jobs. Fit a door to size of opening. Fit on hinges and door lock set. Completely hang a door. Install door in structural steel house.

Related Studies

Drawing.

The following groups of steps represent the successive steps in the drawing of a typical elevation. This is a continuation of the study begun in the previous chapter.

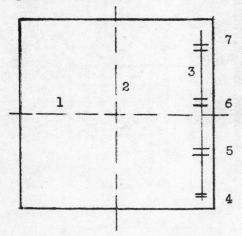

a. Find the center of working space and draw center line #1 and #2.
b. Erect story heights line #3.
c. Locate the basement floor #4.
   "   "   first   "   #5.
   "   "   second   "   #6.
   "   ridge height   #7.

d. Locate width of vertical heights #8.
e. Draw front elevations before side elevations providing the gable faces the front, #9.

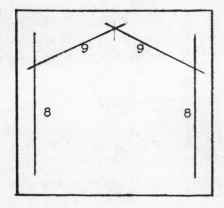

f. Locate windows and doors with cc measurements, #10 and #11.
g. Finish plans by placing in all additional features.

Using the foregoing detailed steps draw the elevations accompanying the floor plan made in the previous study.

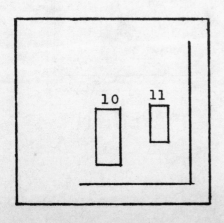

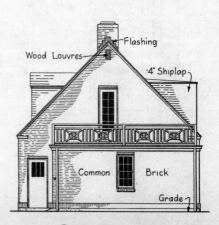

RIGHT ELEVATION

Typical metal door details.

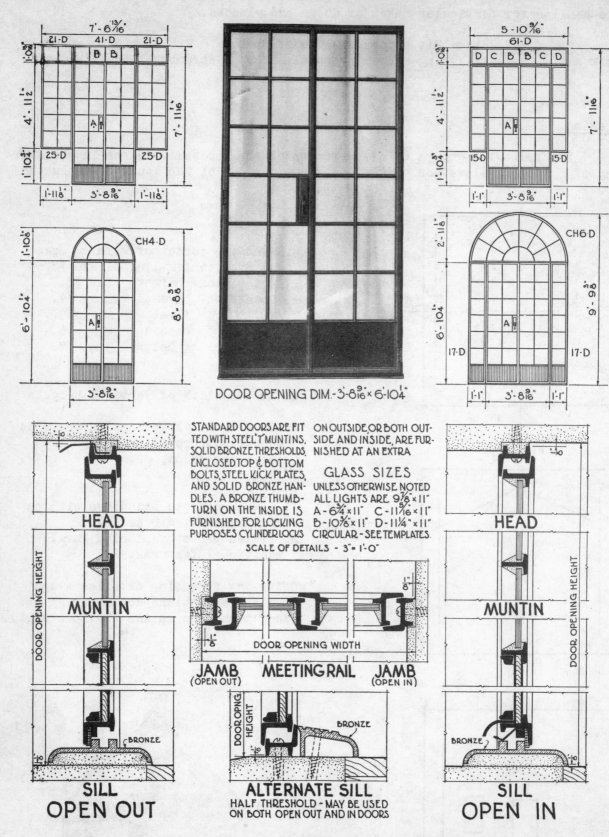

DOOR OPENING DIM.- 3'-8 9/16" x 6'-10 1/4"

STANDARD DOORS ARE FITTED WITH STEEL "T" MUNTINS, SOLID BRONZE THRESHOLDS, ENCLOSED TOP & BOTTOM BOLTS, STEEL KICK PLATES, AND SOLID BRONZE HANDLES. A BRONZE THUMBTURN ON THE INSIDE IS FURNISHED FOR LOCKING PURPOSES CYLINDER LOCKS ON OUTSIDE, OR BOTH OUTSIDE AND INSIDE, ARE FURNISHED AT AN EXTRA

GLASS SIZES

UNLESS OTHERWISE NOTED ALL LIGHTS ARE 9 7/8" x 11"
A - 6 3/4" x 11"   C - 11 5/16" x 11"
B - 10 7/8" x 11"   D - 11 1/4" x 11"
CIRCULAR - SEE TEMPLATES.

SCALE OF DETAILS - 3" = 1'-0"

HEAD

MUNTIN

DOOR OPENING HEIGHT

SILL
OPEN OUT

JAMB (OPEN OUT)   **MEETING RAIL**   JAMB (OPEN IN)

DOOR OPENING WIDTH

BRONZE

ALTERNATE SILL
HALF THRESHOLD - MAY BE USED ON BOTH OPEN OUT AND IN DOORS

HEAD

MUNTIN

DOOR OPENING HEIGHT

BRONZE

SILL
OPEN IN

Mathematics.

Two very important methods or devices of measuring elevation heights are the story pole and the line of heights. The story pole is a long straight piece of stock on which the following heights or levels are measured or marked.

a. foundation wall top; b. sill height; c. first floor height; d. window opening heights; e. door opening heights; f. ceiling height; g. second floor height; h. second floor window opening heights; i. second floor door opening heights; j. multi-floor Heights; k. plate heights; l. attic heights; m. ridge heights; n. chimney heights.

The line of heights on an elevation in drawing is a vertical line at the extreme right hand side of the working space. This vertical line has horizontal lines intersecting it at the right places where, according to exact scale measuring, the several heights occur on the respective or particular elevations.

Produce a line of heights from one of the elevations from one of the sets of plans accompanying this text. Make it a trifle larger in order to bring out the details. Make a story pole, either full size or to scale from wood, using good straight stock.

Science.

The styles of doors and the construction of the several styles is a very interesting study. In general, doors may be classified as panel and as flush type. The design and construction vary greatly.

Sketch the styles of several outside and inside doors. From trade literature discuss and illustrate doors from the following points: cores, panels, stiles, rails, glue, veneers, lumber, glass, hardware and inlays.

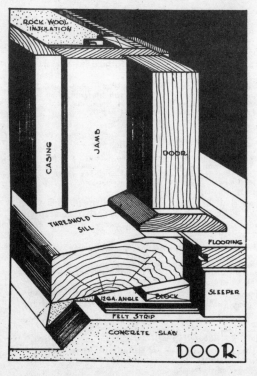

DOOR

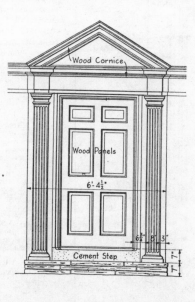

A FRONT ENTRANCE

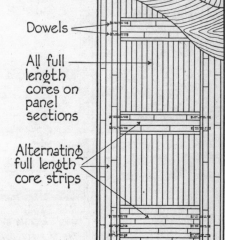

A 'STEELOX' DOOR   A BUILT-UP DOOR

A NEW TYPE OF DOUBLE HUNG STEEL WINDOW

A double hung action window with a fundamentally new principle in design eliminating the usual disadvantages of plate type metal double hung windows. There can be no lateral movement or side play, yet the sash are unbelievably easy to operate due to the use of ball bearing rollers.

Infiltration is reduced by an improved weight box and by weatherstripping on all sides and at meeting rail. Windows are made in fifty standard sizes ranging from 3 ft. 0 in. x 4 ft. 6 in. to 5 ft. 0 in. x 9 ft. 0 in., the same as the Double Hung Windows Types E and F described on page 66.

SPECIFICATIONS

Work Included

1. Furnish and install where shown on drawings, Lupton Steel Double Hung Windows (Type G or H as desired) manufactured by DAVID LUPTON'S SONS CO., Philadelphia, Pa.

Materials

2. Sash members shall be cold galvanized strip steel. Frame members shall be hot galvanized dull coated sheet steel.
3. Members shall be of the following thickness:
Frame members for Type G, head and head cover 20 gauge, sill 16 gauge, jamb 20 gauge and 16 gauge combined.
Frame members for Type H, head 16 gauge, head cover 20 gauge, sill 13 gauge, jamb 16 gauge and 14 gauge combined.
Sash members (for G and H types) 14 gauge (12 gauge for windows over 4 ft. wide), muntin 16 gauge, glazing strips 14 gauge (12 gauge for bottom rail of lower sash).

Construction

4. Windows shall be designed for inside glazing with glazing strips.

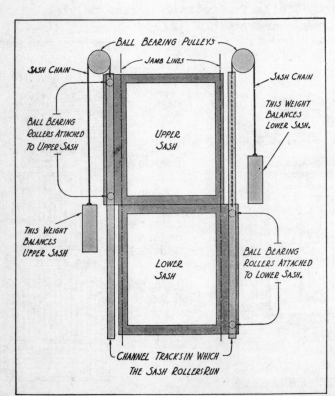

Diagram elevation of window illustrating method of balancing each sash with a single weight attached at one side. Sideplay is prevented by the ball bearing sash rollers which run in a steel channel track.

5. Sash members shall be mitered and arc welded at corners. Muntins shall be spot welded to sash members and at intersections. Frame members shall be arc welded at corners.
6. Sash shall have flanges to enter grooves at head and jambs and to make wide, overlapping contact at sill.
7. Each sash shall be balanced by a weight attached to one side of the sash with a galvanized steel sash chain (No. 113 American Chain Co., 1000 lbs. ultimate strength in tension) passing over a ball bearing steel pulley.
8. Each sash shall be equipped with two ball bearing rollers mounted one at the top and one at the bottom of the flange on the side to which the sash weight is attached. A 13-gauge steel channel track shall be fastened inside the weight box. The rollers shall run smoothly in this track so as to eliminate binding and sideplay or lateral movement of the sash.
9. The flange on the side of the sash opposite the rollers shall be guided by a groove in the face of, but having no opening into the interior of, the weight box.
10. Sash shall be equipped with safety stop to prevent dropping of sash if weight is detached.
11. Weather stripping of nickel silver shall be furnished for meeting rail, sill and jambs. Felt weather stripping shall be furnished at head.

Note:—Where specified, nickel silver will be substituted for felt weathering at the head. See note B, next page.

Hardware

12. Meeting rail lock and pull-down grip of malleable iron, cold galvanized shall be furnished, shipped unattached. Stamped steel pull-down socket for pole operation shall be welded to sash rail. Glazing strips of lower sash shall be formed with a flange to serve as a sash lift.

Note:—If specified the following can be furnished: Pull down handle (substituted for pull down grip) bronze sash lift grips, drop forged pull down socket, bar type lift handles for lower sash, hardware of polished solid bronze. (See note B, next page.)

Erection and Painting

Note:—See page 3 for general information on calking, painting and erection. See also note B, next page. Lupton Double Hung Windows (Types G and H) are shipped assembled. The chain is fastened inside the weight box, and the sash weights are shipped unattached.

13. All windows shall be erected in prepared openings by the window contractor. They shall be set plumb and true, securely fastened in place and counterweighting properly adjusted after glazing.

Note:—Include in the masonry specification that all masonry openings shall be accurately constructed in accordance with the installation details for Lupton Double Hung Windows (Types G and H) and that all mortar, grouting, pointing, etc., shall be performed under other specifications after windows have been erected.

14. All windows shall receive one coat of window manufacturer's standard gray galvanized metal primer before leaving factory.

Glass and Glazing

Note:—(See page 3.) Specify glass and glazing under proper heading elsewhere in specifications.

(a) Do not specify single thickness glass.
(b) Specify high-grade steel window putty (ordinary wood sash putty should not be used).
(c) Specify that all Lupton Steel Double Hung Windows shall be glazed from the inside; that all glass shall be set in a bed of putty and held by glazing strips.

English.

The following list is given to acquaint the apprentice with many works in the field of classical literature.

These books are on the shelves of most all public libraries.

Title	Author
Autoboigraphy	Benjamin Franklin
Journal	John Woolman
The Traveler	Oliver Goldscith
Elia	Charles Lamb
Hero Worshipers	Thomas Carlyle
Addresses	George Washington
Essays	Addison and Steele

Obtain at least one of the above listed books and report on it.

Civics.

The following is a continuation of the study, Health Through The Ages, which was begun in the previous chapter.

Continued from page 249

As WE BEGIN our story, we are, first of all, to imagine that we are living far back in the misty past in the days of the Stone Age.

As the years lift like a curtain, we see before us the face of a cliff studded with pine trees and sturdy bushes. In this cliff are the openings of several caves, partially shielded by the underbrush. A large stone, which can be used to close the mouth of the cave, lies near each entrance and in front are several broad flat stones and many smaller ones serving for chairs and tables.

At one side is a mound of broken stones where some men and boys, dressed in the skins of animals, are laboriously chipping spear heads and ax heads out of stubborn flint. In a pile close by are wooden spears and darts to which the flint heads are to be fixed. When the men go hunting in the surrounding forest, they will carry these spears and darts to kill smaller animals for food and to defend themselves against dangerous beasts.

As we watch this little scene, a woman with a baby in her arms appears at the door of a cave. She weeps and croons over her baby. The child is sick and the mother is seeking the medicine man of the tribe for help in her misery. What will he do for her?

We can guess rather accurately what will happen when the medicine man at last comes from the door of his cave. In the stage of culture which existed in those days, people probably regarded sickness as the work of evil spirits. We still find this superstition today in backward regions of the earth. If people believe that disease is

Continued on page 261

Typical roof framing plan and data.

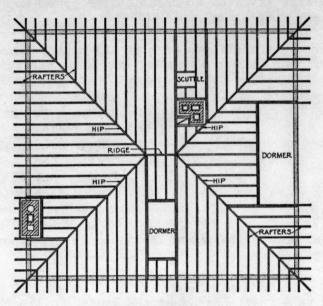

ROOF FRAMING PLAN

NOTES—FRAME BUILDINGS SHOULD BE DESIGNED TO APPLY STANDARD LENGTHS OF LUMBER.
STANDARD LENGTHS ARE MANUFACTURED IN MULTIPLES OF TWO FEET UP TO LENGTH OF TWENTY FOUR FEET.
WHERE GIRDERS OR OTHER MEMBERS ARE BUILT UP, SECTIONS SHOULD BE SECURELY SPIKED TOGETHER.
THE CUTTING OF BEAMS GIRDERS, JOISTS OR OTHER SUPPORTING TIMBERS SHOULD BE DONE IN SUCH MANNER AS NOT TO REDUCE THE STRENGTH OF SUCH TIMBERS.
ALL JOISTS UNDER PARTITIONS, AROUND LARGE OPENINGS, CHIMNEYS ETC. SHOULD BE DOUBLED.
ALL TIMBER BEARING MEMBERS SHOULD BE LAID CROWN EDGE UP TOPS AND ENDS OF PORCH TIMBERS SHOULD RECEIVE TWO BRUSH APPLICATIONS OF HOT REFINED CREOSOTE, OR OTHER PRESERVATIVE.
STUDS SHOULD BE DOUBLED UNDER ENDS OF ALL DOUBLE JOISTS.
DISTANCE BETWEEN ROWS OF CROSS BRIDGING OR CROSS BRIDGING AND BEARING SHOULD NOT EXCEED EIGHT FEET.

WHEN THE SIZE OF LUMBER IS GIVEN IN WHOLE NUMBERS AMERICAN STANDARD NOMINAL SIZES ARE MEANT.
STRESSES SHOULD BE BASED ON THE ACTUAL SIZE OF MATERIAL USED.
THE MINIMUM ACTUAL SIZE OF LUMBER SIGNIFIED BY WHOLE NUMBERS SHALL NOT BE LESS THAN AS FOLLOWS.

NOMINAL SIZE.	ACTUAL FINISHED SIZE.
2 X 4	1 5/8 X 3 5/8
2 X 6	1 5/8 X 5 5/8
2 X 8	1 5/8 X 7 1/2
2 X 10	1 5/8 X 9 1/2
2 X 12	1 5/8 X 11 1/2
3 X 4	2 5/8 X 3 5/8
3 X 6	2 5/8 X 5 5/8
3 X 8	2 5/8 X 7 1/2
3 X 10	2 5/8 X 9 1/2
3 X 12	2 5/8 X 11 1/2

FOR POSTS 5X5 AND LARGER, AND FOR BEAMS 5X6 AND LARGER THE FINISHED SIZE MAY BE 1/2" SMALLER IN EACH DIMENSION THAN THE NOMINAL SIZE.

Chapter XXVII

Hardware

The finish hardware is applied after the house has been painted and the interior finish applied. The hardware consists of door knobs, escutcheons, window latches, sash lifts, etc. The specifications must be followed carefully in order to insure the proper placing of the proper hardware.

Nearly articles of hardware are held in position by screws. These screws should be put in position by the use of a screw driver and never hammered into place.

All hardware should be level and plumb. All window latches should hold the sash together tightly. All doors should work easily. All keys should be properly fitted and the locks work easily. All knobs should be held solidly in place. The carpenter should give extra care to the fitting of finish hardware.

All finish hardware that is difficult to apply, or involves many fittings, is accompanied by detailed directions given by the manufacturers of the articles. This refers especially to door lock sets, door checks, double acting hinges and door hangers used with sliding doors.

Practical jobs. Apply all finish hardware where designated by specifications and plan details.

Related Studies

Drawing.

Develop a complete set of house plans. Use the floor plans and elevations as begun in the two previous studies on drawing. Develop the plans including the following views, phases or sheets: perspective and floor layouts, plot plan, foundation and basement plan, first floor plan, second floor plan, first floor joist plan, second floor joist plan, front framing elevations, left side framing elevation, right side framing elevation, rear framing elevation, wall heights detail, roof framing details, front elevation, right side elevation, left side elevation, rear elevation, moulding details, stair details, garage, list of sheets in set of plans.

Work these drawings up on tracing paper or drawing paper. Do not ink them for tracing but pencil trace and make a set of blue prints.

Mathematics.

Estimate the quantity of hardware needed according to the designations in the specifications. Estimating time or labor needed to fit hardware varies greatly. Installing a lock set in a door takes about two hours time. Hanging a door takes about a like amount of time. Installing and hanging sash takes about three hours per window. In general it is well to figure about a day's labor per room for finish hardware.

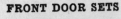

FRONT DOOR SETS

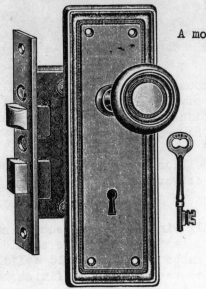

A mortise lock set.

A medicine cabinet.

Typical interior hardware.

DOUBLE HUNG WINDOW HARDWARE

CRESCENT SASH FASTENERS

Cat. No.	Case, in.	Strike, in.
07	$\frac{15}{16}$ x $2\frac{5}{8}$	$\frac{5}{8}$ x $2\frac{5}{8}$
8	1 x $2\frac{3}{4}$	$\frac{7}{8}$ x $2\frac{3}{4}$
9	$1\frac{1}{16}$ x 3	1 x 3
10	$1\frac{1}{4}$ x $3\frac{5}{16}$	$\frac{3}{4}$ x $3\frac{5}{16}$

Nos. 07, 08, 9, 10   No. 102

Sash Fasteners

No. 102 is designed for high sash. Can be fastened or unfastened with a pole hook.

Cat. No.	Case, in.	Strike, in.
102	$\frac{7}{8}$ x $2\frac{3}{8}$	$\frac{7}{8}$ x $2\frac{3}{8}$

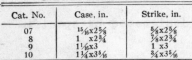

No. 054   No. 22

Nos. 056, 156   No. 14

HOOK SASH LIFTS

Cat. No.	Size, in.
14	$\frac{7}{8}$ x $1\frac{5}{8}$
15	$\frac{7}{8}$ x $1\frac{13}{16}$
015	1 x $1\frac{3}{4}$

No. 22B   No. 022

Flush Sash Lifts

Nos. 026, 26, 27 and 69

Bar Sash Lifts

No. 98

Sash Pull Plate
Cat. No. 98
Size $1\frac{1}{4}$ x $2\frac{1}{8}$ in.

Cat. No.	22	22B	022	054
Size, in...	$1\frac{5}{16}$ x $3\frac{1}{8}$	$1\frac{5}{16}$ x 3	$1\frac{1}{4}$ x $2\frac{9}{16}$	$1\frac{1}{2}$ x $3\frac{5}{8}$

Cat. No.	Size, in.
026	$1\frac{1}{8}$ x 4
26	$1\frac{1}{4}$ x $4\frac{3}{4}$
27	$1\frac{3}{8}$ x 5
69	$1\frac{5}{8}$ x $5\frac{1}{2}$
056	$1\frac{1}{4}$ x $4\frac{3}{4}$
156	1 x 4

Open   No. 0   Closed
Size $1\frac{5}{16}$ x $1\frac{5}{8}$ in.
Ventilating Locks
A safeguard for ventilating rooms.
Permits ventilation with security

S.W.   W.
$1\frac{1}{4}$ in. $1\frac{1}{4}$ in.
No. 8   No. 8
F.H.   R.H.
**Stop Bead
Screws and
Washers**

No. 1x8-in. R.H. Screws
Window Stop Adjusters
Heavy bed prevents
bending in tightening of
screw.

No. 058
$2\frac{1}{4}$ x $1\frac{1}{8}$ in.
**Sash Pole
Hanger**

PULL DOWN HOOK

Cat. No.	Length, in.	Diam. hole, in.
17	$2\frac{15}{16}$	$1\frac{1}{16}$
17L	$3\frac{7}{8}$	$\frac{7}{8}$
017	4	1

INTERIOR HARDWARE

Science.

Assemble as much finish hardware as possible. Try to obtain a lock set. Take it apart and assemble. Take hinges apart and assemble. What is the difference between a butt hinge and a surface hinge? How are lock sets designated? Obtain illustrations of as many items of hardware as possible. What is a safe way to latch a window? Do not confuse finish hardware with sanitary fixtures, which are installed by a plumber.

English.

Write a report on the study or research made in the following study in civics.

Civics.

Metal attachments placed on frame houses have quite a historical background. The development of locks from the medieval days is very interesting. The development of nails from the large headed, thick bodied ones of the early English days to the present wire and cut nails presents a very interesting study

Until recently, hinges were large, crude and cumbersome units. Today the double acting hinge is a very unique apparatus.

Search for the graphic history of hinges, nails, lock sets, etc.

Sketch some of the illustrations. Keep a permanent file of these illustrations.

Continued from
page 257

caused by malign spirits, they usually assume that the way to cure it is to use some form of magic which will appease the evil spirits or frighten them away from the body they have attacked. With offerings and sacrifice, they may try to please the demon, so that he will do no further harm, or, with horrible masks, dances and noises, they may seek to drive him away. Some such help as this we may be sure was offered to our pitiful Stone Age mother.

Today, the carrying of a horse chestnut to ward off rheumatism, the wearing of a bag of camphor around the neck to avoid influenza, and superstitions in regard to horseshoes and the rabbit's foot are survivals of the ages of magic. A few years ago, a famous murder trial in the United States centered about a "charm book" containing magic formulæ for the curing of all diseases. The ages of fear and the ages of superstition are not altogether in the past.

OUR NEXT SCENE is laid in a little country in the hills between the Jordan Valley and the Mediterranean Sea. Here live the Hebrew people in their land of Palestine.

The Message of the Hebrew Priest

Before the steps of the temple is gathered a motley throng waiting for the coming of the priest—soldiers, merchants of the city, herdsmen from the surrounding plains, a group of porters just back with loads of cedar-wood from Lebanon. The old priest comes slowly and majestically out of the temple door and, as the people

Continued on
page 265

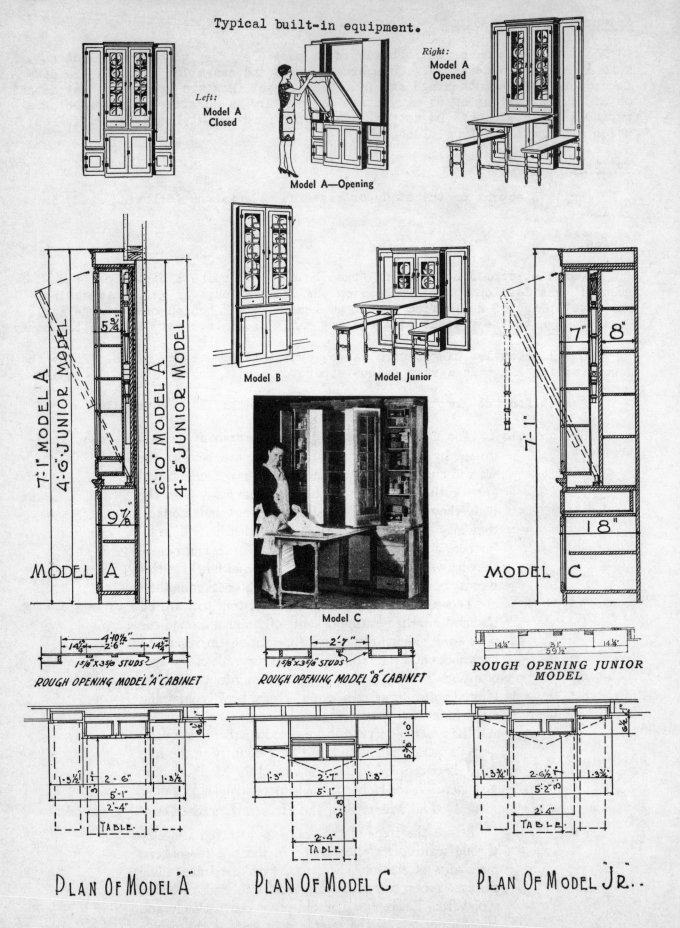

Typical built-in equipment.

Left:
Model A
Closed

Right:
Model A
Opened

Model A—Opening

MODEL A

MODEL C

Model B

Model Junior

Model C

ROUGH OPENING MODEL "A" CABINET

ROUGH OPENING MODEL "B" CABINET

ROUGH OPENING JUNIOR MODEL

PLAN OF MODEL "A"

PLAN OF MODEL C

PLAN OF MODEL JR.

Chapter XXVIII

Closets and Shelving

All trim in closets in worked in with as much care as the trim in any other place in the building. Join pieces as designated or if not designated join with miter or butt joints as the situation requires.

Shelving should be fitted neatly against the plastered walls. A scribed joint should be made if necessary. Join shelving stock with mitered joints. Do not place piece of shelving stock over another where shelving meets at corners. A mitered or butted joint should be used.

Coat hangers and poles in closets should be placed about five feet from the floor and about twelve inches from the rear walls.

Closets and cabinets are shown with much detail in the set of plans and such designations should be followed carefully. Built in cabinets are usually built up at the mill and delivered to the job. The carpenter, in this instance, merely sets the cabinets in place. A cabinet is often delivered to the job knocked down and must be assembled by the carpenter.

Work should be done carefully, plumbed and squared and all surfaces to take a finish should be sanded carefully. All nails should be set and any blemishes in any surface removed or treated.

Practical jobs. Install trim in closets. Install shelving in closets. Install any built in cabinets, fixtures, etc.

Related Studies

Drawing.

Sketch, freehand, various details of built in equipment. The illustrations in this chapter are given as suggestions. Sketch in any one of the several methods. Obtain other illustrations.

Mathematics.

All special cabinet work requires detailed drawings which are used first in estimating cost and then as a guide in construction. Each cabinet is a special job in itself and should be treated as such.

Estimate the cost of material and hardware needed in the special cabinets in the accompanying set of house plans. These items should be worked out on a regulation stock bill and entered in the grand total of the cost of the building as a unit item. The time element in the construction of built-in or ready-built equipment is very difficult to estimate. If one makes a drawing and estimates the material and hardware needed a mill manufacturer can be asked to estimate the unit cost of the project.

Typical built-in equipment.

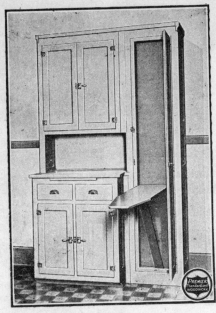

The Broom Cabinet can be used alone as shown below or can be built-in with Practical Six Kitchen Cabinets as shown here.

This shows a 2'6" x 7'0" Dresser joined to Broom Cabinet with Ironing Board Compartment Door.

CORNER CHINA CLOSET

Premier No. 28

This cabinet is cased in with trim to match the doors and other woodwork.   No trim furnished.

No. 28—Corner China Case, Glazed...............K. D. Each, $51.45
No. 28—Corner China Case, Glazed...............N. U. Each, 58.20

Comparative Heights—Top of door lines with 6'8" doors. From floor to counter effect at bottom of upper door 2'6".

Rough Wall Opening—2'8" wide, 6'10" high, 1'3¾" deep.

Upper Section—Base shelf and three adjustable shelves with front edges neatly moulded. Metal ratchet strips secured to ends, metal shelf supports furnished. **Door**—Divided with wood bars and glazed with plain glass free from defects, secured in place with glazing beads. Size of door 2'6" wide, 4'2" high.

Lower Section—Bottom and one stationary shelf. Ends dadoed to receive shelves. **Doors**—Rabbeted and beaded. Panels are 3-ply laminated fir. Pair 2'6" wide, 2'0" high.

Inside of Cabinet—Inside width at front 2'5½" inside width of back (parallel to front) 1'1⅝". Ends extend at right angles to front 6", then converge at 45° for 11". Actual inside depth 1'2". This forms small octagon corner, an added feature for effective display. This construction is necessary when cabinet is set in corner of room—highly desirable when set in straight wall. **Back**—3-ply laminated fir panel.

Packing—Front frame completely assembled, doors rough fitted ready for hardware. One cabinet in carton. Weight—153 lbs.

Installation—Ends, back, top, bottom and shelves are completely machined ready for quick assembling. Doors and front frame are all completely assembled at factory. Ends are dadoed so that no figuring is necessary to locate top, base shelf and bottom. Printed instructions for installation are packed inside the cabinet.

MEDICINE CABINETS

Wall Opening, 20" x 26".
Mirror Size, 14" x 20".

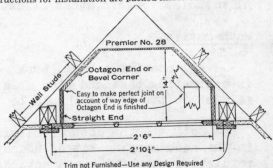

This cabinet without trim offers an opportunity to install a corner china closet that will harmonize with any design of woodwork. It can also be installed in a straight wall where the depth of the wall will permit.

Kitchen cabinet.

Science.

Closets have given place to cabinets as a place for storing household goods. Cabinet construction is seldom done on the job as much better and cheaper units can be built in a mill.

Refer to trade magazines, journals and to trade catalogs and obtain information and illustrations of cabinet equipment for the several rooms of a dwelling. The following illustrations, courtesy the Parsons Co., of Detroit, Mich., show some very recent developments in kitchen cabinet productions. There is an abundance of sales literature available for cabinet work in every room in a house. Search for this literature as much valuable information can be obtained.

Continued from page 261

grow silent, he gives his message. He warns them of the danger of incurring God's anger by running after the gods of the heathen. Then he tells them that persons affected with diseases are "unclean" and that anything which such a one has touched is unclean also. After recovery, the infected person must be quarantined for seven days and then his body and clothes must be washed. The priest then gives the signs by which certain diseases like leprosy may be recognized.

The speaker tells the people that disease must be reported. "He that owneth the house shall come and tell the priest, saying 'It seemeth to me there is, as it were, a plague in the house.' Then the patient shall go out of the house to the door of the house and shall shut up the house seven days." If the priest, after this period, still believes the house to be infected, he will order it to be torn down and its stone and timber carried out of the city.

After delivering his message the old priest turns once more and enters the temple door. The people disperse to their homes, pondering his words.

IN THE Golden Age of ancient Greece, the people loved health and beauty and moral excellence. An exquisite care of the body was part of the training of

Continued on page 271

English.

Obtain a book titled THE TORCH by Louise Collier Willcox. This book is a collection of poems for young people. Read several poems found in this text and report on each. If this volume is not available obtain some of the works of the following authors and make a report: Wordsworth, William; Lowell, James R.; Scott, Sir Walter; Poe, Edgar Allen; Longfellow, Henry W.; Stevenson, Robert W.; Coleridge, Samuel T.; Tennyson, Alfred Lord.

Civics.

A carpenter should have an understanding of the work of all other crafts employed on a frame house. The major portion of the work done on a frame house is done by a carpenter but, if he should not be familiar with the work of the excavator, cement worker, plumber, electrician, painter, glazier, decorator, till setter and plasterer many embarrassing situations will arise.

Describe the work of each of the above named crafts. What relation does the carpenter have with each craft?

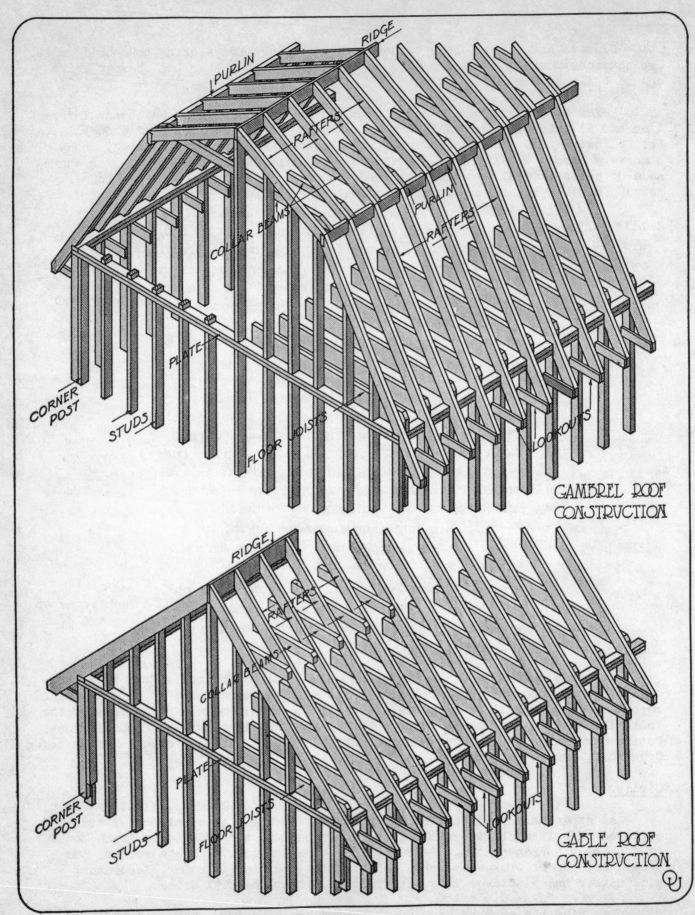

GAMBREL ROOF
CONSTRUCTION

GABLE ROOF
CONSTRUCTION

Chapter XXIX

Finish Flooring

Clear the rough floor of all scrap stock, nails, plaster and dirt. If this material is caked on the floor it must be scraped loose and removed.

If the base strip or carpet strip has been placed on the base board remove it and keep for future use. Nail down any loose boards in the flooring. If there is any pronounced unevenness in the sub or loose flooring it should be leveled before the finished floor is laid.

Lay strip of heavy felt paper on top of the rough floor and make sure it is evenly placed. Lay the paper with about a two inch lap at joints. Often finish flooring is paid before trim is placed in position.

Refer to the plans and note the design to be used for the hardwood flooring. If there is a border it should be laid clear around the room at the beginning of the flooring job. Begin at the extreme edge of the rough flooring and slip the finish floor boards and secret nail in place. Work the border out from the base board piece by piece around the room. Butt all joints. Do not miter any joints. Secret nail all pieces placing nail at a slant so that it will draw stock together.

Work each piece in squarely, one to another and not in relation to the room, as the sides of the room may not be square in relation to itself. See that all stock is held down securely and well matched and joined. Sand the flooring until a smooth finish is obtained. The painter should finish the floor with the required filler and varnish. Replace the carpet strip carefully drawing it down to the finish flooring.

Practical jobs. Prepare a rough floor to receive a hardwood finish flooring. Lay a finish floor with a pattern in it. Lay a finish floor without a pattern in it.

Related Studies

Drawing.

The study in drawing of Chapter XXVIII dealt with an assignment of work of a complete set of house plans. This study will deal with the changing of an existing set of plans. Make some change in the floor plan, such as placing the living room across the front portion of the house. This phase of study is always very interesting as many people will like the exterior of a house but not the room arrangement or vice versa.

Mathematics.

In estimating floor coverings, such as hardwood flooring, linoleum, cork, rubber, etc., one works in units of squares. A square is an area of 10' x 10' in measure. Labor costs run about 250 to 350 hours per 1000 square feet or ten squares.

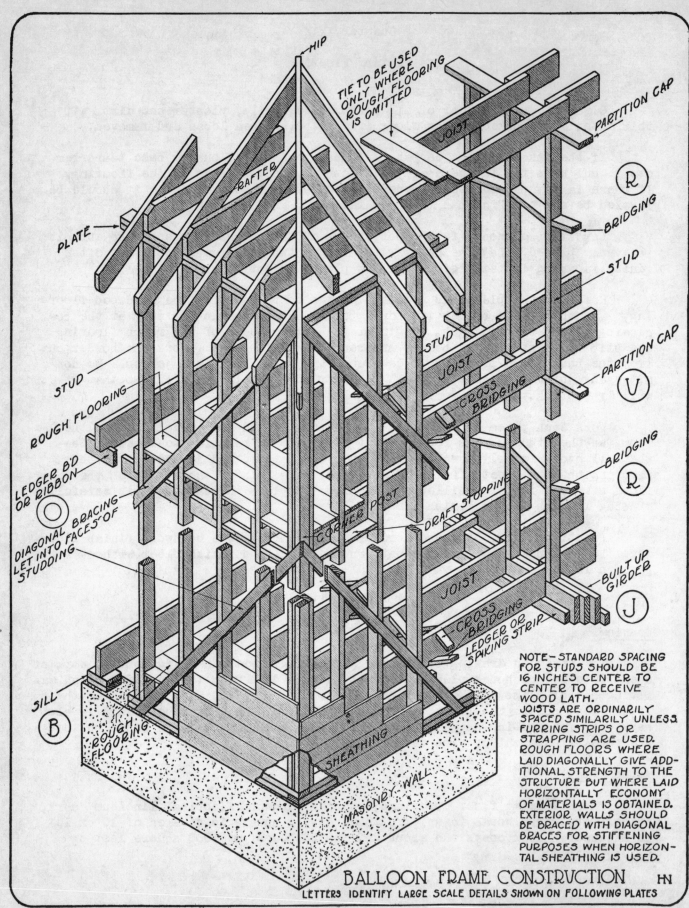

HIP

TIE TO BE USED
ONLY WHERE
ROUGH FLOORING
IS OMITTED

JOIST

PARTITION CAP

Ⓡ

BRIDGING

RAFTER

PLATE

STUD

STUD

JOIST

PARTITION CAP

CROSS BRIDGING

Ⓥ

STUD

ROUGH FLOORING

LEDGER B'D
OR RIBBON

BRIDGING

Ⓡ

Ⓞ

CORNER POST

DRAFT STOPPING

DIAGONAL BRACING
LET INTO FACES OF
STUDDING

JOIST

BUILT UP
GIRDER

Ⓙ

CROSS
BRIDGING

LEDGER OR
SPIKING STRIP

SILL

Ⓑ

ROUGH
FLOORING

SHEATHING

MASONRY WALL

NOTE—STANDARD SPACING
FOR STUDS SHOULD BE
16 INCHES CENTER TO
CENTER TO RECEIVE
WOOD LATH.
JOISTS ARE ORDINARILY
SPACED SIMILARILY UNLESS
FURRING STRIPS OR
STRAPPING ARE USED.
ROUGH FLOORS WHERE
LAID DIAGONALLY GIVE ADD-
ITIONAL STRENGTH TO THE
STRUCTURE BUT WHERE LAID
HORIZONTALLY ECONOMY
OF MATERIALS IS OBTAINED.
EXTERIOR WALLS SHOULD
BE BRACED WITH DIAGONAL
BRACES FOR STIFFENING
PURPOSES WHEN HORIZON-
TAL SHEATHING IS USED.

BALLOON FRAME CONSTRUCTION HN
LETTERS IDENTIFY LARGE SCALE DETAILS SHOWN ON FOLLOWING PLATES

Refer to the specifications, find the floor covering specified, estimate the quantity and labor and add to the grand estimate previously described.

Science.

The following details are offered as aids in the laying of finish flooring. Sketch these details, obtain illustrations of others and keep a catalog of the several illustrations.

TYPICAL FINISH FLOORING DETAILS

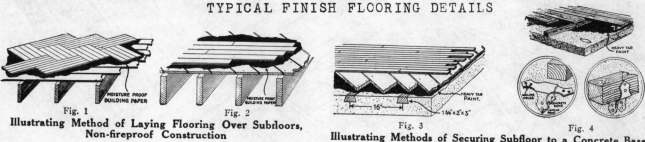

Fig. 1   Fig. 2

Illustrating Method of Laying Flooring Over Subfloors, Non-fireproof Construction

Fig. 3   Fig. 4

Illustrating Methods of Securing Subfloor to a Concrete Base

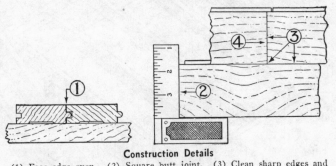
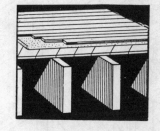

Construction Details

(1) Face edge even.   (2) Square butt joint.   (3) Clean sharp edges and corners.   (4) Hairline joints

English.

Write a description of the accompanying illustration. Describe the items in the picture and relate what is being done.

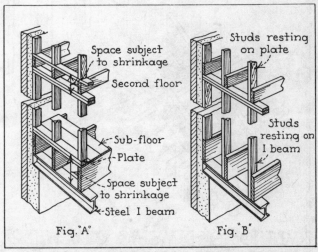

Fig. "A"   Fig. "B"

TROUBLE from shrinkage less in Fig. A framing than Fig. B.

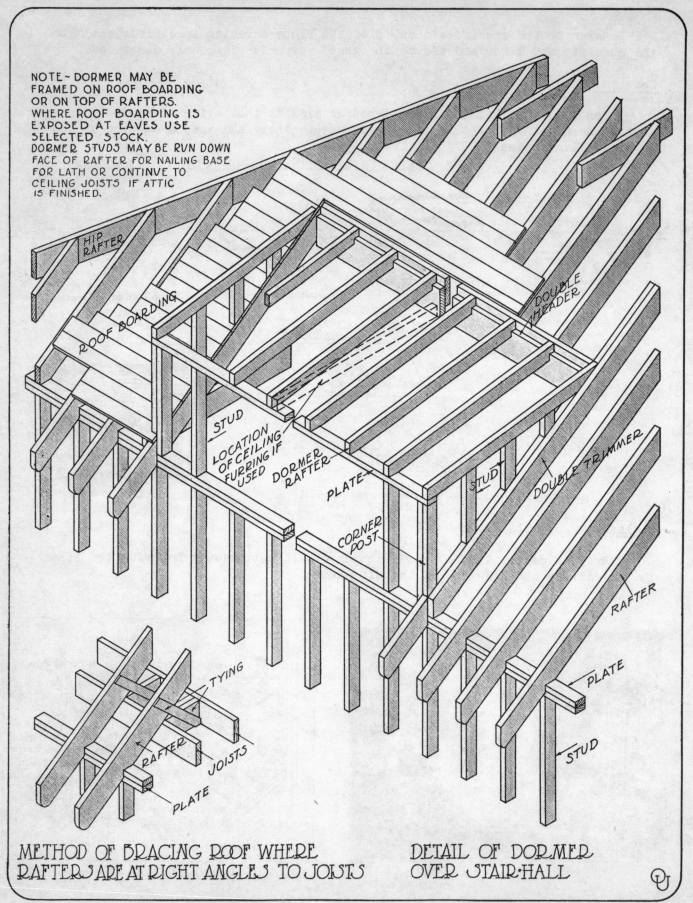

NOTE~ DORMER MAY BE FRAMED ON ROOF BOARDING OR ON TOP OF RAFTERS. WHERE ROOF BOARDING IS EXPOSED AT EAVES USE SELECTED STOCK. DORMER STUDS MAY BE RUN DOWN FACE OF RAFTER FOR NAILING BASE FOR LATH OR CONTINUE TO CEILING JOISTS IF ATTIC IS FINISHED.

HIP RAFTER

ROOF BOARDING

DOUBLE HEADER

STUD

LOCATION OF CEILING FURRING IF USED

DORMER RAFTER

PLATE

STUD

DOUBLE TRIMMER

CORNER POST

RAFTER

PLATE

STUD

TYING

RAFTER

JOISTS

PLATE

METHOD OF BRACING ROOF WHERE RAFTERS ARE AT RIGHT ANGLES TO JOISTS

DETAIL OF DORMER OVER STAIR-HALL

Civics.

The following is a continuation of the study, HEALTH THROUGH THE AGES.

Continued from
page 271

youth. To see the results of this training, we are to pay a visit to the stadium of ancient Athens, where athletic contests took place. It is a sunny day in the year 420 B.C. and the marble benches of the stadium are filled; even the grassy slopes of the hills above are crowded with spectators, for nothing gives greater delight to the citizens of Athens than to see beautiful strong bodies in action.

We watch it all—the running, the jumping, the discus throwing, the spear throwing and the wrestling. These five competitions make up the famous Pentathlon, the most important event in the Olympic Games, because the man who can show superiority in all five must be in truth an all-round athlete. So important are these games to all Greece that the four year periods between their occurrence, called Olympiads, are the Greek units for determining dates.

Long and hard is the training for the candidates who seek to take part in the Olympic Games; but many a youth down there on the racetrack of the stadium dreams of a day when the wreath of wild olive will be placed on his brow to reward a victory in the Olympics.

A man with other dreams sits on the marble bench beside us, watching the ripple of muscles under clear, tanned skins, the light of health in bright, keen eyes. He is a stately middle-aged man, with short, curling beard, massive forehead, and deep-set eyes. He is clad in flowing robes and in his hand he carries a tall staff with a serpent twined about it. In his person we are looking upon Hippocrates of Cos, "The Father of Medicine." He stands for another element in the life of ancient Greece which is as important as the love of life and health and beauty.

The Art of Hippocrates

The greatest gift of the Greeks to civilization was science, or the conception that the universe is ruled by natural laws and that, by studying those laws, we can come into accord with them and so make this world a safer and a better place in which to live. The essence of the art of Hippocrates was the study of the patient—not theorizing, not seeking for magic formulæ, but studying, observing, learning to recognize each particular disease

Continued on
page 272

LAMINATED (THREE PLY) HARDWOOD FLOORING

Construction

Made of thoroughly kiln dried hardwood stock built up three (3) ply with the grain of the center ply set at right angles to bottom and selected face veneers. The flooring is accurately tongued and grooved on all four (4) edges and carefully sanded to a uniform thickness ready for finish.

Advantages

(1) More beautiful selected grain effects can be produced especially in the wider plank flooring.

(2) Elimination of shrinkage, swelling and warpage inherent in ordinary solid strip flooring.

(3) Labor saved in the nailing of the larger units as compared with narrow strips.

(4) Labor saved in the usual scraping and sanding.

Patterns or Types

Plank Flooring—Random widths and lengths showing artificial crack lines, plugs and keys, reminiscent of the days when the size of a plank was determined primarily by the tree from which it was hewn.

Period Patterns—Fontainebleau, herringbone or any of the standard or special period or modern designs.

Thicknesses

Plain or Period Patterns—$1\frac{3}{8}$ in. thick with net $\frac{7}{16}$ in. face veneer; $\frac{7}{8}$ in. thick with net $\frac{1}{4}$ in. face veneer.

Woods

Plain or Quartered White Oak; Plain Red Oak; Walnut; Teak and other accepted flooring woods.

Fuming

Plain or Quartered White Oak can be furnished fumed where required.

Fireproofing

We have a complete plant for fully fireproofing wood which will meet the rigid requirements of the building code of the City of New York. Where required, our flooring can be fireproofed.

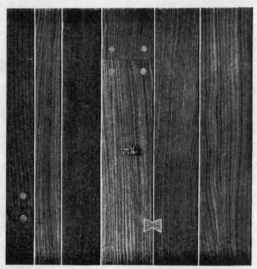

Plank Flooring—Random Widths and Lengths

Fontainebleau Pattern—Quartered White Oak

Courtesy HARDWOOD PRODUCTS CORPORATION, Neenah, Wisconsin.

Continued from page 271

and to find, if possible, its cause and remedy. The actual knowledge of Hippocrates was often slight compared with ours today. Yet it was always a natural and not a magical cause which he was seeking; and his method of questioning nature is the one upon which all modern science and medicine have been built.

During his stay in Athens in 420 B.C., we may imagine that Hippocrates went out to visit Epidaurus, where there was a famous temple of healing. If we had been with him, we should have found a group of splendid marble buildings—temples, hotels, baths, gymnasia, a stadium with a seating capacity of 12,000 and a theater which could hold 20,000. For the patients who came for healing, a regimen of careful diet, rest and sleep, exercise and massage was prescribed. Among the people there

Continued on page 274

Chapter XXX

Finishing

Much of the work of the painter and finisher will be completed before the finish hardware is applied. The exterior work which is painted will be done while the finishing is going on by the carpenter on the inside of the structure.

All work should be completed by the carpenter so that the painter need not be delayed by construction work.

All nails in the exterior and interior work should be set by the carpenter. All surfaces should be planed where needed and sanded where needed.

All rooms should be cleared of all tools and work benches. All extra lumber should be returned to the lumber mill. The floors should be well swept and all wood work dusted.

Practical jobs. Set all finishing nails. Remove all tools. Remove work benches. Sweep up trash and dust all wordwork.

Related Studies

Drawing.

The orders or styles of architecture are supreme developments of a su porting member called a pier or column. Dwellings began with no cellar or basement walls and no supporting walls. In building development, walls, piers and columns were devised. The Romans and Greeks developed the column into a feature of beauty that has been given to civilization. These columns have been reproduced throughout the world since their proportions were fixed by an Italian architect, Giacomo Barozzi of Vignola, Italy, who lived from 1507 to 1573.

The Roman, Greek and Egyptian peoples had certain styles of orders or column development. The best known styles are the Roman order, together with some Greek and Egyptian variations.

A style or order may be divided into the base, column and entablature. The dimensions of all are given in terms of the diameter of the column.

The five orders of Roman origin are shown on the next page.

List the names of the Roman, Greek and Egyptian orders. Produce the above orders, together with the other orders, on drawing paper or in model form in wood. If possible, produce the enrichment of the various parts of the base, columns and entablatures of the orders wherever enrichment is to be found. Name the various parts of the several orders.

Mathematics.

In this study will be found the directions for constructing the hexagon, octagon and ellipse.

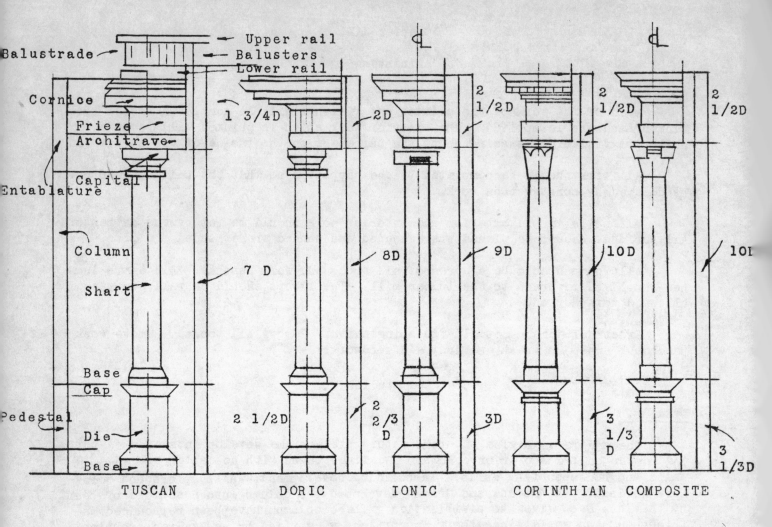

Balustrade — Upper rail — Balusters — Lower rail

Cornice
Frieze
Architrave
Capital
Entablature
Column
Shaft
Base
Cap
Pedestal
Die
Base

1 3/4D   2D   2 1/2D   2 1/2D   2 1/2D

7 D   8D   9D   10D   10D

2 1/2D   2 2/3 D   3D   3 1/3 D   3 1/3D

TUSCAN   DORIC   IONIC   CORINTHIAN   COMPOSITE

FIVE ORDERS OF ARCHITECTURE

Continued from
page 272

was still much reliance on the magic in other forms of treatment which had come down from older times, but the realism of Hippocrates scattered the shadows like a clear ray of sunlight, as he taught his pupils that each disease has its own nature, and that each arises from a natural cause. This method—the method of science—was the great gift of Greece to the Western world.

Note: Space will not permit the placing of the article, HEALTH THROUGH THE AGES, in its entirety. If one is interested in continuing the story it may be obtained from the Metropolitan Life Insurance Co., of New York, or reference may be made in a public library.

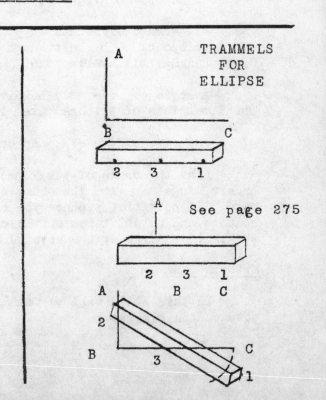

TRAMMELS
FOR
ELLIPSE

See page 275

To construct a hexagon produce a square of any size. Find the center by use of diagonal lines. This is Point A. Produce circle within square so as to touch sides of square. Item B. At point where circle touches sides, say at point C, obtain distance AC on dividers. Step this distance around circumference at points 1, 2, 3, 4 and 5. Join points C, 1, 2, 3, 4, 5, and C with straight lines to produce six-sided figure - a hexagon.

The hexagon

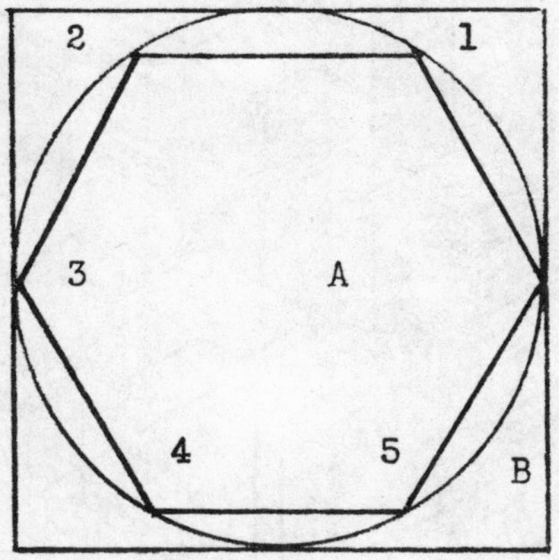

The octagon

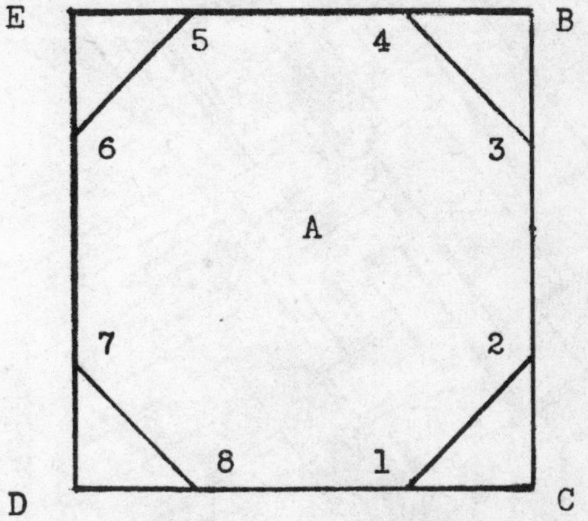

To construct an octagon produce a square. Find center of it by use of diagonal lines. This is point A. Using distance AB as radius and B, C, D, and E as centers, cut sides of square at points 1, 2, 3, 4, 5, 6, 7 and 8. Connect these points 1-2, 3-4, 5-6 and 7-8 with straight lines to produce eight sided figure - an octagon.

To construct an ellipse produce a trammel, which can be a piece of paper or wood, 1/2" x a length slightly greater than BC (the long axis of the ellipse) and mark on trammel points-1-2 equal to CB and 1-3 equal to BA. Place point 2 of trammel at B and point 3 on BC and point 1 at C. Move trammel from C downward to point below B keeping points 2 moving up on BA and 3 moving over on CB. Mark along on line produced to obtain 1/4 of ellipse. Do this for three other portions of figure.

THE COST OF DOING BUSINESS

FIGURED ON THE SELLING PRICE—THE RIGHT WAY TO FIGURE PROFITS.

The following Table shows the percentage which must be added to cost to effect a given percentage of profit on the Selling Price:

Add to Cost	To Make on Selling Price	Add to Cost	To Make on Selling Price	Add to Cost	To Make on Selling Price	Add to Cost	To Make on Selling Price	Add to Cost	To Make on Selling Price
5%	4¾%	16.28%	14%	25%	20%	40%	28½%	66⅔%	40%
7½	7	16⅔	14¼	26.58	21	42.86	30	70	41
10	9	17.65	15	28.21	22	45	31	75	42¾
11.11	10	19.05	16	29.88	23	50	33⅓	80	44½
12.36	11	20.00	16⅔	31.58	24	53.85	35	85	46
12½	11⅛	20.49	17	33⅓	25	55	35½	90	47½
13.63	12	21.96	18	35	26	60	37½	100	50
14.94	13	23.46	19	37½	27¼	65	39½		

TABLE FOR FIGURING NET PROFITS.

If your cost of doing business figured on sales is represented by one of the percentages on top line
And you mark your goods at one of the percentages above delivered cost as shown in left hand column
Your percentage of net profit is represented by the figure at the junction of the two columns

%	10%	11%	12%	13%	14%	15%	16%	17%	18%	19%	20%	21%	22%	23%	24%	25%
25	10	9	8	7	6	5	4	3	2	1	00	1 Loss	2 Loss	3 Loss	4 Loss	5 Loss
33⅓	15	14	13	12	11	10	9	8	7	6	5	4	3	2	1	00
40	18 4/7	17 4/7	16 4/7	15 4/7	14 4/7	13 4/7	12 4/7	11 4/7	10 4/7	9 4/7	8 4/7	7 4/7	6 4/7	5 4/7	4 4/7	3 4/7
50	23⅓	22⅓	21⅓	20⅓	19⅓	18⅓	17⅓	16⅓	15⅓	14⅓	13⅓	12⅓	11⅓	10⅓	9⅓	8⅓
60	27½	26½	25½	24½	23½	22½	21½	20½	19½	18½	17½	16½	15½	14½	13½	12½
75	32 6/7	31 6/7	30 6/7	29 6/7	28 6/7	27 6/7	26 6/7	25 6/7	24 6/7	23 6/7	22 6/7	21 6/7	20 6/7	19 6/7	18 6/7	17 6/7
100	40	39	38	37	36	35	34	33	32	31	30	29	28	27	26	25

Explanation—If your cost of doing business is 15 per cent of your gross sales and you mark a line at 25 per cent. above cost, your net profit is 5 per cent on sales—as shown in the diagram. If your cost of doing business is 18 per cent and you mark a line at 60 per cent, your profit is 19½ per cent on sales.

From 1936 YEAR BOOK of Material Men's Club, Inc. Red Bank, N.J.

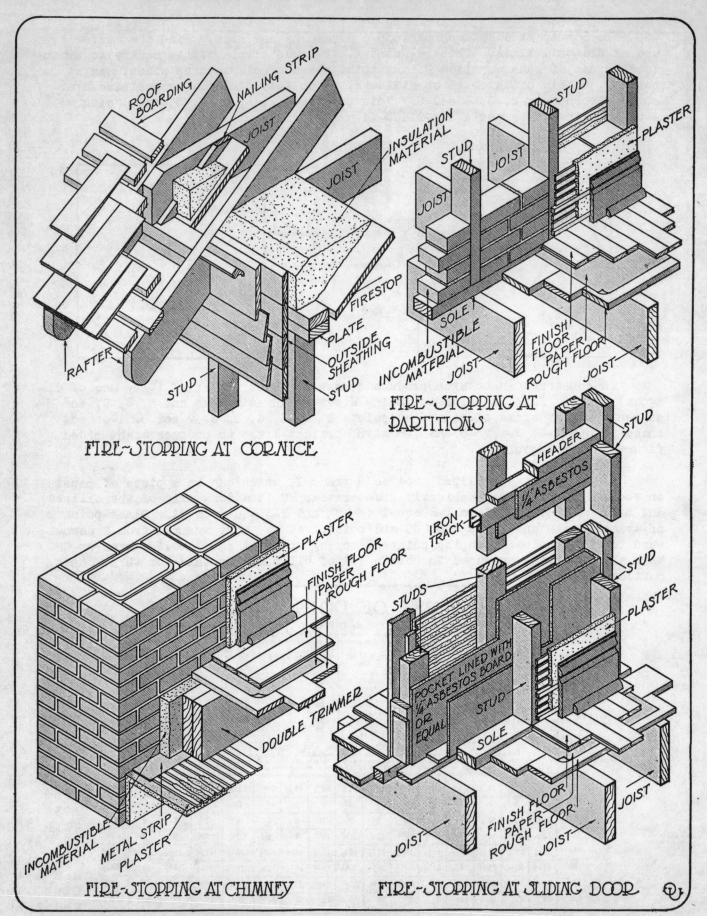

FIRE-STOPPING AT CORNICE

FIRE-STOPPING AT PARTITIONS

FIRE-STOPPING AT CHIMNEY

FIRE-STOPPING AT SLIDING DOOR

Science.

Abrasives, such as sandpaper, flint paper and steel wool are used extensively in finishing. Obtain samples of abrasives, test them on various surfaces such as wood, varnish, paint, etc. State the results obtained in each test. Refer to an encyclopedia for information relative to abrasives.

English.

Visit a dwelling or residence which is just being completed. Takes notes on observations and write a report.

Civics.

Visit a contractor or carpenter. Make yourself acquainted with his work and his jobs in so far as possible. Early in your training career begin to make friends in the construction industry for they will stand you in good stead when training days come to an end.

Constitution and Laws

of the

United Brotherhood of Carpenters and Joiners of America

AND RULES FOR SUBORDINATE
BODIES UNDER ITS JURISDICTION

Established August 12, 1881

Constitution as amended by the Twenty-Second General Convention held at Lakeland, Fla., Sept. 29 to Oct. 9, 1928.

In effect April 1, Nineteen Twenty-Nine

the Local Union of which he was a member, or in which he was rejected, and shall not be received into any Local Union again except by a two-thirds vote of the Local Union.

J   Any candidate applying for admission in any Local Union under the jurisdiction of the United Brotherhood, must be a citizen of one of the countries included in said jurisdiction, or must furnish proof of his intentions to become a citizen in the country where he makes application for membership. All applications of candidates shall give the date and place of court wherein they took out their first citizenship papers, and after five years from said date if they have not taken out their final papers, they shall be dropped from the roll of the organization.

K   An apprentice of good moral character between the ages of seventeen and twenty-two years may be admitted to membership as a semi-beneficial member, and after having served four years as such and qualifying in accordance with the Constitution and International Laws of the United Brotherhood, he shall be classed as a full beneficial member and entitled to the donations prescribed for beneficial members, and notification of his transfer to the beneficial class shall be forwarded in the next monthly report to the General Secretary for record. The initiation fee for an apprentice shall be the constitutional fee of Ten ($10.00) Dollars.

L   An employer who employs two or more journeymen may have one apprentice, but the number may-be increased at such rate as the District Council or Local Union having jurisdiction may decide.

M   All apprentices shall hold agreement between the District Council or Local Union having jurisdiction and his employer, and any apprentice who can be continuously employed by one employer and who violates such agreement shall be debarred from further membership in the United Brotherhood, unless such apprentice shall have sufficient cause to make complaint to the District Council or Local Union against his employer, and which complaint on investigation should be sustained.

N   When an employer cannot provide continuous employment for an apprentice and he is obliged to seek work with another employer, he shall have the actual time he works for each succeeding employer entered on his Due Book.

33

The Carpenter's Union Rules on Apprentices.

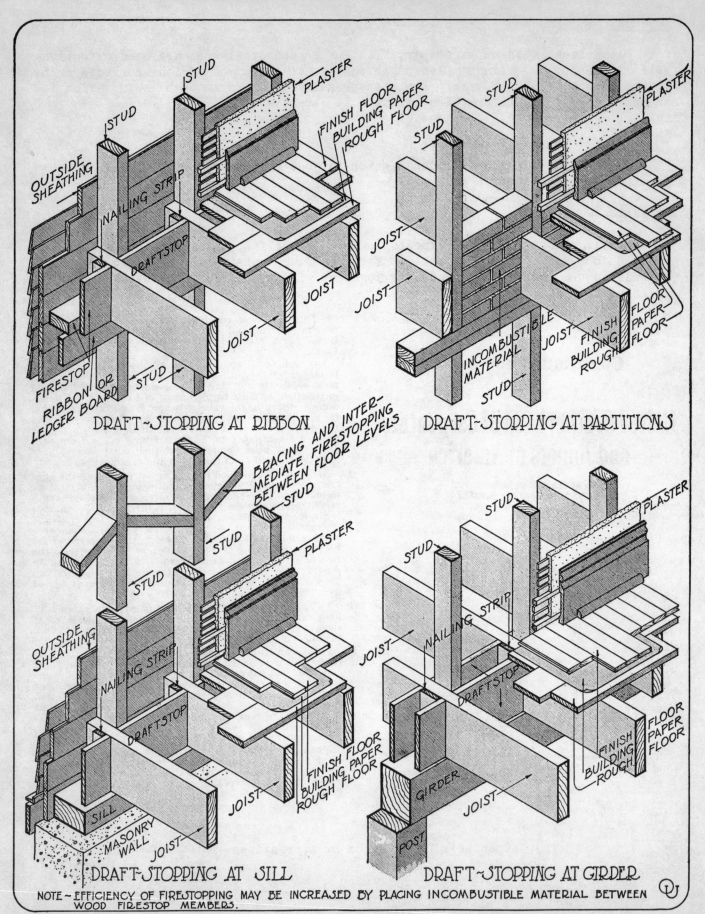

DRAFT~STOPPING AT RIBBON

DRAFT~STOPPING AT PARTITIONS

DRAFT~STOPPING AT SILL

DRAFT~STOPPING AT GIRDER

NOTE~EFFICIENCY OF FIRESTOPPING MAY BE INCREASED BY PLACING INCOMBUSTIBLE MATERIAL BETWEEN WOOD FIRESTOP MEMBERS.

NATIONAL LUMBER MANUFACTURERS ASSOCIATION

Accidents   65, 213
A. I. A.   45, 135
Angle dividers   6
Angular perspective   73
Architect   135, 21
Area   17
Awl   8
Axe   6

Back saw   8
Bay framing   84
Bench bracket   13
Bench stop   13
Bit   10
Bit gauge   10
Blade rule   6
Board feet   43
Bolt clipper   10
Brick chisel   10
Bridging   75
Broom   12
Brush   12
Building code   69, 61
Business letter   59, 229
Butt gauge   10
Butt mortiser   10

Case instruments 140
Ceiling joist   137
Center punch   8
Chalk   6
Chalk line   6
Chalk reel   6
Checking dimensions   19
Chisels   10
Chisels- butt   10
City plan   37
Clamp   12
Closets   263
Cold chisel   10
Commercial law   135
Commercial papers   135
Common rafter   153
Complete sentences   45
Concrete   51
Concrete costs   51
Concrete wall   50
Construction geometry   75
Cornices   171
Countersink   10
Cross cut saw   8
Crow bar   10

Degrees   187
Dividers   6
Doors   252
Drawing equipment 37, 139
Draw knife   13
Drawing paper   15, 185
Drawing pencil   11
Drift punch   8
Drill- power   10
Drill- twist   10

Elevations   109
Equipment   6
Erasers   19
Estimating   172
(and every chapter)
Excavations   33
Extension bit   10
Exterior wall
   covering   203

File   8
Fiction   235
Finish flooring 272
Finishing   273
First aid   213
Floor joists   71
Floor plans   22, 23
Footing   39
Form key   42
Foundation   39
Foundation forms 39
Functional analysis 215

Girder   63, 68
Girder posts   66
Glue pot   12
Gutters   187

Hack saw   8
Hammer- claw   6
Hand drill   10
Hand punch   12
Hardware   260
Health history   249
Hip rafter   165
House plans   22, 23
House styles   232

I beams   66
Inside framed
   walls   109
Insulation   128
Interior trim   82, 237
Interior wall
   covering   215
Isometric
   drawing   91

Jack rafter   152
Joist trimmer   72

Key hole saw   8
Knife- pocket   10

Lantern   12
Letter writing   59
Level- carpenters 6
Level- masons   6
Leveling stand   6
Levers   99
Line level   6
Loads   65
Lumber properties   76
Lumber sizes   68

Mallet   10
Marking gauge   6
Masonite forms   40
Material list   95
Measures   36
Measuring units 36
Mechanical drawing   139
Miter box   8

Nailing   97
Nail set   8

Oblique drawing 91
Oiler   12
Oil stone   12
One point
   perspective   60
Openings   111
Orthographic
   projection   93
Outside framed
   walls   89

I N D E X

Panel gauge   6
Pencil   8
Pencil clasp   6
Personal letter   219
Perspective   48
Pier forms   38
Pincers   12
Pipe wrench   12
Plane- block   13
Plane- jack   13
Plane- jointer   13
Plane- rabbet   13
Plane- router   13
Plane- smooth   13
Pliers   12
Plumb bob   6
Plumbing framed
  work   119
Plumb level   6
Plurals   37
Porch and bay
  framing   69
Portable bench
  saw   8
Portable power
  saw   8
Portable sander   12
Punctuation   125

Ratchet brace   10
Reference books   167
Rigidity   120
Ripping bar   10
Rip saw   6
Rivet chisel   10
Roof framing   153
Roofing   191
Roofs   163
Roof sheathing   171
Roofing bracket   12
Roots   245
Rough flooring   81
Rule   6

Saw filer   8
Saw set   8
Scale   39
Scrapers   13
Scraper burnisher
                      13
Standard lumber abbrevations 105

Screw driver   10
Sheathing walls   127
Shelving   263
Shingling hatchet   6
Shovel   12
Sketching   35
Siding gauge   6
Sill costs   57
Sills   55
Simple sentences   21
Sliding bevel   8
Soft wood structure   76
Specifications   24
Spoke shave   13
Stairs   225
Steel joists   74
Steel line   6
Steel square   8   43
Stock bill   15
Stock order   61
Sub-flooring   81

Termite   59
Three views   93
Tool box   14
Tools   6
Tool box hardware   14
Tool chest   14
Tool history   17
Tool marking   13
Tool material   11
Tool prices   11
Tool spelling   8
Trade terms   78
Trammel points   6
Try and miter square   6
Try square   8
Two-point perspective
                      60

Volume   36

Wheel barrow   12
Windows   239
Wrecking bar   10
Wrench- S   12

Yard stick   6

NOTE ONE: Attention
is directed to the
following groups of
line drawings which
run serially through
out this book.
A. Isometric views
of a two story framed
house, showing all
framed members, in
construction sequence
Refer to pages 56, 80
98, 137 and 138.
B. Floor plans of a
seven room house,
together with framing
plans of each floor
and, in addition, a
roof framing plan
and pertinent data.
Refer to pages 64,
246, 248 and 258.

NOTE TWO: Floor
plans, of various
types, are found
on the following
pages, 22, 23, 27,
28, 30, 32, 62, 64,
106, 108, 122, 136,
148, 150, 178, 180,
204, 206, 210, 212,
246 and 248.

NOTE THREE: Ele-
vations, of various
types, are found on
the following pages,
32, 48, 106, 136,
137, 138, 146, 148,
150, 180, 182, 204,
206, 208, 232 and
234.

NOTE FOUR: Illus-
trations of build-
ing materials and
operations in
Joinery Work are
found on pages 8,
10, 27, 28, 30, 46,
49, 56, 66, 74, 84,
86, 100, 102, 103,
104, 110, 111, 126,
171, 202, 214, 216
and 255.